# Regulating New Drugs
## Edited by Richard L. Landau

The University of Chicago
Center for Policy Study

# Contents

# Contents

# List of Contributors

**Daniel L. Azarnoff, M.D.,** is Professor of Medicine and Pharmacology and Director of the Clinical Pharmacology Unit, Kansas University Medical Center. He is a Markle Scholar in Academic Medicine and a Burroughs Wellcome Scholar in Clinical Pharmacology. He has been a member of the Drug Research Board, AMA Council on Drugs, National Formulary Selection Committee, and U.S. Pharmacopeial Committees on Scope and Bioavailability. In addition, he has been on study sections of the National Institute of General Medical Sciences and the National Heart and Lung Institute, and has served as a consultant for the Food and Drug Administration, the World Health Organization, and various pharmaceutical firms.

**William F. Baxter** is Professor of Law at Stanford University. He has served as a consultant to the Federal Reserve Board, the Brookings Institution, and the President's Task Forces on Antitrust Policy and on Communications Policy. He was Visiting Professor of Law at Yale University from 1964–65. Mr. Baxter's areas of professional expertise include antitrust, government regulation of economic activity, environmental law, and legal and economic impacts of aircraft noise. He is also the author of numerous publications.

**Hubert Bloch, M.D.,** is Director of the Friedrich Miescher-Institut, Basle, an institute for basic bio-medical research sponsored by CIBA-GEIGY. He was Professor of Microbiology and Head of the Department at the School of Medicine, University of Pittsburgh. He later served as Director of Research, CIBA Limited, Basle, and Professor of Microbiology at the University of Basle. Dr. Bloch is also a member of the Research Council of the Swiss National Science Foundation and has served as consultant to the World Health Organization and other groups.

**Guido Calabresi** is the John Thomas Smith Professor of Law at Yale University. He was a Rhodes Scholar and received numerous scholastic honors and prizes while at Yale College, Oxford University, and Yale Law School. In addition, he has been a Visiting Professor at the University of Florence, Italy, Harvard University Law School, and the Kyoto American Studies Seminar, Japan. He has been a consultant to the Department of Transportation and to the State of New York. His publications include *The Costs of Accidents: A Legal and Economic Analysis* (1970).

**Joseph D. Cooper** is Professor of Political Science at Howard University. He has been a member of numerous national committees, and is presently conducting a series of conferences for the Smithsonian Institution under the general title of the Conferences of the Philosophy and Technology of Drug Assessment. He is the editor of *Economics of Drug Innovation,* Washington, D.C., American University, 1970. His articles have appeared in a number of professional periodicals.

**J. Richard Crout, M.D.,** is Acting Director, Office of Scientific Evaluation, Bureau of Drugs, Food and Drug Administration. He has been a Research Fellow and Instructor in Pharmacology at Harvard Medical School, an Assistant and Associate Professor at the University of Texas Southwestern Medical School, and Professor at Michigan State University College of Human Medicine. He was a Burroughs Wellcome Scholar in Clinical Pharmacology, is a Fellow of the American College of Physicians, and holds membership in several other professional societies. He has served on many national committees and is the author of numerous articles.

**Sir Derrick Dunlop** is Professor Emeritus of Therapeutics and Clinical Medicine at the University of Edinburgh. He is a Fellow of the Royal College of Physicians and has served as Physician to H.M. the Queen in Scotland since 1965. Knighted in 1960, Sir Derrick holds several honorary degrees, and has held numerous appointments, fellowships, and lectureships.

**Leon I. Goldberg, M.D.,** is Professor of Medicine (Clinical Pharmacology) and Pharmacology and Director of the Clinical Pharmacology Program at Emory University School of Medicine. He has been a Research Assistant and Associate in Pharmacology at the Medical College of South Carolina, a Research Fellow in Anesthesia at Massachusetts General Hospital, and a Clinical Associate at the National Heart Institute. He has served on numerous national and international committees, and is on the editorial boards of several publications. He has also published extensively. From 1961–66 he was a Burroughs Wellcome Scholar in Clinical Pharmacology.

**William Neil Hubbard, Jr., M.D.,** is Executive Vice-President of The Upjohn Company. A member of various professional organizations, honorary societies, and advisory committees, Dr. Hubbard has also been Associate Dean of the New York University College of

Medicine and Dean of the University of Michigan Medical School, Director of the University of Michigan Medical Center, and a consultant to the U.S. Public Health Service.

**Reuben A. Kessel** is Professor of Business Economics in the Graduate School of Business at The University of Chicago. He has previously been an economist for the RAND Corporation, Professor at UCLA's School of Business Administration, and a Research Associate at the National Bureau of Economic Research. He is the author of many publications, and has received awards from the Merrill Foundation for the Advancement of Financial Knowledge, the Volder Foundation, the Commission on Money and Credit, and the National Science Foundation.

**Edmund Kitch** is Professor of Law at The University of Chicago. He is the co-author (with Harvey Perlman) of *Legal Regulation of the Competitive Process* (1972). His article, "Graham v. the John Deere Co.: New Standards for Patents" appeared in the 1966 *Supreme Court Review*.

**Louis Lasagna, M.D.,** is Professor of Pharmacology and Toxicology and of Medicine at the University of Rochester School of Medicine and Dentistry. He is a member of the Institute of Medicine, the American Society for Clinical Investigation, the American Federation for Clinical Research, and other professional organizations. His many publications include *The Doctors' Dilemmas* (1962) and *Life, Death, and the Doctor* (1968).

**Sam Peltzman** is Professor of Economics at the University of California at Los Angeles. He has also been a Faculty Research Fellow, National Bureau of Economic Research, a Visiting Associate Professor in the Graduate School of Business at The University of Chicago, and a senior staff economist for the Council of Economic Advisors, Executive Office of the President. His articles have appeared in a number of professional and scholarly journals.

**George J. Stigler** joined The University of Chicago faculty in 1958 as the Charles R. Walgreen Distinguished Service Professor of American Institutions in the Graduate School of Business and the Department of Economics. He has also been a lecturer at the London School of Economics, a member of the Attorney-General's National Committee for Study of Anti-Trust Laws (1954–55), a

Guggenheim Fellow (1955), and a Fellow of the Center for Advanced Study in Behavioral Sciences (1957–58). He is a member of several professional associations. In addition to many articles on economics, his publications include *The Theory of Price* (1946, 1952, 1966), *The Intellectual Market Place and Other Essays* (1963), and *The Organization of Industry* (1968).

**Lester G. Telser** is Professor of Economics at The University of Chicago. He is a fellow of the Economic Society and the American Statistical Association, associate editor of the *Review of Economics and Statistics*, and a member of the Economics Advisory Panel, National Science Foundation (1971–73). His most recent publication is *Competition, Collusion and Game Theory* (1972).

# Foreword

It is the interesting fate of this book to have been controversial before it ever went to press. A reading will tell you why, perhaps.

It grew out of a conference on the introduction of new pharmaceuticals sponsored by the Center for Policy Study at The University of Chicago in December 1972. Invitations to the conference were sent to many persons in agencies of government and in the Congress, as well to academics and some officials of drug manufacturing companies. These invitations were followed by repeated conversations with some of the government people in which they were urged to attend. Not enough did. But shortly after the conference some of these same people were widely quoted in the press as offended by some of the presentations at the conference and as demanding that the information be made public. Well, here it is. There was never any effort to keep the papers secret and there was a good deal of effort to make them known to the very people whose protests indicate that they understand the arguments here.

Books of this kind are not treatises, but contributions to a continuing debate about an issue of public importance, or postcards from a volcano. Because the fortunes of industries and bureaucracies are involved in this particular debate, as well as the health of all Americans, perhaps a certain amount of controversy is inevitable.

The papers printed here speak to many different audiences with different kinds of expertise, but the central problem they address is the same; it provides them with a certain unity.

A transcript was made of the discussions on these papers during the conference, and from it Margot Doyle and Dr. Richard Landau have extracted brief summaries, which can be found in the appendices.

The conference project which results in this publication was supported by grants from the Charles R. Walgreen Foundation for the Study of American Institutions and from the Drug Abuse Council, and the Drug Abuse Council has given support in its grant for the publication of this volume.

D. J. R. Bruckner
Director, the Center for Policy Study
and Vice-President for Public Affairs
The University of Chicago

# Preface

The 1962 Amendments to the Food and Drug Act resulted in a number of new federal regulations governing the sale and development of pharmaceutical agents. The Food and Drug Administration was empowered to require that available drugs are effective and safe enough to justify their intended application. Hundreds of approved drugs have had to be re-evaluated for efficacy. However, the major impact of the new regulations has been on the development and the marketing of new chemical entities. New regulations promulgated by the Food and Drug Administration coupled with the expanding disciplines of pharmacology and clinical pharmacology have substantially lengthened both the preclinical and clinical phases of new drug testing. The cost of developing each new drug and the time required for it to reach the market has increased substantially. However, the new pharmaceutical agents when approved by the FDA are both safe and effective.

Ten years of new regulations and a more aggressive Food and Drug Administration have produced a number of strains. Although a portion of the public seems to believe that its concerns about new drug safety and efficacy are now dealt with more effectively, the pharmaceutical industry, members of the academic medical community, and some medical practitioners have the feeling that regulations are keeping valuable and potentially useful drugs from the market, to the detriment of the health of the American people.

This concern about the possible adverse effects of the 1962 Amendments and the regulations derived from them was felt by several members of The University of Chicago faculty. Thus colleagues from the University's Graduate School of Business, Law School, Medical School, and the University's Center for Policy Study planned an international conference on "The Regulation of the Introduction of New Pharmaceuticals." The program was developed in the main by Professors Reuben Kessel, George Stigler, Richard Posner, Frank Zimring, Daniel X. Freedman, John Rust, and Richard L. Landau. Eddie N. Williams was Vice-President for Public Affairs and Director of the Center for Policy Study until July of 1972 when he was succeeded by D. J. R. Bruckner. The conference was held at the University's Center for Continuing Education on December 4 and 5, 1972. This volume consists of the proceedings of that conference.

Position papers commissioned by the Center for Policy Study were distributed to conference participants in advance of the proceedings. They were presented at the meeting in abstract form only, and were followed by a formal critique of each position paper.

The ensuing discussion was recorded and was later edited and partially rewritten by Margot Doyle and Richard L. Landau. They appear in Appendix I, as synopsis of commentary.

Richard L. Landau

# Introduction

## Regulation: The Confusion of Means and Ends
George J. Stigler

## Purpose, Technique, and Strategy in the Regulation of New Drugs
Joseph D. Cooper

# Regulation:
# The Confusion of Means and Ends
George J. Stigler

[There is widespread agreement on the regulation of economic and social affairs in the United States.][The subject is a relatively uncontroversial one.

Public regulation is relatively uncontroversial in an ideological sense: there are only a few people who go to the extremes which surround current policy. A few people, indeed, believe that almost all regulation is bad, and by a singular coincidence a significant fraction of the academic part of this group resides within a radius of one mile of this University. Rather more people believe that regulation is wholly insufficient or inefficient, and that the explicit vesting of much privately-owned enterprise in direct governmental ownership and operation is essential to satisfactory social performance. These old-fashioned socialists have always had some trouble discussing the post office: when the sovereign cannot carry small rectangular pieces of paper with either economy or dispatch, one must inevitably worry about his capacity to manage an entire economy. Recently the socialists have been dealt a fierce and unscrupulous blow: nationalization of passenger train service.

[The great majority of Americans would not dream of abandoning the important regulatory policies, and are in full agreement with a regime which adds five or ten new regulatory items a year. As recently as October 21, 1972, this majority had the good fortune to obtain a law authorizing the Secretary of Transportation to order heavier bumpers for automobiles and to jail men found tampering with the mileage on an odometer. We may confidently await new regulations of other parts of a motor vehicle and of the thousand other ingredients of everyday living.

Accordingly, the regulatory policies are uncontroversial in a political sense. The major parties do not dispute their existence, and seldom their detailed policies. Each year the appropriations of each regulatory body grow about 8 percent on average: 1 percent for population, 5 percent for prices, and 2 percent for growing evil. The momentum of events is awesome.

Most basically, there is scarce a murmur of controversy on the goals of social policy. Everyone wants a good deal of purity in goods and wholesomeness in environment, they want safety in automobiles and in financial institutions, they want reliable service in airlines, competence in doctors, erudition or at least incomprehensibility in professors, and sunshine on weekends. Everyone wants poverty eliminated, families united—no matter what the cost in psychiatric care—and crime abated, or at least confined to certain localities.

To be sure, a list of good things will seldom create controversy if each person is allowed his own priorities, or, differently put, if the price tags are not attached. In fact, there is no substantive difference between hating a thing and professing love for it if only the price were not undeniably exorbitant. With our opulent nation and our rapidly growing public sector, publicly-supplied good things seem hardly to confront a problem of scarcity: almost every old and new program can be, and in fact has been, increasing rapidly.

In this connection, a special word of praise is due to Professor Galbraith, the leading spokesman for the underprivileged public sector. As of the recent past and present time his message was, of course, absurd. The non-defense budget of our nation—state and local as well as federal governments—has been growing at the rate of 10 percent a year since 1960. The public sector has been starved for only one thing: remotely promising enterprises on which to spend money. In another decade, however, that picture will change radically, and no doubt that prospective picture was what Galbraith had or should have had in mind. The aggregate expansion of the public sector will slow down rapidly, and the theory of opportunity cost will return from exile to full residence in Washington and the state capitals. Granting that scarcity eventually intrudes on all of men's activities, however, up to now we have been spared the harsh controversies of difficult public choices.

One may distinguish two kinds of public regulations, and I wish to discuss the problems of enforcement of regulation of only one kind. The kind of regulation I propose to ignore is industry-oriented and almost invariably industry-dominated: the various petroleum programs, the regulation of transportation and communication industries, and the like. Regulations in these industries are directed primarily to industry benefits, and the industry usually plays a large role in their enforcement.[1]

The second kind of regulation is general purpose: the collection of a general income tax; the control of monopoly wherever it arises (antitrust policy); the protection of consumers against fraud and defective products. The distinction between this kind of regulation and industry regulation is not unambiguous: the Food and Drug Administration (FDA), the subject of the present conference, is directed to a few industries, and is part of a program of general

1. George J. Stigler, "The Theory of Economic Regulation," *The Bell Journal of Economics and Management Science*, Spring 1971.

protection of consumers. Yet the distinction is useful, and I propose to discuss in the remainder of this paper the problems of efficient enforcement of these general economic policies. The laws with any and all of their blemishes will be accepted as goals, but reconsidered as instruments to achieve these goals.

What is not commonly realized is that there are several ways to skin even a reforming cat. The traditional, not to say unthinking, reliance upon the appointment of a regulatory body is not the only, or even often a reasonable, method of advancing our regulatory goals. To tell an agency to go out and see that others sin no more is not to solve a problem except in the important sense of getting it off the agenda for the time being. One must ask of every regulatory agent:

1. Is he qualified?
2. Is he given proper incentives?
3. Is there an audit of his performance?
4. Is it possible to challenge failures or weaknesses in his performance?

I propose to submit our regulatory agencies to these tests. I shall make extensive use of an article by Gary Becker and myself on the enforcement of rules.[2]

## 1. Are Regulators Qualified?

I assert that regulators are or can be fully qualified. If the state wishes, it can employ skilled men with specialized knowledge, it can persuade them to be diligent, and it can achieve good levels of integrity. Of course it can fail in all these respects, but so too can profit-making institutions. If the state wishes to pay the market rate, it can hire men of high ability.

Thus I reject the popular view that bureaucrats are inherently incompetent or lazy or timid in the conduct of public affairs. This view is often based simply upon ancient prejudice, but it is sometimes supported by the argument that in a non-profit-making organization there are no definite measures of and incentives to efficient performance. I postpone that issue, and simply reaffirm that the state can and does hire able people, whether they use their ability properly or not.

General ability is not the whole content of a qualified person,

2. Gary S. Becker and George J. Stigler, "Law Enforcement, Malfeasance, and Compensation of Enforcers," forthcoming.

however. Consider the enforcement of the Sherman Act. Presently it is enforced by a troop of lawyers, aided by some FBI agents and occasionally a stray economist—all, let us assume, of the highest quality. How can this collection of people, removed from commerce and largely concentrated in the nation's capital, know whether company W in industry X is violating the Act in state Y with respect to commodity Z? The only way in which the Antitrust Division could possibly learn of this violation is through a letter of complaint from an aggrieved party. Many such letters are received, but there is surely no serious presumption that the most serious violations call forth the first and the most helpful complaints—that would be fortuitous in the extreme.

Or consider the determination whether a given product is produced under sanitary conditions. The probability of a violation depends upon the production process, the raw materials, the quality of labor, and similar factors known primarily to the industry and its suppliers and customers. These circumstances change frequently, and vary widely from plant to plant, and even from one manager to the next, and from one shift of operations to the next. Even an experienced corps of inspectors will be less skilled than the people directly concerned with the industry in detecting violations.

The argument can be generalized: very seldom, indeed, will the regulators be well situated in experience and knowledge to detect and prove violations. A dozen people are more likely than the Internal Revenue Service to know whether X is cheating on his tax, and a score of truckers know better than the ICC whether firm Y is violating its certificate restrictions. Professional competence and integrity are not sufficient to qualify one as a superior enforcer.

## 2. The Incentives of Regulators

A rational man must be guided by the incentive system within which he operates. No matter what his own personal desires, he must be discouraged from certain activities if they carry penalties, and attracted toward others if they carry large rewards. The carrot and the stick guide scientists and politicians as well as donkeys.

An efficient enforcement system, therefore, requires intelligent guides to the regulators, telling them which things are good and also important, which good but unimportant, and which positively harmful. In too many cases, the system of values, or incentives, is now badly skewed. This is a fault, not of the regulators, but of the legislatures and executives who establish the incentives. Let me give three examples.

Very often the regulators proudly tell us how many cases they have won: how many adulterators they have apprehended, how many false advertisements they have challenged, how many thieves they have jailed. This is as if General Electric told us proudly how many items it had produced last year, counting aircraft engines equally with turbines and refrigerators and light bulbs. Such a report would properly expose General Electric to ridicule, but each year the Federal Trade Commission (FTC) gravely reports the number of cease and desist orders it has mailed out. [We should demand measures of performance which take account of importance.]

Second, failures are not free to regulators, but they are seldom charged the full cost. If a violation is improperly charged, and the party is acquitted, he is reimbursed neither for the costs of his defense nor for the damage done to his reputation. This tyrannical vestige of the age of absolute sovereigns is so indefensible that it is impossible for me to conceive of a defense sufficiently respectable to deserve examination. At a very minimum, I should think that after every acquittal, the regulatory agency should be required to reimburse direct expenses and insert a quarter-page ad in 10 national newspapers and magazines withdrawing all accusations with apology. This practice should of course be associated with an increase in agency appropriations: the purpose of the scheme is to place the cost of error on the society rather than on the victim. Error is inevitable, but regulators should be given incentives to minimize it.

There is another kind of regulatory failure, nonfeasance. To act slowly (which has one special but non-empty sub-category, taking forever to act) often has no easily identifiable costs to society. If the Federal Communications Commission (FCC) takes interminable ages to allow the introduction of pay-TV, only one or two pioneer companies seem to be mildly injured. In fact, of course, a thousand firms have been denied existence, and you and I have been denied programs for which I would have been an eager purchaser for half a generation. The suppression of this boon to minority audiences has surely done me more harm than all the other actions of the FCC have ever done me good. Professor Peltzman's study of the cost of the FDA's restriction and delay of new drugs is both pathbreaking and monumental, and I look forward confidently to the expansion of our knowledge of these costs of nonfeasance in regulation as other scholars follow his example and methods.

Unlike the problem of charging innocent people, there is no simple solution to the problem of delay. Regulation is an activity of human beings in a complex and imperfectly understood world, so regulators—like brides, musicians, and professors—are entitled to some mistakes, or rather, cannot possibly avoid all mistakes. There are almost no effective sanctions upon delay if the consent of the regulator is necessary: even if the regulatory body is given a short period within which to act (as is true, for example, of SEC review of new prospectuses), the agency has such large discretionary powers in asking for further information or otherwise burdening an enterprise as to rob the time limit of content. Unless the controversial behavior may continue until stopped by the regulator, a time limit should be an element of every statute, although a uniform time limit is a crude tool to shape a variegated world. A better remedy for delay will be proposed later.

The first problem of regulation, the lack of guides to the selection of important cases, does allow of substantial correction even with our present regulatory procedures. The penalties for violations of statutes should be proportioned to the harm which these violations impose on society. A technical violation which simply affronts the dignity of the regulatory body should call forth a small fine. A major violation should correspondingly incur a major fine. We should not specify the fines in statutes—saying, as the Sherman Act does, that a maximum offense will be fined $50,000, or, with the Copeland Act, that a second offense of food adulteration will have a maximum fine of $10,000. The fines should be proportioned to the severity of the harm done by the violation, and should be larger, the smaller the probability of detection of the offense. Then the violator will face a rational system of deterrence, and the regulatory body will face a rational system of incentives and of measurement of performance.

# 3.  Auditing the Regulator

The auditing of the performance of a regulatory body is now seldom undertaken by any responsible public body. A congressional committee may subject the routine operations of an agency to close, and possibly headline-oriented, review once every 20 or 80 years. The Office of Management and Budget (OMB) will ask for some numbers of the kind I have just deplored. The main check on the agency comes from the industry or activity it regulates. That is where one finds the combination of strong and continuing financial interest and intensive knowledge—and of course the knowledge is a result of the financial interest—which guarantees close, informed scrutiny and vigorous legal and political action.

This is a splendid check, but of course it is a check against only certain types of error in regulation. Industry review will guarantee that the Federal Deposit Insurance Corporation (FDIC) does not charter too many new banks (as if that were conceivable) or fail to close down those without charter. Industry review will guarantee that rates of domestic and international airlines do not become too cheap. But industry review will not combat the monopoly-creating propensities which inhere in virtually all regulation, and almost by definition it is inappropriate to the class of general regulatory policy which I am discussing.

The only non-industry audit that an agency must fear is that of the reformer, be he a professor or an evangelical lawyer. The professor is an easy burden: if he is responsible and competent, we can be certain that his audience will be at most in the hundreds, not in the hundreds of thousands or millions. The Nader type of reformer is more fearsome, because he is armed with passion, and any irresponsibility and slovenliness in his accusations seem to have little cost to him. He is, however, a feeble reed on which to rest the public welfare, and for two reasons. First, he lives on headlines, so he must flit from one sin to another, and for him one fresh $5 million scandal is worth $100 million of day-in, day-out routine inefficiency. Second, because he is untrained or half-trained, he has no real remedy for a regulatory failure except indignation, a new set of faces, and a stern admonition to sin no more. Consider what is basically a shallow, shoddy piece of work, the Fellman-Cox study of the FTC. They seek to strengthen some of the silliest activities of the Commission, such as the regulation of advertising. They calmly ignore its nearly 60 years of history, and ask now for only five new faces! This sort of audit of regulation cries for regulation of auditors.

The appraisal of the achievements of a regulatory body is not impossible: a whole series of such appraisals is gradually developing an arsenal of techniques for measurement. I may cite the Coleman study of school segregation, the forthcoming New Jersey study of income maintenance plans, as well as a large number of economic studies, many of which have appeared in the *Journal of Law and Economics*. It would be at least a minor improvement of our world if once a decade each major regulator was reviewed by a committee appointed by the appropriate scientific body, with funds and subpoena powers provided by the OMB.

## 4. The Improvability of Regulation

Suppose a citizen becomes convinced that a particular regulatory agency is thoroughly remiss in its enforcement of a statutory policy. This is not a strenuous supposition: even the most exemplary regulatory body has its periods of inanimation or even of perversion of policy, and this period will sometimes be very long.

The one recourse this citizen now has, aside from resignation, is to launch a crusade: to write to his congressman, who receives many letters; to his editor, who publishes few; and to what always proves to be so embarrassingly small, his public. Even a professor of economics is, as I observed in connection with the auditing function, a very small voice for the excellent reason that there are so many professors that if each had a loud voice, the noise would be deafening. There is no satisfactory recourse for the informed citizen when he encounters a regulatory failure.

Indeed, the shield of invulnerability seems almost impenetrable to assaults even by substantial groups, let alone individual citizens. Consider the fixed commission structure of the New York Stock Exchange, which has dwelled under the shelter of Security and Exchange Commission (SEC) patronage and hence presumable exemption from the Sherman Act. Major changes brought about by major groups have resulted from this grievous malfeasance of the SEC: the third market has developed; the "give-ups" were developed to a high level; and institutional membership in the regional exchanges has begun. The SEC continued its bland neglect of the public interest in this area until a year ago, when negotiated rates were commanded where they are not needed—for very large transactions. The great mutual funds and pension funds and insurance companies could not bring about an appropriate, fully authorized SEC decision to instill competition in this price structure.

The present system does not allow small groups to operate effectively on the great stage of national regulation: one must launch a large political campaign or remain silent. This discontinuity, this permissible insularity of the regulatory bodies, no doubt has its merits: the agencies are not engaged in constant disputes, listening to fools and knaves as well as angels, but it builds an all-or-none element into regulatory reform.

## 5. A Modest Proposal

One of the greatest merits of the economic system is that it has
learned to overcome precisely this problem. Suppose I wish a kind
of textbook in economics different from all those now available.
It is not necessary for me to convince a Federal Board of Editors,
or the Congressional Committee which controls it, to make a substantial shift in its publishing program. The very size of such a
Board, and the very diversity of interests of affected parties, would
normally lead the board to file my suggestion in a paper shredder.
No, now I can appeal to any one publisher, argue the commercial
promise of the venture, and, if I can succeed in persuading a single
publisher (or become one myself), my idea will be tried. If I am
wholly correct in my view of what the market wishes, a herd of
publishers will then follow my successful (meaning profitable)
leadership.

This suggests, and I now wish explicitly to propose, the introduction of competition into the enforcement of regulation. Our
survey of the problems of enforcement found four difficulties with
the system of enforcement by a specialized regulatory service:

1. The public agents, even though trained and diligent, are often
very poorly situated to discover violations, and never *better* situated
than all other groups in the society.

2. The incentives to regulators to concentrate on larger problems
and to speed are weak because legislatures have not been persuaded
to strengthen them. Improved legislation may provide guidance on
the importance of cases, but it does not seem possible to devise an
efficient incentive on speed.

3. The auditing of regulatory agencies requires a continuous
expenditure of substantial resources, and only one group in the
society—those primarily subject to the regulations—have the incentive to provide these resources.

4. If a regulatory agency performs badly, there is no recourse
open to individuals or small groups.

All of these difficulties except the provision of proper incentives
will be resolved if any person who wishes to do so is allowed to
enforce regulatory statutes. In particular:

1. Those best informed about violations will be enlisted to stop
them.

2. Since enforcement will be a profitable undertaking for superior enforcers, we can expect diligence, dispatch, and innovation.
If fines are made proportional to the harm done by a violation,

incentives to enforcement will be proportional to the demonstrated damage from violations, so enforcement efforts will be concentrated on the most damaging violations.

3. If public agencies also enforce statutes in competition with private parties, the auditing of both will be undertaken by competitors in the process. If a public regulator overlooks large violations, private enforcers will find the area profitable.

4. Anyone who detects an enforcement failure can enter into the enterprise of enforcement.

Support for these propositions will be found in the paper by Becker and me.

This proposal is not so radical as may appear. The triple damage suit has become much the most important sanction of the Sherman Act, and the lawyers specializing in this area are even preparing the evidence required to show violation of the statute. Class action legislation, intended to codify (and no doubt to limit) this new type of enforcement, will presumably be passed soon by Congress. The only deterrent I would put on class actions is the requirement that if defendants are acquitted, complete compensation of all costs be provided by the plaintiff. We have traditionally used private assistance extensively in public enforcement, although under such opprobrious titles as informers. Indeed the most popular lawyers' reaction is that private competition will lead to too much enforcement!

Anyone who rejects this proposal, for good reasons or bad, ought to face squarely the question: how will he discharge the four main tasks of enforcement? How will he find the information, direct the regulators to the expeditious pursuit of major violators, assure himself of the continued reliability of the regulator, and bring about needed reforms? Public regulation, for all its enormous momentum, lives by its goals and not by its achievements, and surely we ought eventually to tire of promising preambles and unpromising achievement.

# Purpose, Technique, and Strategy in the Regulation of New Drugs
Joseph D. Cooper

It sometimes happens that when an institution or movement is at peak in carrying out or tidying up its affairs, it is actually at the beginning of its decline. A corollary is that when complex solutions for the handling of complex problems have been long in the making their solutions may no longer be appropriate. In both cases, the environment that governs all purpose has undergone change that has not been perceived by mortal beings who cope with the experiences of the past within the means and technologies of the present.

Current efforts to modify and up-date the present system for scientific assessment of the safety and efficacy of new drugs (or medicines) under the Food and Drug Administration (FDA) come squarely under this "rule." Never before have so many people been working so diligently in pursuit of this aim within the FDA, assisted by consultants within the pharmaceutical industry and among interested academic authorities. All are in agreement, although for different reasons, that the present arrangements need to be superseded by an improved assessment model.

We need a new model—one that will encompass all or most of the elements of the evolving assessment system that will be discussed by others, but also one that will redistribute responsibility for the operation of the model. I envisage: (1) a more powerful FDA achieving its aims more selectively through existing institutions of society; (2) a greater role for academic and professional institutions in actual assessment; and (3) for industry, a greater self-regulatory responsibility, short of judgment on technological novelty or innovation, which should be subject to challenge.

Whatever the system that evolves, fundamental changes in assessment technology are needed as remedies for the ills of excessively elaborated systems and as means of side-stepping the insoluble conflicts that continue to arise under the existing system. Consider, for example, the following:

1. During the last session of the Congress efforts were made by individuals who designate themselves consumer advocates to replace the present FDA with a new organization that would, in new organizational surroundings, be more directly consumer-oriented. Presumably, those consumer advocates would have a stronger voice in program control. These efforts came very close to being successful, notwithstanding the absence of any thorough consideration of the impact of change on pharmaceutical innovation. The infusion of responsible consumer interest is certainly desirable, but the question is: should scientific assessment be of service to consumer

advocates who have no public accountability or should the latter have an input and monitoring role of service to the assessors and the general public?

2. The development of new drugs, as a consequence of demands for greater premarketing proof of safety and efficacy, is becoming so costly as to force research-based manufacturers to abandon interest in minor, although important, medicines.

3. For whatever reason, pharmaceutical innovation in general has been slowing down. It is a worldwide phenomenon, although some people believe that other countries are becoming relatively more innovative than the United States due to the imposition of more rigid requirements by the latter. The FDA rejects this hypothesis, while asserting that the lag in innovation is more reasonably attributable to lags in fundamental scientific discovery. Both sides might be right. The truth might also lie between them. Nevertheless, existing approaches to regulation in the more advanced countries tend to be inherently constraining. Interestingly, although constructive challenge can stimulate creative endeavor, beyond some optimal point of intervention it becomes counterproductive.

4. Measures of beneficial outcome, in terms of public health, need to be devised for evaluation of FDA operations. What do we know of the cost to the public of a single approval or rejection action by the regulatory agency? Can we know when we have reached a point—assuming we have not already passed it by—at which greater numbers and sophistication become counterproductive? How can we know that the assessment apparatus of one country, operating at a tiny fraction of the cost of FDA review, within brief time, is any less effective or any more so in terms of actual public outcomes?

5. Many American companies have been exporting early clinical trials on developmental drugs in order to gain valuable time, or to enable them to make many more screening trials, or to save money. For whatever reason, this appears to be a trend. What will it avail the United States to have the world's most elaborate system of evaluation if this should force a flight of clinical research to other lands and if foreign markets should become of increasingly greater interest than the domestic one? Without relaxation of realistically prudent standards of acceptance, can we get to the end of the line at less cost?

The pharmaceutical industry, as regulated clientele, charges the FDA with demanding unnecessarily elaborate data presentations, with taking too long to reach decisions, with blocking the approval of new drugs (or medicines) whose benefits are available to the peoples in other countries, and with pricing innovation out of the market.

On the other hand, the so-called consumer advocates, whom one would presume to be supporters of the FDA, charge it with being soft on the industry, thereby putting the public at risk. The consumer advocates have taken the FDA to court to compel it to move faster to remove products from the market that were adjudged by FDA advisers to be less than fully effective.

The present Commissioner of Food and Drugs has brought new talent into the agency—both resident staff and outside advisers— and has accelerated or introduced major procedural changes. In spite of these actions (or perhaps because of them) there is great dissension within the FDA as existing notions of how best to do the job are displaced.

Some academic leaders in medicine expect the FDA to take up where the medical schools have failed in teaching doctors how to prescribe. When, however, the FDA attempts to include guidelines in product labels for deciding on the comparative values of particular medicines, it meets with resistance on grounds of interference in professional medical judgment. An example of this was the FDA's decision to specify order of therapeutic choice in treatment of maturity onset diabetes.

The generic issue has united a broad range of interests: those who hope to promote competition and bring down prices through eliminating brand names; those whose sole professional interest is in having a single nomenclature for all products of identical chemical formulation, thereby simplifying inventory and prescribing practices; those generic manufacturers who hope thereby to gain a greater share of market; and those who are inherently opposed to advertising.

The advertising issue has long evoked spirited interest from those who believe that doctors should obtain their medical information from medical schools or the government or both; from those who are opposed to advertising on economic grounds; from those who simply want more truth in advertising; and, more recently, from those who believe drug abuse is encouraged by advertising medicinal products, especially non-prescription products promoted through mass media.

In the long run, what the FDA (or any other administrative agency) puts on its agenda is governed by a combination of en-

vironmental pressures—including those of the legislature and the
political administration above it—and its own bureaucratic aspira-
tions. The examples I have given are illustrative of the complex of
motivations and pressures. None of the issues is clearcut; each
tends to generate new problems and issues. The generic issue led
to a great deal of expensive preoccupation with the problem of
biological equivalence—how to ensure that different products of
identical generic nomenclature achieve identical biochemical reactions in patients. It has been an expensive issue for all concerned,
of dubious cost/benefit outcome. The assault on advertising in
journals won many academic adherents until they discovered that,
deprived of advertising revenues, the journals might perish. And
then they, too, might perish for want of publication. Meanwhile,
leading brand manufacturers have begun to market their own
generic lines. The ultimate consequences of this are yet to be seen
and felt.

We could cite numerous other examples, only to conclude that
nothing is as simple as it seems—or as cost-free, or as beneficial.
The important question is whether the hard-core mission of the
FDA is being imperiled by systems adventures, efforts to accom-
modate political pressures, the initiating of systems refinements
and improvements of possibly marginal returns, and the simulta-
neous undertaking of too many new activities, particularly when
substance and outcomes are clouded by unknowns.

The scope of FDA responsibility for assessment has become
progressively broadened since enactment of the Food and Drug
Act of 1906. That first federal legislation related to adulteration and
misbranding—that is, to assurance of purity of products and to
requiring that manufacturers more accurately describe the claims
for their medicines. Safety was covered under the adulteration
section that prohibited inclusion of any substance that would be
poisonous or deleterious to health. This Act stemmed from the
contemporary efforts of the muckraking writers and journalists in
league with public-spirited legislators. The 1906 Act was followed
by disappearance of Kickapoo Indian Sagwa, Peruna, Dr. Hostet-
ter's Celebrated Stomach Bitters, assorted rum-laden tonics and
cures, anti-cancer remedies, and innumerable specifics for that ill-
defined "entity" known then as catarrh.

Administration of the 1906 Act was only partially effective,
within its limitations. Consumer groups, mainly women's organizations, pressed for reform which was eventually achieved through
the enactment of the Federal Food, Drug, and Cosmetic Act of

June 25, 1938. This law expanded greatly on provisions pertaining to adulteration and misbranding. It required manufacturers to demonstrate the safety of new drugs under the prescribed or recommended conditions of use, and to submit applications for FDA approval prior to marketing. A defect was the provision that absence of a positive or negative determination by the FDA within specified time periods would lead to automatic approval.

The 1938 Act was first drafted in the U.S. Department of Agriculture in 1933 as an early New Deal response to the populistic pressures of the day. It went through five years of hearings, debate, and resistance by both food and drug interests before final passage. The deciding factor was the elixir of sulfanilamide catastrophe—the death of at least 73 and possibly 93 people due to the marketing of sulfanilamide dissolved in di-ethylene glycol, a poisonous substance used generally as an antifreeze for automobile radiators. The Food and Drug Administration was at its finest in retrieving or accounting for every last ounce of the preparation. The national conscience was aroused as never before, and passage of the Act was assured.

This legislation was amended in 1962. Most important was the inclusion of requirements that efficacy as well as safety be demonstrated before positive approval. The efficacy provision made explicit that which was always implicit.

Of course, safety cannot be determined except with reference to efficacy. The FDA always had authority to require demonstrations of efficacy as a prerequisite to approval for safety. In fact, on the eve of the 1962 Amendments, the FDA had a draft of new regulations to that end, but these were never issued. The efficacy provision was accepted by industry interests who believed that some relatively unimportant changes in the 1938 Act should be made as a substitute for efforts by the late Senator Estes Kefauver to control profitability as a primary objective. How wrong the industry representatives proved to be! The explicit efficacy requirements have revolutionized pharmaceutical assessment in the United States.

As in 1938, passage of the Kefauver legislation was uncertain or unlikely because of sustained opposition. Another catastrophe moved the issue. This time it was thalidomide, the infamous sleep-inducer, which was linked to deformities in newborn babies. A great deal of mythology has surrounded this event. The story given out to this day is that a valiant FDA physician, foreseeing danger, had blocked the approval of thalidomide, thereby demonstrating the competence and value of FDA review. The facts are that thalidomide had been blocked for non-relevant reasons, and was actually moving toward approval when the drug company itself reported the terrible news. At that time, approximately 2.5 million thalidomide tablets—potential cripplers—were in the hands of physicians as samples. It took the FDA more than four months to realize that many, many people were still at risk, but even that comprehension was provided from the outside by Dr. Helen Taussig of The Johns Hopkins University. More months then passed before the FDA moved with dispatch, this time with the aid and insistence of President John F. Kennedy. The FDA had, in this episode, been at its bureaucratic worst.

Months after the entire matter had been reported in the literature, Senator Kefauver and his staff contrived to dramatize the catastrophe through the medium of the press as a means of securing passage of his bill. The world was at last shocked into action, the 1962 Amendments were passed, new heroes were manufactured, Great Britain set up a Committee on Drug Safety, and other happenings ensued.

Nothing in the new legislation offered assurance against another thalidomide-like event. No one can legislate for the unforseeable. To this day, however, the phrase "another thalidomide" evokes public reaction and therefore arouses political and journalistic sensitivities. Furthermore, the safety component of assessment technology revolves largely around the avoidance of unlikely major catastrophes. It is a cost burden attached to the simplest of innovations.

Since 1962, the FDA has broadened its concepts of its scope beyond safety and efficacy. It is attempting or tending to control or make determinations pertaining to the following, although not specifically provided for in law:

1. Relative efficacy of drugs for stated indications.
2. Conduct of clinical research.
3. Rational therapeutics as practiced by physicians.
4. Rationality of pharmaceutical formulations, particularly as pertains to combination products.
5. Public access to relatively safe compounds used in self-medications.
6. Prices and profits in the pharmaceutical industry.

Understandably, as the FDA has entered into each of these areas through flexible interpretation of its authorities, it has engendered hostile reactions from the pharmaceutical industry and elements of the medical profession who have said: "Here you are building up your activities while you have not yet solved more fundamental problems related to safety and efficacy. Why do you spread yourself so thin when you could be using staff to get rid of backlogs?"

Hence, the decade since 1962 has been marked by increasingly strident controversy. Appropriations for staff have continued to increase, but there has been no evidence as yet of marked improvements in capability at the "desk" level of the assessment function, notwithstanding an upgrading in the leadership echelons and the acquisition of many well-qualified persons for work in the line. The most critical of the long-term personnel problems is to find incentives for medical scientists to work in an organization that presently offers little opportunity for professional growth and recognition in medical science as academically recognized.

In parallel, the consumer movement has become more vocal and legislatively more powerful—a force for good with a potential for overkill. Although many people in science are associated with consumer reform, this as-yet-undefined movement tends to be anti-science and anti-elitist. The blend of selective use of technological capabilities to conduct research and of know-nothingness is curious indeed. Augmented by insider leaks as sources of privileged knowledge, consumer advocates have utilized the existence of a politically sensitive response to achieve credibility and leverage. The consumer advocates have moved easily into a great vacuum in our technological age. They have directed their attention to problem areas that were ignored by others. In time, they will have dulled their thrust due to the inexorable workings of the institutional processes of aging, feedbacks from errors and excesses, and the inevitable diversion of public interest to more refreshing targets. One day, though, the cycle will replicate itself, as it has done before.

Let us turn now to the future. The FDA is presently developing a highly sophisticated apparatus for assessment of safety and efficacy. It may not yet exist as a perceived totality, but indications of directions can be found in utterances of top FDA officials. Nevertheless, the following elements can be discerned in being or in development:

1. Specification by the FDA of requirements for animal pharmacology and toxicology.

2. Specification of guidelines to govern scientifically-controlled clinical research on medicines by clinical categories.

3. Prior approval of protocols for the conduct of clinical research designed to validate assumptions of safety and efficacy.

4. Review of product research progress at critical stages of clinical investigation prior to submission of applications for approval.

5. The conduct of the review of new drug applications (NDAs).

6. Specification of the purposes or indications for which a medicine may be prescribed as well as circumstances under which alternative therapies are to be preferred.

7. Indirect control of doctors' prescribing practices, mainly through making them more liable to malpractice actions to assure that they conform to approved indications.

8. Monitoring of long-term clinical effects for the validation of efficacy, the modification of dosage-effect relationships, and the discovery of long-term toxicities.

I suggest for all of this the term "total linear control." It constitutes total monitoring of pharmaceutical research and development by the government, with minimum acceptance of independent discretion by otherwise private firms that would, in effect, become regulated utilities.

The activation of this apparatus would require:

1. Creation of an elaborate network of outside academic advisers to serve as *de facto* decision-makers on critical issues.

2. Upgrading of the scientific assessment staff of the FDA to perform the functions of backstopping and channeling the activities of advisory committees, participation in administrative decision-making in execution of the Commissioner's responsibilities, monitoring of clinical experience with approved drugs, and monitoring of clinical development in assigned areas.

3. Development and expansion of ancillary services, such as testing facilities, biostatistical analysis services, information retrieval and analysis services, and facilities for informational dissemination.

4. Access to extensive clinical facilities for use in testing proposed and approved medicines under a variety of conditions.

5. A substantial increase in appropriations.

Let us bypass arguments over details. The problem is systems complexity. Any complex system devised to cope with dynamic conditions is a form of utopia. It aims to define and characterize all essential components and to order and relate them within the total systems configuration. It depends for successful performance on minimizing the number of variables and on the predictability of defined performers.

A critical fallacy of this utopia is that it attempts to bring into predictable relationships matters that defy precise definition and description. To this day, no one has yet defined safety and efficacy. Nevertheless, distinguished panels attempt to make what are termed "scientific assessments" in the absence of objective basing points. A more important fallacy, among others, is that there is aways a lag between the spontaneous manifestations of conditions and problems and the solutions propounded by man. By the time solutions are devised and put into effect, conditions have changed and the solutions belong then to the past.

Elaborate systems tend to take on an elegance of their own—a baroque elegance. They become massive dust-catchers, never capable of being tidied up. As a bureaucratic phenomenon, a pre-occupation with details tends to become an end in itself—as with much of the masses of data which bureaucracies of all kinds continue to accumulate without apparent use; original purposes having long since been forgotten.

Among the more serious criticisms of utopian schemes is that if they are subject to political or administrative domination, they will be—with consequent impairment of aim and execution. The activity becomes the means, or is subsidiary to other ends. Idealized aims may be compromised for reasons of political gain or administrative advantage or survival.

The advisory function, a component of the system, is an example of idealized aim diluted politically and administratively. The aim is to bring the brightest and the best into voluntary public service in order to provide people with the benefits of the most outstanding judgments. Let us observe, however, how the environment reacts in co-opting the advisory function. First, one must observe the political imperative that under-represented components of society be drawn upon. Laudable as this is as an ancillary aim, it may exclude some of the best minds in particular areas of competence. So also with what may well be an outmoded concept of conflict of interest, which excludes medical scientists who have done work for pharmaceutical companies, thereby putting the government and industry into competition for the same leading consultants. Since administrators are concerned with outcomes, they generally tend to select advisers who are at once prominent, credible, very busy, and most likely to fulfill administrative expectations, and then to provide those busy people with reinforcing staff assistance. I see no reason to believe that the Food and Drug Administration would be different in this regard.

As an alternative to the present model, society should consider a lean structure of elegance—one that would be less elaborate as a system, but more productive of benefit. I can envisage a future FDA that is indirectly more powerful and productive, yet less directly powerful in its execution of paper operations. As a powerful catalyst, it would operate through existing institutions of society.

I propose the following principles as starting points:

1. The FDA must be concerned primarily with assessment of outcomes rather than with direct monitoring of the successive stages of research and development.

2. A preoccupation with the attainment of the risk-free or fail-safe society—not attainable in any event—should be replaced by the aim of achieving maximum benefit matched by least- or max-imum-tolerable risk as particular circumstances warrant. The growing burdens on society of constitutional and degenerative dis-orders must be relieved, in part, through a shift from an attitude of "above all do no harm" to "above all do good."

3. The people to be convinced that medicines are safe and efficacious should be the leading competent peers of the medical profession, rather than governmental functionaries. The monitoring role of government must be to see that the best decisions are reached by the best people.

4. Subject to the imperatives that there be prudent safeguards against gross and irreversible toxicity, the movement of medica-tions into the marketplace must be made much easier as a spur to innovation. The ultimate test of safety and efficacy is how man responds in significant numbers under diverse conditions over relatively long periods of time. We have tended to substitute for that ultimate test one of the fads of the times—the scientifically-controlled double blind trial. At best it is one potential source of evidence. Its limitations are mainly in the inabilities of designers and investigators to identify and to properly interrelate all key variables in the face of biological and situational unknowns.

5. There are no certain simplistic solutions. Neither are there complex ones except as conceptual exercises. The essence of de-cision in the face of complexity and mystery is to attempt to en-compass those select factors that account for most of the problem. The remainders of problems are usually not assimilable *a priori* in any event although they might account for most of the burden in decision-making.

6. Guidelines for investigation and assessment should be neither too few nor too many. Guidelines are constructed out of the past

while innovation seeks a base in new art. Guidelines and systems should be carved in plastic rather than in concrete.

7. The only way a scientifically-based bureaucracy can become part of the society of science is to become a true activity of science. To accomplish this, the FDA should vest scientific decision-making responsibility in others, reserving to itself responsibilities for co-ordination, review and oversight, and for promoting and seeing to the communication of professional goals, standards, and meth-odologies.

8. Routine decision-making should be decentralized to local academic groups subject to certification by review bodies under FDA auspices, peer groups that review evidence in support of applications for approval of plans to investigate new drugs in man. Some or many decisions could be made by certificated pharmaceu-tical manufacturers subject to standards promulgated by the FDA.

9. Non-routine decisions, or those based on important new art, should be made on referral to national standing.

10. A commission form of organization for the FDA should be considered. Apart from insulating decisions from undue political intervention, it could propound policies and regulations, mediate disputes, and administer appeals machinery.

Any fundamental changes in the organization and technology of drug assessment would have to be preceded by extensive open dialogue. Public perceptions and expectations, after many years of indoctrination in the belief that there is already in being a good system for assessment and control, cannot easily be superseded. Nevertheless, I have great confidence that reasonable and reason-ing people, dedicated to a common cause, will be able to achieve constructive and progressive results.

# Part I:
# Preclinical and Clinical Problems of New Drug Development

## Preclinical Problems of New Drug Development
William N. Hubbard, Jr.

## Comments
Guido Calabresi

## New Drug Investigations in Man: Continuing Unresolved Problems
Leon I. Goldberg and Daniel L. Azarnoff

## Comments
J. Richard Crout

# Preclinical Problems
# of New Drug Development
William N. Hubbard, Jr.

The obligation of preclinical research is to identify new compounds with biological activity of potential medicinal value in humans. It is then the responsibility of the preclinical investigator to accumulate data that justify initial single dose studies in man of the absorption, distribution, metabolism, and excretion of the compounds. When this single dose study is initiated, the clinical phase of new drug development has begun. In order to meet the elementary definition of his social function, the preclinical investigator must have strategies calculated to produce in the first instance new compounds with useful biological activity. Once such a compound is produced, the subsequent planning of preclinical investigation poses a dilemma. On the one hand there is the risk of premature abandonment of a compound that could under proper circumstances become a useful medicinal; on the other hand there is the risk of too hasty clinical administration with resultant adverse responses that are ethically indefensible. In order to serve its social function optimally, therefore, the preclinical research protocol must be designed to obtain data that are adequate to make an informed judgment, while avoiding redundancies which do not further improve that judgment as it relates to the initial studies in man. The negative statement of this dilemma is to have the preclinical systems protect against the administration of a new compound to man where the risk is not justified by the potential benefits.

In my discussion I will first consider the problems of the investigation itself. I will then describe my own understanding of the problems created for regulatory agencies by the nature of preclinical investigation. Finally, I will offer some suggestions for enhancing the process of development of new medicinals while minimizing the risk to humans.

## The Source of New Agents to be Studied for Medicinal Potential

There are three principal strategies used to develop new compounds with medicinal potentials:

First, the observation of spontaneous human biological processes with the identification, isolation, purification, and modification of the agents that are the primary causal factors in these phenomena.

The second strategem is the purification and standardization of compounds of so-called "natural" origin which are not native to, but have an effect on, the economy of the human body.

The third approach is via the broad field of medicinal chemistry, which has simultaneously been described as the ultimate rationale of structure/action drug development and the exercise of trivial molecular manipulation.

Each of these three strategies has its own characteristic problems for the discovery of new biological activity and these problems in turn create difficulties for the regulatory agencies.

## Observations of Natural Biological Activity in Humans

The success that has been achieved by this strategy is most impressive and at the present time it is the most active and fruitful line of action. The understanding of replacement of fluids and electrolytes which was developed early in this century, along with the early use of whole blood, was fundamental to the feasibility of wide use of major surgical techniques.

The subsequent development of blood fractions that are specific for human disorders represents a complex path leading from the early isolation of whole plasma to the more recent development of subtle fractions that replace genetically deficient elements in the blood of patients with rare dyscrasias.

The story of the hormones is still being unfolded in fields ranging from fertility control to the disorders of mineralization of bone. The prostaglandins and the still-controversial chalones are new chapters in this story whose significance for medicine is not yet well defined, but whose biological actions are of such importance that one can predict that they will be of high significance.

Of monumental complexity but great promise is the development of natural products associated with the manipulation of immune responses. The induction of antibodies by the use of vaccines was the historic beginning of this effort, but we now find more subtle uses such as the cellular transfer factor and antihuman thymocyte globulins. From inflammation to neoplasia, the potential manipulations of the immune response make it one of the most stimulating fields in human biology. Unfortunately, the wide interspecies differences that are observed make preclinical information of very limited use in predicting the biological effects that these compounds will have when introduced into man, much less the efficacy and safety that may be associated with them. It is a truism that no drug has a single effect, but the implications of the general systemic effects of such compounds as the prostaglandins, or compounds that interfere with the competence of the immune response, are so extensive that they create a whole new level of difficulty.

## Purification and Standardization of "Naturally" Occurring Compounds

Modern pharmacology had its origins in this strategy and so did the pharmaceutical industry. It is probable that the first compound subjected to purification and standardization was alcohol. The development of local standard wines and beers and their subsequent distillation to produce this simple chemical goes well beyond the time of recorded history. In many of the developing countries alcohol is the most widely abused drug, and is responsible for the greatest morbidity and mortality. Except as a solvent, its medicinal uses today are for the most part trivial. Historically, however, it is a compound of great interest which has been widely used with therapeutic intent.

Continuing in this reflective vein, one recalls that the most important source of medicinals until this century has been extracts from plants and herbs. The Galenical compounds have now largely passed into history, but there is still widespread value in the use of digitalis, quinine, and the derivatives of opium. The search for compounds of medicinal value in plants still continues, and the marine biologists have opened up a whole new environment for exploration.

The identification of the vitamins as prime factors in a variety of disorders beginning with scurvy and pellagra and continuing up to the present time with a new understanding of the influence of these nutritionals in the development of human intelligence, is one of the most satisfying records of the contribution of the strategy of study of naturally occurring compounds. It is probable, however, that the greatest contribution to therapy by this strategy has been made by the identification of biologically active metabolites of microorganisms. The antibiotics represent a classic story of *in vitro* observations that led to profound improvement in the therapy of human disease. The screening of soils for microorganisms whose metabolites have antimicrobial action continues annually to produce antibiotics of interesting potency. More recently some of these products of bacterial metabolism have been found useful in the treatment of malignancies. A side issue that deserves exploration is the observation that although the frequency with which such new antibiotics are discovered has not decreased, the identification of those that are suitable for human therapy has sharply fallen off in the last few years.

Because of the lack of predictive value in the structure-function relationships of naturally occurring compounds, it has been necessary to undertake laborious extraction and purification approaches. Furthermore, the unpredictability of the occurrence of useful natural compounds has resulted in massive screening programs that are intrinsically inefficient as the only available search technique for interesting activities in new compounds. Because all of these compounds are derived from sources external to the body economy, they require extended examination in an effort to predict their effects. The difficulties in achieving this latter goal with any degree of certainty creates serious problems for the authority that must certify their use in human beings.

## Medicinal Chemistry and Molecular Manipulation

Medicinal chemistry and chemotherapy had their beginnings in the observation of an exquisite specificity of the binding of organic dyes to proteins. It was recognized early that this remarkable selectivity opened the way for a bactericidal action that would not be lethal to the human host. The name of Paul Ehrlich is permanently identified with this strategy. It is of some interest to recall that his early career was devoted to the development of biological staining techniques and it was only in his later years that he turned his attention to the synthesis of arsenicals that would be tolerated in humans but would be lethal to microorganisms.

In 1909, one of his students demonstrated that the 606th compound that had been developed through molecular manipulation, which had failed to demonstrate any effectiveness against trypanosomes, was effective against the spirochete of syphilis. This monumental observation led to the development of salvarsan.

It is an interesting coincidence that in 1909 also, Höerlein suggested that the azo dyes used for wool and silk might have a medicinal value in bacterial infections. It was not until 1913 that Eisenberg demonstrated the *in vitro* bactericidal action of chrysoidin and subsequently of pyridium. In 1932 the dye, prontosil, was synthesized, and in the same year, Domagk made his classical demonstration of mouse protection. The following year, Foerster successfully used prontosil to treat a baby with a staphylococcal infection, and we entered a new era of medicinal chemistry and chemotherapy.

The antimalarials of World War II, the antitubercular compounds that came in the early 1950s, and the antitumor compounds that have been evolving since the late 1940s are all examples of the effort of the medicinal chemist in a direct lineal descent from the protein specificity theories of Paul Ehrlich.

A medicinal chemical effort of more recent origin, which holds great promise for the future, is the structural modification of naturally occurring antibiotics. The first significant success in this field was achieved in the synthetic penicillins which produced a new variety of agents with gram-negative activity. More recently the synthetic cephalosporins and lincomycins have given hope that through the molecular modification of natural antibiotics an important series of new compounds with highly sought-after novel antibacterial activity will become available.

The feedback from clinical observations to the medicinal chemist has a vital influence on the direction of chemical effort. It occasionally happens that chemical modifications are made in order to take advantage of the fortuitous clinical observations of "side effects" that represent unanticipated opportunities for therapy. The classical example of this is in the sulfonamides. It was recognized early that the antibacterial sulfonamides had diuretic and hypoglycemic activity. These observations in the clinic were a stimulus that led the medicinal chemist to manipulate the parent sulfonamide molecule in order to enhance a selected "side" effect. The result has been a whole family of diuretics and hypoglycemic agents.

Similarly, the tubercularstatic agent, isoniazid, was observed to be a mood elevator, and from this there has flowed a series of monamine oxidase inhibitors. A similar story can be told about the sedative properties of the antihistaminic promethazine, the observation of which led through molecular manipulation to the chlorpromazines and phenothiazines which have done more to diminish the incarceration of mentally-disturbed patients than all of the other therapeutic efforts combined. Finally, one recalls the effects of using phenylbutazone as a solvent for amidopyrine. Whereas phenylbutazone has no anti-inflammatory effect in laboratory animals, it was soon recognized that it had a very potent effect in man, and so began the story of the nonsteroidal anti-inflammatory agents, the earliest chapters of which are still being written. Serendipity, therefore, continues to characterize the very unpredictable events in this strategy.

Because there is no general theory that can predict the most successful line of attack in any one of these three strategies, there is a very high degree of uncertainty in all of them. Although we are learning slowly some of the elementary relationships between molecular structure and biological function, these understandings are not yet generally predictive and, in spite of some limited successes, they have generally been disappointing.

One of the most serious current problems in preclinical research aimed at the identification of new compounds of biological significance is the persistent indictment heard from regulatory agencies and from some segments of the scientific community that the medicinal chemist's efforts are usually trivial molecular manipulations rather than basic investigations. This concern has been discussed in many settings (reference 6) and except for the intensity and persistence of the attacks on medicinal chemists in the pharmaceutical industry, it would seem fatuous to discuss the biological significance of minute variations in molecular structure. The molecular defect in sickle cell disease is subtle enough that the mechanism of this politically-sensitive disorder should have persuaded those who doubted the importance of minor variations in molecular structure. The presence of a single methyl group which makes the molecule of codeine different from that of morphine should also offer to politically-sensitive critics a persuasion of the importance of small structural differences. In the preclinical phase where there is a steady feedback between the chemist and the biologist as the former proceeds with molecular manipulation, the difficulty, of course, is the ill-defined relationship between structure and function. This difficulty is exaggerated by the specific interspecies and individual intraspecies differences in animal test systems. There is no way for the chemist to know when he undertakes the synthesis of a new molecule whether he will be accused of a trivial effort or praised for a biological breakthrough. Indeed the chemist tends to be pleased if his minor modification has not entirely destroyed the biological activity of the molecule. Since, however, there is no more effective test system available than the animal model, we continue to deal with the cumulative uncertainties of molecular manipulation and variation in species response. It is, however, this very high degree of uncertainty which creates the problem. It seems to me, therefore, that the explanation of the attack by spokesmen of regulatory agencies upon molecular manipulation must be sought outside of the realm of science.

## Animal Experimentation and Evaluation of Efficacy

When a compound with interesting biological activity has been identified, it then becomes necessary to test more fully the reaction of living systems to that agent. Universally it is agreed that the test systems should in the first instance be laboratory animals rather than human beings. The reasons for this are now taken for granted, but the science of comparative pharmacology is less than 150 years old and is still considered to be in its infancy. The problems inherent in testing compounds in animals with the expectation that the results will be predictive of those obtained in man have been reviewed repeatedly in the recent literature (refs. 1, 3–7). No systematic discussion of these general problems will be offered, but I will refer to a few of the central issues in order to continue the development of the thesis that the high degree of uncertainty inherent in the research strategems for the development of new medicinals is at the root of the problems created for the regulatory agency.

Efficacy in humans is the ultimate test of a potential utility for a new medicinal compound. Medicinals are, by definition, used for the amelioration or cure of human disease. The unique quality of disease in humans creates a high degree of uncertainty that efficacy demonstrated in animal models will necessarily be valid across species lines. The obverse is also true and creates a problem. It was long thought that by moving from rodents and dogs to primates the difficulty of cross species observations of efficacy would be greatly diminished, but this has not proved to be the case. Animal models of disease are most particularly unsatisfactory in cases where the very high level of organization of the human central nervous system is at issue. Since disorders of behavior are still the greatest cause of morbidity among the human diseases, this lack of cross species specificity in animal models is crucial. The same principle also applies to animal disease models of the human cardiovascular-renal systems.

Indeed, it may be proper to say that the greater the level of complexity of the system involved in the human disease process the less the likelihood that a relevant animal model can be produced to study it. The broad field of immunology exemplifies this problem of comparative pharmacology in disease models. Although the immune response is one of the earliest biological systems to develop in evolutionary terms, adequate animal models of the most common disorders of hypersensitivity in humans have not been developed. Efficacy in disease states is the most important observation to be made about a medicinal compound and such observations have a low degree of certainty as one compares animal with human models. Positive correlations between animals and humans are relatively easy to deal with, but negative results in animals extrapolated by inference to humans cause very great difficulties indeed for regulatory agencies.

The differences in efficacy between species is mimicked in the different rates of "adverse" reactions. The toxicity of compounds in animals has a more satisfying predictive relationship to humans than the study of therapeutic efficacy. This relative degree of satisfaction, however, has an obverse side since any toxicity observed in animals leads to attempts to prove that such toxicity is not relevant to man. The enthusiasm for seeking this proof is based on the relative consistency of cross species toxicity as compared to cross species efficacy.

The following anecdote will serve to describe the kinds of problems that develop. In the very early sixties, in the laboratories of The Upjohn Company, a highly substituted pyrimidine was found to have a profound vasodilator activity in animals, its site of action being apparently in the peripheral vasculature and independent of the autonomic nervous system. When this new compound was administered to the dog, however, it was found that a lesion, which was primarily microhemorrhagic in nature, developed in the right atrium. The compound was then tested in a multitude of other animals, including primates, and no other animal demonstrated the lesion. Because of its potential benefits in humans and the very strong probability that this was an isolated species-specific lesion, the compound was submitted to a probing test in patients with life-threatening hypertensive vascular disease. The striking efficacy observed in these probing tests suggested that there was a high medicinal value in the treatment of severe hypertensive disease.

The compound was then submitted as an investigational new drug on a limited emergency protocol in January 1968. By Spring 1970, the single investigator who had been handling it on an emergency protocol sought to expand the work into a Phase II effort, that is, clinical investigations on a limited number of patients. In this two-year interval, patients who had come to autopsy as a result of their hypertensive disease after having been treated with this new compound showed no evidence of an atrial lesion. Unfortunately, because of the anxiety created by the early dog lesions, we were unable to undertake a Phase II effort. Now, in late Fall 1972, after accumulation of more animal data, it is likely that Phase II will begin.

In August 1971, one of the principal investigators of this compound submitted for approval a protocol for a simple, single dose response study in patients with moderate to severe hypertension.

After visiting the regulatory agency in September 1971 and revising the protocol according to their suggestions, the new protocol was submitted in November and recruitment of patients was initiated. No formal approval, however, was forthcoming, although no further protocol changes were proposed. Several meetings were arranged, but were postponed until January 1972, when a third revised protocol was submitted. At that time there were further requests for changes and a fourth revision of the protocol was submitted later in the same month. This appeared to be satisfactory, but it was not until mid-February that approval of the single dose response protocol was finally received—six months after the initial request for a compound which by then had been subjected to over three years of intensive study in humans with life-threatening hypertension.

During these three years it had been demonstrated that the metabolic path of the compound in dogs is different from that in primates or man, and that the principal metabolite in dogs does not occur in primates or man. On the emergency protocols, reports continue to come in of dramatic and even life-saving responses to this compound in patients who had been resistant to all other medicinals. This anecdote emphasizes the difficulty created for the regulatory agency in handling interspecies differences in toxicity under the present degrees of uncertainty about the relationship of toxicity in one species to that in man.

The problem of intraspecies differences becomes increasingly important as efforts are made to standardize the animal strains that are used in preclinical investigation. The greater variability of responses of mongrels as contrasted to inbred strains is well understood. In this connection it is important to note that man himself, as he occurs in his natural setting, is a mongrel, and it is a clinical truism that each patient's responses are different. This, of course, is also true of the responses of animals. It becomes difficult to know in specific instances where small groups are being tested whether one is dealing with species or individual differences. Among human beings the wide individual differences in response to medicinal compounds is in part a reflection of the genetic differences of these humans. Theoretically, it should be possible to unravel the genetic background of many of these differences both in animals and in humans. Up to the present time, however, little success has been achieved by this route. The result of this uncertainty is to require the examination of larger numbers of more species of animals. How much this contributes to reliability of prediction of action in humans is, to say the least, very uncertain.

In establishing a reference animal group, it is necessary to be concerned not only with the genetic configuration of that group but also to be aware of age, sex, nutritional, and health status, as well as the mood of the animals. Given the statistical and practical advantages of an inbred strain in a controlled environment, there is a growing tendency to utilize this model to minimize intra-species differences. The risk that is run in this effort is to emphasize characteristics not ordinarily observed in the mongrel strain. In our own laboratories the inbred beagle strain has an incidence of thyroiditis that is well beyond the limits of chance from the orig-inal blood line which was itself supposed to be highly refined. The most stable inbred strain of mice is so given to agitated behavior that it is useless in psycho-pharmaceutic research. There is also the problem within the inbred community of genetic drift with no obvious markers for this drift except for changes in response to standardized test systems.

The field of comparative pharmacology and toxicology originated with observations of mongrel strains. The variability in these re-sults and the increasing utilization of biostatistical techniques for confirming differences has led to the dependence upon highly in-bred strains in controlled environments. The data from many laboratories on the behavior of a given species to standard expo-sures need to be collected if we are to rely upon the significance of the observed differences as a basis for judgment of efficacy or toxicity. Without such baseline data, there is always difficulty in determining whether the efficacy or toxicity observed is drug-related in a general sense or whether it is an intraspecies differ-ence. The current method of dealing with this problem is to increase the numbers of animals and strains employed. This strategy is minimally effective and extraordinarily inefficient.

There is a clear theoretical possibility that if one could reduce the complexity of the reaction to a standard drug exposure to the level of enzyme reactions that are common to both the test system and to the human internal environment—or even at a higher level of organization if one could deal with a cellular system—then the laboratory results would be more reproducible and many of the statistical problems created by whole animal systems could be avoided. This possibility is part of the reductionist strategy that has characterized the physical and biological sciences in this cen-tury. It is beyond dispute that in making causal inferences about operations of complex systems the reductionist approach is the most powerful analytical strategy we have. It does not assure, however, that observations at the most reduced level can be utilized as a satisfying description of events in complex organizations. In the physical sciences the weak force and strong force descriptive systems now have a fair degree of independence in analytical terms. One cannot, by observing interaction of elementary particles in weak force systems, derive from these observations predictive statements that satisfy observations in the field of chemistry or mechanics. In an analogous manner, it is not possible to reconstruct from observations at subcellular and cellular levels predictive statements that will be valid at the level of organization of whole human beings.

It is paradoxically true in biological research that with reductionist approaches, the observations become more explicit and more reproducible while at the same time becoming less useful for predictive statements regarding the whole organism; much less his conscious or unconscious interaction with his external environment. Nevertheless, this reductionist approach does hold a long-range promise of avoiding many of the issues that are so troublesome in the biology of the whole animal. One must, however, exercise modesty and caution in the temptation to extrapolate from cell or extract systems to whole living beings. We now recognize that the temptation to extrapolate from animal data to human data is fraught with danger; nevertheless, the degrees of certainty available in these systems make them essential because they represent the best available strategies we have to rationalize the introduction of new compounds into humans for medicinal purposes.

Those adverse reactions that occur very rarely or in patients who may be taking more than one medication simultaneously are special problems for animal test systems. The technique of testing increasing number of animals and species while at the same time introducing increasing number of drugs simultaneously in an effort to expose these uncommon events creates a high probability of the random occurrence of negative findings simply as a function of numbers of tests performed and the number of animals participating in each test. As a statistical problem, this is not a matter of great significance; but the inability of regulatory agencies to assimilate even random negative information makes the problem severe. It becomes the responsibility of the investigator to demonstrate that a random occurrence does not have significance in man, even as a rare adverse response. Since there is actually no way to construct a direct proof of this negative postulate, one is left with further dependence upon larger numbers and a greater variety of strains in order to deal statistically with the issue of random events. The problems of the regulatory agencies in dealing with negative data, therefore, exert a profound influence on the strategy and efficiency of preclinical research. It is in this area, in my opinion, that the highest likelihood of noncontributory redundancy exists. Ultimately the decision to introduce a new compound in man must be subjective and based on values. It cannot in the final analysis be strictly scientific and surely it is not a biostatistical phenomenon. Just as surely as one cannot depend entirely on intuition for this important decision, so one cannot depend entirely upon scientific explanation and biostatistical analysis. Since opinion is easily attacked at the political level and scientific explanation tends to be obscure enough to provide itself with some protection, there is a human tendency to act upon this difference in liability to political exposure.

## The Problems Created for Regulatory Agencies by the Uncertainty of Preclinical Research

It has been stated that it would be very difficult today to introduce digitalis or penicillin as new medicinals because of the toxicity they demonstrate in animals. It has further been suggested that no pharmaceutical company would attempt to introduce aspirin because of the problems of distinguishing aspirin from placebo in most situations. In my opinion these speculations are not justified. My own impression is that over some extended span of time both digitalis and penicillin would be released under today's regulations for trials in man. The question, therefore, is whether the delay imposed by current regulations serves human purpose and the public interest in a positive way.

The sad fact is that the present regulations have been formulated as a result of terrible tragedies. The 1938 regulations were stimulated primarily by the deaths caused by the use of an elixir of sulfanilamide that had a toxic vehicle. The regulations under which we operate now in the United States, dating to the laws of 1962, were derived from the public reaction to the thalidomide tragedy in Germany. One result of the origins of the present legislation, unfortunately, has been to create an adversary role between industry and the regulatory agency as if their purposes were in contest, with the public interest being threatened by the industry and protected by the regulatory agency. There is in the legal structure for the agency no franchise to offer a positive environment for the development and introduction of important new therapeutic entities. On the contrary, the entire regulatory structure is negative in its language and based on an implicit reiteration of the assumption of conflicting social goals. In actual practice, it is not a difference of understanding of the nature of science nor a difference of intent insofar as the public good is concerned that separates the positions of the regulatory agency and the responsible pharmaceutical company; rather, it is a problem of judgment in degree, not in principle. The agency itself does not and, in fact, cannot be expected to maintain on its staff the full range of scientific competence which is necessary to interpret all the data presented to it. In its role as political adversary, however, it is obligated to be the instrument of this interpretation. One of the most confused issues in the present setting is the role of advisory committees, of which there surely is no shortage. The problem for the regulatory agency is what is to be done with their advice. The committee itself has no legal status since the obligation for decision rests with the agency. There is therefore a tendency for the agency to utilize such advice as is consistent with its own prior views and to be reluctant to accept deviant opinions. Since those who offer the opinions carry no legal responsibility for their implications, it is reasonable that the responsible party rests most heavily upon the advice that supports its own final judgments.

This question of the location of the final judgment is a crucial one. The regulatory authority works with value judgments such as safety, efficacy, risk-to-benefit relationships, and even the general public welfare as contrasted to individual benefits. In making these judgments it places its nominal reliance upon adequate controlled clinical trials. The jump from scientific explanation to value judgment is across an abyss that is nearly infinite. These comments are made, not to detract from the importance of scientific explanation, but to discriminate between that effort and the effort to make value judgments. Intuition and an anecdotal kind of life experience have no place in scientific explanation. On the other hand, these portions of human life are at least contributory to undertaking value judgments. In point of fact, these matters are very well understood both by those in the regulatory agency and those in the pharmaceutical industry, but both of these partners must operate in the real environment of the regulatory function.

This real environment has three realms. The first of these is the scientific. There is really very little problem in dealing with scientific explanation between the participants, but the judgments of causal inference can be heavily influenced by the other two components of the realm. The second component is the legal one. This is made up of the basic law that creates the agency, and the regulations and legal precedents that have accumulated over the years. The agency is not able to deal freely with scientific inferences of causation, but must make these inferences in the light of legislation. The Delaney Amendment, although the most notorious, is by no means the only example of this constraint. Reference has already been made to the adversary relationship that the law imposes on the regulatory agency, and this adversary relationship is exaggerated insistently by the demands of the third and most important component of the realm.

The most important influence on the actions of the regulatory agency is the political pressure exerted upon it. In concert with the mass media, the regulatory agency is continuously badgered for not fulfilling adequately its role as adversary. It is almost never criticized for failing to make any decisions—particularly where any negative information at all is in hand—and indeed the history of the handling of thalidomide in the United States is a classic example of the rewards of procrastination. The continuing tendency in the United States to imply conspiracy between government and industry against the interest of the general welfare finds particular emphasis in the case of the regulatory agency. The result is inevitably to complicate and delay the decision-making process.

In my view, it is only by the active participation of preclinical and clinical scientists from all sectors, but particularly from the academic community, in support of the regulatory agency's efforts to optimize the introduction of new medicinal agents that we will improve the way in which we handle the dilemma that we confront. The public welfare demands assurance that pharmaceuticals are safe and effective for their intended use. This assurance must be monitored by an independent agency. That agency, however, needs the support of, and indeed the protection from, its political and legal antagonists if its judgments are to be most heavily dependent upon scientific explanation and the opinions of experts in the field. I have had abundant opportunity to be well aware that the academic community does not welcome this kind of assignment. I would only suggest that in avoiding this obligation it is failing to serve the best public interest.

In a concluding postscript let me refer briefly to some of the economics of the pharmaceutical industry and the implications of today's discussion for it. I am assuming that the function of a pharmaceutical industry, which is the development of a therapeutic entity to a useful final dosage form and its distribution to the medical community, is a function that will be served by some institution, whether state or private.

The first essential for the pharmaceutical industry is to recognize a health need that can be met by medicinals. If the agent produced by the pharmaceutical industry is ineffective for its intended use, then it is not worth developing or promoting in a company that is based on research.

In an effort to improve upon existing medicinals, companies frequently come upon minor changes, any one of which is relatively insignificant, but offers a potentially useful difference. These so-called "me too" compounds are at least a sure antidote for the monopolistic problems of the original entry. Every company would prefer to market only major breakthroughs that represent unique contributions to therapy. In fact, companies survive between such rare experiences by introducing variations of compounds which may have more potency, may be more convenient in dosage forms, or may have variations in side effects which are of potential value to some patients. No company sets out in the first instance to avoid major findings by emphasizing minor endeavors.

Ultimately, however, as the costs of introducing a new therapeutic agent increase and the inherent uncertainty of research efforts is not reduced, while the adversary role of the regulatory agency is increasingly emphasized through political pressure, a change will take place in the conduct of new drug development. This change will be a reluctance to pursue any but the most promising observations and to limit the investment in preclinical research, since it will obviously be possible to pursue only a very few clinical investigations. A few pharmaceutical companies have already either reduced or abandoned research efforts. There is no other institution in our society now constituted to initiate such endeavor. The long-term effect is therefore inevitably to delay and diminish the number of new entities introduced. This trend is less apparent on the continent of Europe and in Japan. It would be a matter of some interest to know what the reasons for this difference might be and to what degree the public interest is served by it.

In the last analysis the public's interests will be served by the development of medicinal agents that do not yet exist. This positive purpose must be served both by the investigator and the member of the regulatory agency. The negative political and legal pressures exerted on the regulatory agency and the negative economic pressures exerted on the preclinical investigator do not support this positive purpose, and are therefore, in my opinion, contrary to the public welfare.

# References

1. Carr, E. A., Jr., "Extrapolation of Pharmacologic Data: Lower Animals to Man," *Federation Proceedings* 26, No. 4, July–August 1967, pp. 1089–1096.

2. Carr, E. A., Jr., (personal communications), Address: "Relating Animal Data to Man," International Society of Clinical Pharmacology, San Francisco, California, July 28, 1972.

3. Koppanyi, T., and Avery, M. A., "Species Differences and the Clinical Trial of New Drugs," *Clinical Pharmacology Therapeutics,* 7, 1966, pp. 250–70.

4. Modell, W. (ed.). *Symposium on Clinical Drug Evaluation and Human Pharmacology.* St. Louis: C. V. Mosby Co., 1962.

5. Schein, P. S., et al., "The Evaluation of Anticancer Drugs in Dogs and Monkeys for the Prediction of Qualitative Toxicities," *Clinical Pharmacology Therapeutics,* 11:3, 1970.

6. Schueler, F. W. (ed.), "Symposium on Molecular Modification in Drug Design," American Chemical Society, 1964.

7. Wolstenholme, G., and Porter, R. (eds.). *Symposium on Drug Responses in Man.* Boston: Little, Brown & Co., 1967.

# Comments on Preclinical Problems of New Drug Development
Guido Calabresi

I'm not quite sure why I have been asked to comment on a paper which in many of its aspects is technical, but I have decided that, if I am to be here, my only function is to be argumentative. So I shall proceed to be argumentative.

I think that Dr. Hubbard's paper is a very elegant description of the central problems. If any of you have not looked at it, I would urge you to read at least the marvelous example about the anti-hypertensive drug and the dog, which suggests the problems involved. Although I enjoyed it, when I got to the conclusions that seemed to follow from this paper, I was rather troubled, because the conclusions seemed to be that what we need is a better agency with more academic participation and better understanding of the problems. This is not really very different from the type of conclusion we associate with Mr. Ralph Nader.

Dr. Hubbard shares with Mr. Nader the view that what we need is a better agency, but he would probably disagree on what the better agency should do. I would suggest that that ought to be troublesome. When one finds oneself saying that everything would be fine if only the regulators were wiser, one ought to realize that one is in trouble. The object the "wise regulators" should seek is to maximize benefits and minimize harms: fine; that's a pretty common object. But how should they go about doing this? That is the issue worth worrying about.

I would suggest that in situations like this there are two polar ways of deciding whether the benefits are worth the harm. I would like to talk about these, though my own inclination has generally been to seek a middle way. Either we can decide in some collective, regulatory manner if a risk is worthwhile, and then bar the risky activity (levy costs, inflict stigmas, use the whip, the thumbscrew, or anything you want on the person or company who dares violate that Rule); or we can decide instead who is best suited to decide whether a risk is worthwhile and let him get the profits and benefits of a correct guess and bear the costs of a bad guess. The first way is what I call the regulatory way, the second is the incentive way.

Everybody here tells me that all we can do is guess about the risks or benefits of introducing a new drug; that it is impossible to be certain. Under such circumstances, it is still possible to set up a system that will award the profits or benefits of a correct guess to the person or activity that is best suited to make a guess, and let the losses or costs (however we choose to define them) fall on that same person or activity if the guess is wrong. We then can relax and let that person or activity guess.

Now, in a perfect world, in a utopia, both the regulatory and the incentive methods I have described would work perfectly. In our world, neither does. Dr. Hubbard chooses a variant of what is still the most popular way, the regulatory way. I would suggest that the variants of this way are really more complicated than we think. I said that Mr. Nader would choose another variant of the regulatory way, and I would suggest that what we did before we had an FDA was yet another variant of the same way. This is the negligence or fault system, a variant of the regulatory method of which Professor Richard Posner is very fond. This system involves having a judge and jury tell us whether an individual company should have realized that the benefits of introducing a new drug were less than the costs to society of doing so. If so, the costs and some stigma would be put on the company, "the wrongdoer." I don't think the fault system worked very well in this area. At least, we all know that it did not work well enough to keep us from getting the FDA.

I would suggest that the traditional method employed for deciding how goods and services should be produced in our society is, instead, a variant of the incentive way, since it involves putting the profits or losses on the party best suited to guess. In easy cases, it's an easy variant to prefer.

We might consider, by way of contrast, how either Dr. Hubbard or Professor Posner would feel about a regulatory agency deciding such "easy cases," as for instance whether a new type of shoe or a new industrial plant is needed, or is likely to be wasteful. That is whether, looking at it prospectively, the benefits from having the new shoes are greater or less than the costs. There are, of course, areas where just such decisions *are* made by regulatory agencies. One instance is where what lawyers call a certificate of public convenience and necessity is required to undertake an activity.

A similar choice could, instead, be left to a judge and jury. They could decide, retrospectively, whether the entry of a new plant or a new product was foreseeably likely to create greater benefits or losses. If foreseeably the results seemed to be good, even though in fact they turned out to be catastrophic, this ("fault") approach would say: "You who came in (the new facility) do not need to bear any of the losses which you have imposed on society."

Both these variants of the regulatory method should be contrasted with the approach that we usually take in this area. The usual way says: "Let the person who would produce a new shoe evaluate the costs and benefits of the innovation. If the benefits are sufficient, he will make money. If there are losses, he will bear them." The fact that this is a situation of uncertainty, that we don't know ahead of time whether the new shoe is worthwhile, doesn't really bother us. Indeed, there is a theory in economics, associated, I think, with Frank Knight in this country and Gustavo Del Vecchio in Europe, which suggests that such situations of uncertainty are the only sources of "true profits" (as against economic rents, monopoly profits, and interest). That is, profits are viewed as the returns for taking an uninsurable risk that works out well. The other side, of course, is that the enterpreneur can be wiped out if the uninsurable risk proves to be a bad one.

By instinct, I prefer the incentive system. I say "by instinct" because it is not clear that because one system or approach works better in one area it is going to work better in another. I think each situation has to be looked at individually. Thus, I do not think there is any necessary inconsistency between Professor Posner's criticism of regulatory agencies in the utility area and defense of the fault system in the accident area. It is always an empirical question whether a variant of the regulatory or the incentive system will work better in a particular area.

Now, let us consider pharmaceuticals. In the FDA we have a regulatory system. Could an incentive approach be established? The first question under such a system would be who is better suited to evaluate the harms and benefits of new drugs and to decide when the introduction of one of these is worthwhile. That is, whom do we wish to reward for good guesses and charge for bad ones, because they are most likely to guess well.

Professor Cooper said that business decisions ought to be made by business people, and automatically assumed—and I rather agree with him—that "business people" in this context are the drug companies, with the academic establishment and medical doctors tied into them as consultants. What was missing, in my view, from Professor Cooper's presentation was the notion that the costs of a bad guess should be put on these same business people, although that may have been implicit in his presentation. I would agree with that general approach because I suspect that there is very little that the ultimate consumer can actually know in most situations about whether a new drug is likely to require more research or not. Compared with the drug companies, or conceivably the doctors, he is not very well qualified to make this kind of guess.

The problem, then, is not so much in identifying who is better suited to guess—I think most people would agree on this—it is rather that the drug industry itself probably does not much like that solution. Industry (as was suggested by Professor Milton Friedman a while back, and by Adam Smith even further back) on the whole prefers regulations, or standards, on the assumption that although standards are rough for a while, basically they can also be lived with. They involve less risk and often create opportunities for excluding innovators and other potential competitors. And yet, in the longer run, the only reason we have a private drug industry rather than a governmental drug industry is because we want some organization that can take this kind of risk.

As a result, in the very long run, I think the drug companies are talking against their interests in supporting, as Dr. Hubbard does, standards set by "wise regulators" instead of full risk bearing. Still, one cannot expect the head of a drug company to say "we would rather have a situation where we bear great risks than standards with which we can live today, because in the long run the first is better for free enterprise." He is not likely to have that much patience or understanding. I would suggest that one function of people like us is to help drug company executives to try to understand that argument.

Once we decide that the incentive approach may be worthwhile in the drug licensing area and that the drug companies are those whom we wish to reward for good guesses and charge for bad ones, we immediately have another series of very difficult problems. The first one is: what are the costs, and how can we define the costs when they involve people who die or suffer in different ways as a result of the introduction of new drugs?

This terribly difficult problem occurs in a variety of areas in our society and although no solution to it is perfect, an attempt at a solution is inevitable. Obviously, the more a society is interested in erring on the side of safety and the status quo, the higher the value it will give to the costs which will be put on the drug companies when there is an untoward drug reaction. To the extent that the society is more interested in the earlier introduction of new drugs, presumably because it guesses that, over long periods of time, such early introduction of new drugs is going to pay off, then it will value these costs less. In short, if we use a free enterprise system to strike a balance, we will express our views, as to which errors are most harmful, in the concept of cost we use in the balancing.

I would emphasize, though, that if it is difficult to evaluate these costs, it is no less difficult to do the same thing under a regulatory system. That is, we may think we are avoiding the problem by giving it to a regulatory agency like the FDA, because we do not *monetize* the cost of people killed as against the cost of having others die because new drugs have not come in, but the same problem is there. It is true that monetizing such costs (which incidentally we would still do if we used the judge-jury type of regulatory system) creates some problems of its own, because we hate to be told that human beings are worth money. In this sense, therefore, there is an advantage to the FDA in that it avoids *monetization*. There is, however, an equivalent, and as great, a problem with non-monetization. This is the fact that when some centralized collective agency makes a mistake, that very mistake amounts to a statement by society that lives are not worth very much to it. And there are costs attached to that kind of statement which are, to my mind, as great as the costs of monetization.

If I may wander a little afield to give you an example of this: last year there was a case involving the Pentagon Papers. When the case came up to the Supreme Court, Mr. Justice Stewart asked counsel for *The New York Times*, Alexander Bickel, whether he would argue against prior restraint (whether he would argue that the newspaper should be allowed to publish) in a case in which it could be shown that a hundred people would die if publication occurred. Justice Stewart said: "Would this not amount to a judicial sentence of death to a hundred people?" Mr. Bickel answered, in effect: In this case, there is no such problem; don't worry about it until you get a case which has the problem. Justice Stewart didn't, and decided the case the way; he wanted to.

I take it that Mr. Justice Black sitting near Stewart would have said: "The issue is precisely as you put it. It is not that a hundred people might die for the sake of freedom of the press. That would be a very small cost indeed. The problem is that there would be a court, in effect judicially, sentencing a hundred people to death! *That* is the problem. A hundred people die for far less interesting reasons all the time. What we have to do is create a system where we don't have the federal judiciary or any other branch of government in some sense directly saying that a hundred people should die for this reason."

I would argue that, on the whole, a system that puts the costs which arise from the introduction of new drugs on the drug company is less likely to create the kind of situation in which it can be said that some victims have clearly been sacrificed by our government, than does a system where the choice of allowing a new drug rests with a centralized government agency. A mistake by the FDA based on a wrong cost-benefit analysis is the same as the government saying that lives are not worth much. A mistake by a drug company for which it must pay compensation may be a tragedy, but it is not the equivalent to "a judicial sentencing to death."

The second of the series of problems which would arise if we were to use an incentive system of new drug control is fairly specific to the drug area. If we were to put the risks of errors on the industry, there may be a danger that adverse reactions from drugs will be hidden, and successful hiding of adverse reactions would destroy the effectiveness of the incentive system. If we assume not only that the patient is ignorant, too ignorant to make an adequate choice (which I'm willing to assume in this area, though not in all others), if we assume further that that ignorance need be just a little bit greater in order for the patient not even to know that he has been injured, then we have to be very sure that we have a system that induces others to reveal the existence of adverse reactions. For we need this information in order to put the correct cost incentive on what I have elsewhere called the cheapest avoider, the one best suited to guess.

This is not the place to spell out specific proposals to deal with such problems. I will mention one way of dealing with the question not as a proposal but more as an example of how the problem can be approached. We could co-opt the doctors by giving them immunity from malpractice suits in cases of adverse drug reactions if they make a timely report describing the facts which indicate that an adverse reaction may have occurred. Such information would be reported to some collating agency, preferably governmental.

There are, of course, problems with how one would deal with immunity of doctors in such situations; how would one keep them from inventing adverse reactions in order to be free from a malpractice suit in a case where they made the error and the drug did no harm. It is the existence of such highly technical issues which would make any "proposal" far too premature. Let me suggest, however, that these problems, and the administrative costs of resolving them, are likely to be nowhere near as great as the administrative cost and the baroque elegance which the FDA would achieve were it to begin to do the job we have assigned to it.

My conclusion, without going further into details, is to say that I think Dr. Hubbard is, like Mr. Nader though for very different reasons, barking up the same wrong tree when he suggests that the trouble with regulation is mainly that we need better regulators.

The trouble with this view is that it ignores the fact that there are things which regulators are not likely to be able to foresee well, and hence to regulate well, no matter how well disposed they are.

My view does not exclude regulation where there is reason to believe that regulators can guess well, or in some situations where guessing is not involved. Thus, I have not discussed the issue of the "harmless" but "ineffective" drug because that issue presents quite different practical problems of who can judge the facts best. I have focused on the introduction of effective but potentially dangerous drugs. Here, no one will be able to foresee perfectly. As a result, we should seek out the people who are most able to foresee reasonably well and give them an appropriate cost incentive to make that decision well. Then, foregoing the search for ultimate wisdom, we are likely to come out with a wise result.

# New Drug Investigations in Man: Continuing Unresolved Problems
Leon I. Goldberg and Daniel L. Azarnoff

Ten years have elapsed since the passage of the Kefauver-Harris Bill, and now would seem a good time to evaluate the influence of this bill on investigations of new drugs in man. One way to accomplish this is to consider from scientific, ethical, and regulatory viewpoints, the current problems faced by clinical pharmacologists.

To carry out their charge under the drug regulatory laws, the Food and Drug Administration (FDA) has promulgated regulations dividing new drug evaluations into three phases. Each represents a different type of effort and requires different expertise. Therefore, we will discuss them separately.

## Phase I: Clinical Pharmacology

In Phase I, the drug is administered for the first time to a human being. The principal goals of these studies are to determine (1) how the drug is absorbed, metabolized, and eliminated; (2) levels of the drug that are tolerated; and (3) any obvious toxic effects. Normal subjects are usually enlisted for these studies, which are primarily conducted in hospitals or institutionalized environments where the subject can be continuously followed. One of the more common subject groups is prisoners. Elaborate testing facilities have been developed in state and county prisons by private foundations, universities, and the pharmaceutical industry.

This phase of investigation represents an intense collaborative effort by many different scientists. The clinical pharmacologist must be well versed in pharmacology and toxicology in order to understand the preclinical data and to communicate with the basic scientists. This communication must be maintained, for additional laboratory studies are usually required as the initial human observations suggest need for further information. For example, when the metabolic pathway of a drug is determined in the first few humans, more definitive animal studies can be carried out, utilizing the species which handles the drug most similarly to man. Although there are some generalizations concerning the more preferred species there are so many exceptions that each drug must be studied individually. This is one of the pressing reasons for administering the drug to a human being as soon as possible. Clearly many hours, dollars, and experimental animals are wasted in the shotgun approach that is used before the human studies.

Several unresolved (and perhaps unresolvable!) problems are met in Phase I.

1. For how long, in what dose, to how many animals, and by

what route must a drug be administered to experimental animals before it is given in one small dose to a human being? One adversary of the present regulations has concluded that all drugs must be administered to experimental animals for two years before a single human study is done in order to minimize the danger of carcinogenesis. There are many cogent arguments against this approach. First, tumors may be produced in animals by metabolites that do not occur in man and, thus, have no clinical significance whatsoever. Second, the risk of producing a malignancy with a few administrations of the drug in doses hundreds of times smaller than those used in animal studies is probably very slight. Third, withholding a potentially useful drug for two years may delay treatment of thousands of patients badly needing the agent. A most extreme example would be penicillin. The problem should not be belittled, but the fear of cancer should not obstruct new drug development. Isoniazid induces cancer in experimental animals although it still is used clinically with no evidence of an increase in the incidence of malignancy in patients who have received it for many years. The need must obviously outweigh the risk. A recent example of a drug that was speeded through trial was the anti-Parkinson agent, L-dopa.

2. The next problem that troubles many of us is the extent to which trials should be carried out on the normal subject. This is an extremely difficult decision, with eloquent and well-meaning adversaries at two opposite poles. One group of experts would like the FDA to demand the most painstaking investigations including the potentially dangerous procedures such as cardiac catheterizations and liver biopsies. The other position is that no normal subjects should be used, and all new drugs should be administered to diseased patients in whom the risk can be morally defended since they may possibly benefit from the drug.

It is obvious that neither extreme can be accepted, and that clinical pharmacologists with the advice of appropriate ethical committees must have a certain amount of freedom in this area. We may want to examine this dilemma a little further. The advantages of using normal subjects are that the metabolic and laboratory data obtained would not be altered by disease processes, nor would subjective and objective signs of toxicity be mistaken for symptoms of the disease. The advantages of studying patients are similarly persuasive. Since a drug must ultimately be utilized by patients, would it not be better to discover immediately how the disease process affects the metabolism of a drug? A second and perhaps more important reason for studying a drug in patients with disease is the determination of efficacy. If a drug is effective, then further basic studies can be carried out in normal subjects; if it is ineffective, the risk to normal subjects can be eliminated.

A more detailed discussion of this problem was presented by Dr. Azarnoff at the first Deer Lodge Conference on Clinical Pharmacology.

3. The third problem that might be considered is whether Phase I studies should be regulated by the FDA or whether they should be handled more appropriately by local committees. Not too long ago, it was possible for an investigator to submit a Phase I study plan, following approval by his local committee, and begin his studies immediately. Now he must wait 30 days to obtain clearance from the FDA and this period may be greatly prolonged by continuing minor reservations. The argument against federal regulation of Phase I studies is that these investigations do not represent a public health hazard, and primarily involve questions of ethics which at present are handled principally by local peer group committees. It is in this area that much criticism of regulations has been based. Academic scientists in particular are frustrated by FDA regulations since their research frequently involves administration of compounds that are not generally classified as drugs nor ultimately intended for commercial purposes. Such compounds are administered as research tools to investigate biochemical and physiological mechanisms. One example might be the use of an amino acid that is obtained in its purest form from a chemical corporation and represents no more of the ingredient than is taken in normal foodstuffs; yet an FDA monitor could interpret this investigation as a new drug study and demand all of the animal data required of a new chemical substance. The unfortunate result of the regulations as now written is that law-abiding investigators who submit their plans to the FDA may be prevented from undertaking the study at all. Review of the medical literature suggests that literally hundreds of compounds have been administered to man since the Kefauver-Harris regulations were approved, without receiving FDA sanction. The legal implications of this state of affairs are obvious.

## Phase II: Clinical Investigations

Clinical investigations involve treatment of a limited number of patients with the new drug. The observations are frequently as detailed as Phase I, but there is the additional objective of observing the effects of the drug on the prevention or control of a disease or symptom. These studies usually begin in a very few patients, but may include several hundred before clearance is obtained for progression into the next phase. The problems faced in Phase II are similar to those in any experimental study with patients. The disease process of the selected patients must be reasonably expected to be affected by the drug. Only rarely is it of value to study patients with terminal disease. Much of the effort from this phase is expended in choosing appropriate patients and designing the study so that changes that would occur by chance can be minimized. At this stage, false negative results may forever stop investigations on a class of compounds that are indeed therapeutically beneficial to patients. It is important to emphasize that a rigid set of guidelines for all disease categories can never be written, even though the FDA is now making an effort to establish guidelines for each disease category and for drugs used in their treatment. We consider that it would be a mistake to set guidelines so rigidly that innovative methodology cannot be employed.

During Phases I and II, the drug is usually administered in capsules or dosage forms that may not be similar to the marketed product. An attempt should therefore be made to delineate the effective blood level range as a guide to future bio-availability problems.

# Phase III: Clinical Trial Phase

The purpose of Phase III is to establish the safety and appropriate dosage of the drug for the various patients on whom it will be used. Large numbers of patients are studied in this phase, usually in an outpatient environment. The principal problem is to design an investigation that will give accurate results with the smallest number of patients. Frequently, when subjective symptoms are being investigated, a double-blind control study may be most appropriate. In other cases, when clear objective findings are the end points, it may not be necessary to employ double-blind techniques.

One of the major problems in this area is to recruit patients sufficiently motivated to comply completely with the requirements of the design. Many studies have failed because many patients were not reliable in taking their medications or were erratic in returning to the clinic. In order to minimize these difficulties, an even larger number of patients must be screened and special facilities must be provided so that those chosen can be followed easily. Great progress has been made in this area by the establishment of special clinics in a number of universities. The National Institutes of Health (NIH) has supported controlled outpatient studies for specific drugs and provided adequate support for the cooperating clinics. Large, multiclinic, long-term cooperative trials are essential to the proper evaluation of drugs to be used for treatment of chronic ills. It is no longer tenable to treat biochemical changes associated with an illness (for example, sugar diabetes or plasma lipids in coronary heart disease) without evidence that the patient is being benefited. Such long-term trials are difficult and expensive. It is time to decide how much of the cost will be borne by governmental agencies and how much by industry. Taxes and the price of drugs ultimately pass the cost of these studies on to the consumer.

By the time the drug reaches Phase III, hundreds of thousands and sometimes millions of dollars have been spent in its development. It is thus extremely important to make a careful view of the adverse reactions which may require that the investigation of the drug be discontinued in this phase. Here, improvement of the communications between the regulatory officials and the monitors of the drug company is of great importance. As investigators, we can recite many instances where an investigator has obtained one set of instructions concerning the continuation of a study from the drug company monitor, and another from the FDA official.

## General Problems and Suggestions for Improving New Drug Investigations

It is obvious that each phase of new drug development requires individuals with specific expertise, and that clinical pharmacologists or someone with similar training must be involved in each phase of the investigation. Clinical pharmacology as a special branch of pharmacology has made considerable progress since the passage of the Kefauver-Harris legislation. Substantial grants have been made by the NIH, the Burroughs Wellcome Fund, and the Pharmaceutical Manufacturers' Association Foundation to support clinical pharmacology units in a number of medical schools. The field, however, is still in a developmental phase and it is difficult to predict whether it will survive as an academic discipline. Universities in general have been unable to provide the long-term support required to recruit outstanding faculty members. Several well-known clinical pharmacologists have accepted chairmanships of departments of pharmacology and other academic positions ranging from dean to directors of clinical research facilities. It is unfortunate that, faced with a dire need to educate medical students, house officers, and postgraduate students in the principles of modern clinical pharmacology as well as to participate in new drug research, these individuals have not continued as full-time clinical pharmacologists. It is to be hoped that they will be able to influence development of the discipline from the vantage point of their administrative positions. The trend away from active participation in clinical pharmacology could be reversed by establishing chairs of clinical pharmacology such as those at Harvard and Johns Hopkins. It remains to be seen whether these two chairs will serve the purpose, since the holders have been individuals who have distinguished themselves in molecular biology rather than in clinical pharmacology.

Another disturbing problem has been the relative lack of recruits into clinical pharmacology. Despite the establishment of several training programs and the large demand for clinical pharmacologists, there have been too few trainees to fill all the available positions. Several reasons for this bear discussion. Many young people feel that they must become proficient in an organ-oriented discipline such as cardiology or neurology in order to have patient privileges in the more government-oriented medicine of the future. Clinical pharmacology is not a recognized sub-specialty, and the progressive young man who chooses academic life may not wish to spend two or more years after completion of an internship and residency unless he can acquire sub-specialty certification. Clinical faculties of medical schools are also usually organized on a sub-specialty basis. One approach to the problem has been to train other sub-specialties in clinical pharmacology, but this unfortunately does not result in the development of a well-rounded clinical pharmacologist with a broad interest in drugs. Instead, such individuals tend to favor their sub-specialty and are willing to investigate drugs used only in their particular area.

The second reason may be economic pressure. The practice of medicine has become increasingly lucrative, particularly in the sub-specialties. The training in clinical pharmacology does not give immediate promise of a secure financial future, particularly at a time when most clinical faculty members supplement their salary with professional fees. After two years of specialty training, the clinical pharmacologist cannot hang out his shingle, as can the individual completing training in cardiology, hematology, or pulmonary disease, and expect patients to flock to his door as a subspecialist. Thus the trainee in clinical pharmacology sees his career in academic medicine, the pharmaceutical industry, or government.

Finally, many medical schools still do not have clinical pharmacology units and the students and house staff are not aware of it as a career choice. Since the supply of clinical pharmacologists will depend primarily upon the numbers trained in medical schools and upon faculty positions available to them, the number will not increase significantly until chairmen of clinical departments accept the idea that clinical pharmacology is as necessary and important as any other sub-specialty. Although this may sound like an academic problem, it is easy to see how the number of clinical pharmacologists available for new drug development is dependent upon such acceptance.

## Ethical Problems of Clinical Investigators

The ethical issues in human experimentation involve problems that can never be satisfactorily solved. Thousands of words have already been written on this subject, and thousands more will undoubtedly be added. There will never be a perfect solution, because we must deal with the rights of individuals on one hand and the needs of society on the other. At the present time, both the FDA and the NIH require a peer group review by other physicians and informed laymen before any human investigation can be carried out. The investigating institution is required to provide assurance to the NIH that the committee will be assigned responsibility to determine for each activity planned and conducted that: (1) the rights and welfare of subjects are adequately protected; (2) the risks to subjects are outweighed by potential benefits; and (3) the informed consent of subjects will be obtained by methods that are adequate and appropriate. The institution must also provide evidence that informed consent of the subjects *is* obtained and that the projects are under continuing review. Initially, the universities were permitted to develop procedures in a flexible manner, but recently the Department of Health, Education and Welfare (HEW) has insisted upon more rigid interpretations which could impede research. There is, however, evidence that some local committees are far more restrictive than HEW or the FDA. To strengthen the system, the investigator needs some type of Court of Appeals, and it is then hoped that this subject will be discussed. It should be obvious that, despite all these guidelines, the question of informed consent and adherence to regulations depends primarily upon the ethics of the individual investigator.

In addition to all the written regulations, the investigator faces many untested legal problems which must often restrain individuals from entering our field. The question of no fault insurance should again be considered.

# The Future

There is, we believe, general agreement that many of the problems of clinical investigation and of the regulations that control it are based on the fact that the issues are not clear cut. We lack sufficient scientific information in many areas to be certain of the best way to conduct either animal or human investigations. Thus, research must continue to provide regulatory agencies with more sound information.

To facilitate its work, the FDA must be permitted to bring in the best available minds to assist in making their sometimes awesome decisions. Although there are many who would debate this point, we have observed distinct changes in the FDA since the present administrators took office. In the first place, the present commissioner has been successful in attracting several outstanding scientists and clinical investigators into the FDA. Secondly, consultants from the universities, private practice, and industry are much more frequently called upon for opinions than in the past. It is one of the paradoxes of today's world that although the use of consultants by the FDA is for the benefit of the ultimate consumer of drugs, the patients, a serious attack against use of such consultants recently came from one of Ralph Nader's groups, the Health Service Committee. In a report signed by Dr. Sidney Wolf and Ms. Anita Johnson, it was insisted that no consultant who has ever studied a new drug provided by industry should be called in by the FDA. Since most new drugs are supplied by industry, adopting this suggestion would necessarily eliminate most experienced consultants. The conclusion of the report was that only full-time government employees are sufficiently disinterested to make unbiased decisions. Unfortunately, one of the major problems confronted by the FDA is that these purely regulatory officials occasionally are not adequately trained for their task and certainly cannot encompass the entire area of science. Therefore, the advice of consultants should be eagerly sought.

Perhaps one of the problems we can discuss at this conference is how an unbiased consultant can be brought in without endangering the secrecy of new drug applications and without permitting the possibility of profit-making.

We have set forth our ideas in this manuscript to stimulate discussion. Undoubtedly there are problems in new drug development that have not been mentioned and solutions we did not foresee. The differences in the number and dates of licensing of new drugs in the United States compared to the United Kingdom will provide adequate evidence that we are slower in bringing new drugs to the patient. If it can be demonstrated that patients are being deprived of worthwhile drugs, we have a problem for which it behooves us to find solutions as quickly as possible.

# References

Azarnoff, D. L., "Physiological Factors in Selecting Human Volunteers for Drug Studies," *Clinical Pharmacology and Therapeutics*, 13, 1972, pp. 796–802.

*Daedalus*, Spring 1969 (entire issue).

I. Ladimer (ed.), "New Dimensions in Legal and Ethical Concepts for Human Research," *Annals of the N.Y. Academy of Sciences*, 169, 1970, pp. 293–593.

Tabor, B-Z. *Providing New Drugs—A Guide to Clinical Trials*. Los Altos, Calif.: Geron-X, Inc., 1969.

# Comments on New Drug Investigation in Man: Continuing Unresolved Problems

J. Richard Crout

I'm responding to Drs. Goldberg and Azarnoff's paper for myself. I think that too often in the past representatives of the Food and Drug Administration have been hung up on commenting in public because they felt they were commenting for the agency, and this inhibits a free kind of communication. One of the factors that is changing the FDA is that we are having a lot more free communication than we used to.

The problems discussed by Goldberg and Azarnoff may be divided into two categories: (1) scientific or administrative problems relating to the Food and Drug Administration; and (2) policy issues relating to the general process of new drug regulation.

Some examples of the former—that is, scientific and administrative problems related to the Food and Drug Administration—include the authors' comments on carcinogenicity testing, on the use of normal subjects in clinical research, on the need for flexible guidelines, on the value of measuring blood levels during Phase II testing, and on the importance of outside consultants to informed decision-making. The suggestions they offer on these matters are sound and are in accord with FDA policy. The FDA is making every attempt to implement these suggestions as well as many others concerned with the everyday work of new drug regulation.

Technical problems of this type must be handled by any regulatory agency, be it the Food and Drug Administration, the Federal Trade Commission, the Environmental Protection Agency, or any other comparable governmental body; and it is inevitable that some of these decisions will generate controversy. However, this controversy need not be as bitter or protracted as has occurred on some occasions in the past, particularly between investigators in the cardiovascular field and the FDA. These problems can be addressed—and are currently being addressed—by improved communication between FDA scientists and investigators, by improved management practices in the agency, and by much wider use of consultants and advisory committees.

I will therefore not consider in any greater detail the specifics of the scientific and administrative proposals made by Goldberg and Azarnoff. Instead I will turn to the second category of problems they have considered, namely, policy issues which influence drug regulation in general. This is the most important area of interest for a conference such as this.

The first policy question they raise is: how should Phase I research best be regulated? This is a difficult question not only for the reasons they cite, but also because such research is conducted in widely differing facilities by investigators of widely differing competencies.

Phase I research is not regulated in most countries of the world with the exception of Canada and the United Kingdom, and in the United Kingdom approval by the regulatory body is required only if studies are done in patients, but not if they are done in normal volunteers. However, an international trend toward increasing regulation of Phase I research is definitely occurring, and I suspect that within a few years a more uniform practice will prevail among the drug developing countries of North America and Western Europe.

As emphasized by Goldberg and Azarnoff, regulatory agencies must recognize that individual investigators often use drugs only as research tools; most academic scientists are not basically in the business of new drug development. To facilitate the use of common compounds (such as amino acids) as research tools, the FDA has asked certain firms to submit information on these compounds in the form of a Master File which can be used by any investigator as part of his investigational new drug (IND). Cooperation from firms has been excellent. In addition, we have recently revised Form 1571 to make it more readily usable by individual investigators. I cite these only as examples that the Food and Drug Administration is attempting to be sensitive to current problems.

In regard to the regulation of Phase I research under INDs, I believe that if the institutional review system in universities has developed to the point where it can do a better job of reviewing these matters than a federal agency can, then it is time to alter our approach to regulating Phase I studies. I hope this topic will be discussed at this conference. We need well-thought-out guidelines on what kinds of research should be regulated and on how the institutional review system can be used to best advantage in consumer protection.

A second policy question raised by Goldberg and Azarnoff is: what are the criteria for safety and efficacy in various drug classes, or phrased alternatively, what evidence is required for approval of a new drug for marketing? Under the law, a new drug application may be denied if there is lack of substantial evidence that a drug will do what it purports to do, and the law goes on to say that substantial evidence consists of well-controlled studies, including clinical investigations conducted by experts qualified to perform such studies on new drugs.

This law has been interpreted to mean that before marketing his drug, the manufacturer must provide not only basic information on the efficacy of the drug, but also more extensive information on its use in the treatment of disease. Such information may include dosage schedules in sub-groups of the population such as children or the aged, or it may include documentation of the safety of a drug in the hands of non-expert physicians, or it may include studies of toxicity in specific organs during long-term therapy, and so on. This information is gathered during Phase III testing, and extensive Phase III work is one of the most important differences between the United States and most other countries in the requirements for marketing approval.

In the United Kingdom, for example, drugs are approved for marketing on the basis of evidence developed in a few hundred patients; the maximum duration of exposure of patients to the drug is usually measured in months rather than years. However, in the United States the typical new molecular entity has been given to 1,000 to 3,000 patients by the time of marketing, and at least some of these patients have been followed with detailed toxicological studies for more than a year. There are examples, of course, of drugs marketed with lesser experience, but this usually occurs only for new formulations of already marketed drugs, or for drugs used in the treatment of an uncommon disease.

The point I would emphasize is that the scientific requirements for marketing, whatever they may be, are not scientific in the usual sense, but are judgmental and arbitrary. Furthermore, these requirements are independent of the mechanics of the drug review process. The drug regulatory system in the United States presumes that longer and more extensive testing during the investigational phase will lead to better benefit/risk judgments and to more accurate prescribing information for the physician who uses the drug. One can reasonably debate whether Phase III testing favors consumer protection by providing doctors with effective well-labeled drugs or whether such testing delays the marketing of new drugs which doctors will use as they please anyway. However, it is not correct to attribute the longer time for investigating a drug in the United States as compared to the United Kingdom simply to differences in the efficiency or reasonableness of the review process; the big difference is the scientific evidence required at the time of approval.

The standard used for approval of a new drug is a major factor influencing regulatory decision-making, and meaningful appraisal of this factor cannot be done by such superficial techniques as comparing the number of drugs marketed in one country versus another or the timing of marketing in various countries. Many factors besides the drug regulatory system influence the marketing of new drugs, including societal desires in consumer protection, the opinions of advisory committees, the competencies of investigators, the cost of research, and the sales and marketing practices of international drug firms. This conference could do the field of new drug development a service by stating the major factors influencing new drug development and identifying better ways of acquiring accurate data on these factors.

A third policy question in the preceding paper is: what is an appropriate standard of quality for the clinical research submitted in support of the efficacy of a new drug? What I'm about to say comes as a shock to most investigators, but there is common agreement between the Food and Drug Administration and the drug industry that clinical investigators hold the key to providing more rapid new drug development today. Far too many drug trials are performed which fail to answer important questions. The major reasons for this are failure to state properly the objectives of the trial in the first place, poor experimental design, improper patient selection, high drop-out rates, use of concomitant medication which confounds interpretation of the data, and sloppy documentation in case records.

Drs. Goldberg and Azarnoff have made an enlightened plea for improved clinical pharmacology and improved clinical trials. Nothing would be more helpful to the process of new drug development than the realization of these goals. One of the major new thrusts of the FDA is to become more involved in the planning of research and the review of protocols for clinical trials, in an attempt to solve some of these problems. In the past, strategic planning has been left entirely to the firm, but it is our belief that such planning would be improved by including both investigators and the FDA in the process. Far too much regulatory energy has been spent in the past in searching for flaws in new drug applications after the fact, and far too little energy has been spent in planning efforts during the investigational phase. We strongly believe this emphasis must be reversed.

In addition to these unresolved problems identified by Drs. Goldberg and Azarnoff, I would like to add three others for consideration by the conference.

1. The first is that individual investigators, those who have worked the most with a drug, are basically left out of the decision-

making process by both the industry and the FDA. Research planning for a new drug and the development of protocols are done by industry employees who are often unknown to clinical investigators. The results collected by these investigators are in turn presented to the FDA by the firm. The investigator himself does not see the way his own results are presented in a new drug application. The application is then reviewed by physicians at the FDA who for the most part do not know and are not known to the clinical investigators.

This whole system leaves investigators out of the planning process, the dialogue with industry, and the decision-making process. Although investigators view themselves as impartial evaluators of new drugs, they are often treated by the industry as simply technical servants and by the FDA as parties in interest. The final bargaining over a new drug and its package insert—and recall that much of Phase III research is aimed toward getting a well-rounded package insert—is done by people who have no first-hand experience with the drug. This statement applies to both FDA reviewers and their counterparts in industry. In my opinion, we need to develop better strategies for identifying those investigators who are in essence working for the firm and those who are independent evaluators of the drug—and our world includes both—so that the latter can be brought more closely into the decision-making process.

2. A second problem relating to clinical investigation that I would emphasize is that the review of data at the FDA is shrouded in far too much secrecy. Clinical data and animal toxicological data have traditionally been considered trade secrets by the drug industry. This means that unpublished data submitted in a new drug application (and the bulk of such data are unpublished) are reviewed only by the FDA. The concept of privileged information works to keep the data in new drug applications from being scrutinized and judged by the usual mechanisms of science, namely, open review by those with the greatest expertise in the field.

In my opinion, the drug industry has created many of its own problems in drug review by insisting that clinical and toxicological information be kept secret. Many matters which should be debated freely and openly by scientists and practicing physicians are considered only behind closed doors. Decisions made under these circumstances tend to lack credibility in the scientific community even if they are correct.

The concept of privileged information also tends to isolate FDA reviewers and their industrial counterparts from open conversation with other scientists at meetings. It teaches those who work in the FDA that the industry can and does hide important data from public view for nonscientific reasons. For example, we now know of several drugs which are no longer being investigated in the United States because of animal or human toxicity but which are nevertheless being marketed in foreign countries; yet the data in our files on these drugs are considered secret. Patients who participate in a clinical study on a new drug, and most investigators, do not realize that unless the study in which they are participating is published, the results become privileged information useful for that firm only. In my opinion, patients should either be told this as a part of informed consent or the concept of privileged information should not apply to any data deriving from human research.

The same principle should also apply to animal toxicological data which seriously impinges on the safe use of drugs in man. Drug firms cannot claim to be engaging in health research and at the same time bury toxicological data at the FDA under the cloak of privileged information.

I am convinced that the industry does not understand the enormous price it pays for forcing data on safety and efficacy to be reviewed apart from the usual mechanisms and traditions of science. The tragedy of this situation is made worse by the fact that it also ineffective (or perhaps only "possibly effective") as a strategy for keeping information out of the hands of other firms. Any knowledgeable scientist who attends the appropriate scientific meetings can easily determine where any important investigational drug is in its phase of development and who is doing the work. Investigators like to talk freely, as everyone knows. I hope this conference will help to identify new ways of opening clinical and toxicological data to scientific scrutiny while still providing firms with appropriate protection for their legitimate trade secrets.

3. The final problem I would mention is the failure of most drug regulatory systems, including that in the United States, to recognize that research on a new drug is a continuum which lasts from the first moment of discovery through the life history of the drug on the market. Almost every regulatory system places too much emphasis on the act of approval of a new drug application and too little on subsequent review. The administrative approval of new drug applications, and the use of innovative approaches to Phase IV testing during the early marketing phase, would be much easier if approval were granted for a finite period of time, perhaps every five years.

# Part II:
# The Legal and Economic Effects of Drug Regulatory Policies

## The Patent System and the New Drug Application
Edmund W. Kitch

## Comments
William F. Baxter

## The Benefits and Costs of New Drug Regulation
Sam Peltzman

## Comments
Lester G. Telser

# The Patent System
# and the New Drug Application:
# An Evaluation of the Incentives
# for Private Investment in New Drug
# Research and Marketing
Edmund W. Kitch

# I. Introduction

The 1962 Amendments to the Food and Drug Act[1] have had a
significant impact on the process of introducing a new therapeutic
drug or device into the American market. The three major changes
introduced by that legislation are in form quite modest. First, the
Act was amended to provide that a new drug or device cannot be
marketed until it has been approved by the Food and Drug Administration.[2] The previous legislation had provided that if the
FDA did not act within 180 days to exclude the drug, then it could
be marketed.[3] Second, the Act was amended to provide that a firm
seeking to market a new drug or device must demonstrate that
it is not only safe, but also effective for the purpose for which
it is sold.[4] Third, the Act was amended to provide that permission
must be obtained from the FDA before human clinical testing can
be undertaken.[5] In the context of the thalidomide tragedy which
aroused widespread fears about the dangers of drug technology,
these amendments seemed relatively mild.[6] The old requirement
that the FDA hold a hearing and act within 180 days if it wished
to exclude a drug from the market seemed unduly hasty in light of
the newly-apprehended risk. In its place was substituted a hortatory
provision urging an "expedited" procedure.[7] Then, too, the Kefauver hearings of the previous years had indicated that some drugs
marketed were of questionable therapeutic effectiveness. It did not
seem unreasonable, in light of the risks that might be involved
in any new drug, to require that effectiveness be demonstrated.
Finally, the thalidomide actually distributed in the United States
had been distributed only for clinical testing, hence the reasonableness of an advance clearance procedure for such testing.

Ignored, or perhaps simply assumed, was the fact that the increased length and complexity of the procedure for the marketing
of new drugs would increase the cost. This was probably thought
to present no problem because the Kefauver hearing[8] had

1. Public Law 87–781, 76 Stat. 780 (1962).
2. *Id.* § 104(b), 21 U.S.C. § 355(c).
3. Public Law 75–717 § 505(c), 52 Stat. 1052 (1938).
4. Public Law 87–781 §§ 102(b), 102(c), 21 U.S.C. §§ 355(b), 355(d).
5. Public Law 87–781 § 106(b), 21 U.S.C. § 355(i).
6. Even though thalidomide had not been marketed in the United States
and none of the deformed babies were born in the United States.
7. Public Law 87–781 § 104(b)(2), 21 U.S.C. § 355(c)(2).
8. For a sympathetic account of the Kefauver hearings, see Richard Harris,
*The Real Voice.* New York: MacMillan Co., 1964.

demonstrated that the drug industry was, when compared to other industries, relatively more profitable and that high markups over factory cost were obtained for some drugs. Overlooked was the fact that an industry faced with increased costs for introducing new products would preserve its profitability simply by reducing the number of new products introduced. This would increase the profitability of old products and the profitability of those products introduced. Also ignored was the problem that any firm wishing to pioneer the introduction of a new drug would necessarily have to obtain information of great value to its potential competitors. If a firm pioneering a new drug had to absorb these costs only to see the market for the drug largely captured by others, it would not make the required investment. This problem was probably ignored because the legislators assumed that any pioneer would hold a patent on the drug to be marketed. The Kefauver hearings had emphasized the role of patents in protecting pharmaceutical manufacturers from competition and indeed the original Kefauver bills contained provisions, not ultimately passed, designed to weaken the available patent protection.[9]

This paper will examine the problems of cost recovery created by the structure of the present drug clearance procedure. It will assume that an administrative clearance procedure is desired and will not evaluate the possible use of the tort system as an alternative quality control mechanism. The paper will first examine the uneven and diluted impact of the patent system on the technology of chemical therapy; the implications of the fact that the FDA market clearance procedure has emerged as an awkward substitute for the patent system will then be discussed; and finally, the paper will consider possible alternative arrangements for financing drug research and marketing.

## II. The Patent System

The patent system is designed to enable those who invest in the development of new technology to capture a significant portion of the economic returns resulting from their investment. In the absence of a patent system, investment in new technology by private firms operating in competitive markets would be less than the potential social returns would justify. The importance of the patent

9. S. 1552, 87th Cong. 1st Sess., § 3. The amendments required for patentability an improved therapeutic effect, changed the patent term, and provided for compulsory licenses.

system for the drug industry is dramatized by the refusal of the drug manufacturers to be involved with any government-sponsored research if it would affect their ability to claim patent protection for their new products.[10] In spite of its importance, however, changes in technology have weakened the ability of the present patent system to serve as an appropriate incentive for the development of new drug technology. For students of the patent system this should come as no surprise. The present statute, subject to numerous subsequent technical changes that are unimportant for this discussion, was passed in 1836, long before drug research, development, and sale had assumed significant commercial importance. The problems of the patent system are many and varied: first, the long delay between early synthesis and commercial sale caused by the increasing complex clinical testing and clearance procedures has substantially reduced the return to be obtained from a patented new drug; second, the requirements of patentability appear to make unpatentable many possible new therapeutic uses of chemicals, particularly in light of the developments over the last fifty years in the chemical arts. Given the increased cost of simply obtaining clearance to market a new drug, the absence of patent protection may mean that even substances of known therapeutic utility will not be made available to the public.

## A. Timing and the Statutory Period

The patent statute provides for a 17-year term beginning on the date of the issuance of the patent. The term is one which, while giving to the patent owner over 90 percent of the present value of his invention, avoids the complexity of an economy encumbered by exclusive perpetual rights over all technology. In the simple model assumed by the statute, a firm that has developed a new patentable product can apply for a patent and begin marketing its product. During the two to three years that elapse before the patent is issued, the firm is not protected, but usually the simple act of marking the product "patent pending" will deter competitors from copying it. Thus the firm can hope to enjoy as much as

10. For a review of the problem, which arose in 1962 when the Department of Health, Education and Welfare asked drug companies which provided free screening for compounds produced by government-sponsored research programs to waive their patent rights, see Harbridge House, Inc., *Government Patent Policy, Final Report*, II–15 to II–45 (1968). See generally, Howard I. Forman, "How the Chemical-Pharmaceutical Industry Views the Government's Patent Policy," *Food-Drug-Cosmetic Law Journal* 25 (1970), p. 204.

20 years of exclusive commercial exploitation of its new product.
This simple model, however, cannot be followed in the pharmaceutical industry. A firm must apply for its patent almost as soon as a compound with possible therapeutic utility has been identified. This will often occur early in the animal testing stage. Commercial marketing, however, cannot begin until the FDA has been persuaded (1) that the non-human tests justify clinical trials, and (2) that the human clinical trials establish safety and effectiveness. If this process takes six years, then the 20-year protection is reduced to 14. If it takes longer, the period of protection is further reduced. There are devices that patent lawyers can and do use to delay the issuance of a patent in the Patent Office. To the extent that they are used, the date of issue can be brought closer to the date of marketing clearance. However, these devices—which essentially involve filing defective initial applications so that the Patent Office is forced to take more actions—are unethical and weaken the patent, since courts are likely to be suspicious of a patent that had difficulty getting through the Patent Office.

A patent application for a pharmaceutical must, as a practical matter, be filed as soon as the substance is identified and there are indications of possible utility for a number of different reasons: first, delay in filing increases the chances that some other firm may be able to claim priority and either invalidate the patent or obtain the patent for itself; second, and perhaps more important, any delay increases the risk that the patent will be invalidated by public discussion or disclosure of the compound in a printed publication. Under the § 102(b) time bar of the patent statute,[11] a patent is invalidated by the public use or printed description of its subject matter more than one year before filing. It is quite probable that either the investigational use of a compound by a person not subject to an obligation not to disclose his work, or the submission to the FDA of an application for clinical testing will constitute the public use that activates this time bar. It is possible to proceed without filing for a patent by subjecting all investigators to a secrecy requirement and taking the position that an application for clinical testing to the FDA is not a public document. Secrecy constraints, however, have substantial costs since they complicate, if they do not prevent, meaningful interchange about the drug within the research community. If all investigations of the possible therapeutic uses of new substances proceeded in secrecy, wasteful dupli-

11. 35 U.S.C. § 102(b).

cations of research would increase. Moreover, in spite of the willingness of the FDA to cooperate, it is questionable at best whether an application for clinical testing can be treated as a non-public document. Finally, for reasons to be discussed further, an early filing decreases the amount of information that must be disclosed in the patent. In the typical case, a patent application will be made at the outset of an investigation of the therapeutic effects of a new substance. Thus the effect of the complex marketing clearance procedures has been to reduce the effective period of patent protection, and, correspondingly, the private investment likely to be made in the detection, development, and marketing of new drugs. It is important to emphasize that this is an effect quite separate from the fact that the marketing clearance procedures increase the cost of introducing the new drugs. The procedures not only increase the cost, they decrease the time period over which the drug pioneer can rely upon his patent to enable him to recoup his expenditures.

## B. The Scope of Patent Protection

**1. The known compound.** Most drug patents are patents that claim as the invention the composition of matter constituting the drug. It can be argued that it is possible to claim as an invention the therapeutic use of a compound, but the doubtfulness of that approach—to be discussed in depth shortly—has meant that the usual approach is to claim the compound itself. However, a compound that is already known cannot be patented for lack of novelty. Thus the patent system offers no protection (subject to the possibility that a patent can be issued on a therapeutic use) for discoveries relating to new therapeutic effects of known drugs. As the techniques of chemical synthesis, isolation, and purification have been improved, a larger and larger number of substances have entered the public domain. The patent system provides no incentive for the investigation of known substances for beneficial therapeutic effects, much less for payment of the costs of obtaining a marketing clearance for them. Since there is no reason to assume that drug research should be focused on structurally new substances, this characteristic of the patent system skews the incentives for drug research in an undesirable manner.

**2. The non-obviousness requirement.** In order to prevent the granting of a patent monopoly on inventions which are trivial, the patent statute imposes the requirement that the invention must not have been obvious to those skilled in the art to which the invention pertains. The requirement creates considerable difficulty when applied to a patent claim on a compound or combination of compounds. There are three characteristics of a compound which might be said to be non-obvious: (1) the method of making it; (2) the fact of its existence; and (3) the nature of one or more of its properties. An example of a case in which the first two conditions were satisfied is *Merck & Co. v. Olin Mathieson Chemical Corp.*,[12] involving the patent on Vitamin $B_{12}$. Here, the substance had not existed previously in pure form, nor had the existence of such a chemical structure been predicted. The technique for isolating the substance had been developed by the inventor. The only feature that was obvious was that the substance was effective in curing pernicious anemia, for it was that trait that had been used to guide the effort to isolate the patented substance. Where, however, drug research has not proceeded by attempting to isolate a natural substance of known or suspected therapeutic value, but rather by identifying therapeutic effects of known or easily synthesized substances the patent situation is more difficult. If the method of preparing the substance is known to the art, or if its existence is predicted by chemical theory, it is difficult to argue that the substance itself is non-obvious. In these cases it is the therapeutic effect which is non-obvious. How, then, can the claim on the substance itself be supported by the discovery of one of its properties? Is not such a result difficult if not impossible to justify in view of the fact that a patent on the substance gives the patent owner a monopoly right on all uses of the substance, even those discovered by someone else? This would seem to be a simple case of claiming as a patentable invention more than has actually been invented, a practice consistently condemned in patent law.

The Patent Office and the patent bar have not proceeded in the manner which this logic would suggest. There are several reasons for this: the first may well be historical. There was probably a time when the state of the chemical arts was such that any claim on a previously non-existent substance was a disclosure worthy of a patent. The custom thus established has continued in spite of the changes in science. Second, a claim on the substance may be the only possible way to patent a drug in light of the possible unpatentability of therapeutic uses. Third, a claim on the substance is easier to enforce since any maker or seller of the substance is in

12. 253 F.2d 156 (4th Cir. 1958).

violation of the patent and it is unnecessary to prove that he is selling it for any particular use. Fourth, a claim on the substance enables the patentee to file his application earlier and to disclose less about his invention while preserving all rights against any subsequently discovered use. This last reason requires further explanation. The patent statute requires an applicant to disclose the best mode contemplated by the inventor of carrying out his invention.[13] The theory is that the patentee, in exchange for his patent rights, discloses to the public how to use the invention. But this is interpreted to mean the best mode contemplated by the inventor at the time of the application. Thus it is arguable that if an application were filed for the use of a drug that had been approved by the FDA, the applicant would have to disclose the contents of the new drug application, since without that information it would be difficult for the public to make use of the invention. On the other hand, if the application is filed while the invention is still in a primitive state, then only the primitive mode of use need be disclosed, even though the patentee is protected against more useful versions of his invention. If a patent application for a drug is filed at a time when research only indicates some standard beneficial effects on animals, only those effects will be disclosed in the patent. This strategy, however, will work only if a claim is allowed on the substance rather than on its use. If the patent is confined to those uses disclosed, a later discovered therapeutic effect will not be covered by the patent and another patent application will be required for protection. The second application would then have to disclose the best mode of using the later discovered therapeutic effect. Of course a patent owner selling a drug will have to disclose to the world the techniques for administering the drug, but he will not have to disclose the therapeutically preferable version of the chemical nor how to prepare it for marketing.

Whatever the reason, it is clearly the general practice of the Patent Office bar to include references to possible uses in the general description of the patentable subject matter while confining the patent claims to the chemical substance itself. Indeed, most chemical patents do not even contain a use claim as an alternative "fall-back" position even though the statute would permit such a defensive strategy. It is difficult to understand the origin and original rationale of the Patent Office practice, both because the interpretation of each decision turns in part on the contemporary understanding of the chemical arts and because the Patent Office and

13. 35 U.S.C. § 112.

its specialized review court, the Court of Customs and Patent Appeals, have been confused and contradictory about the role of a disclosure of utility in a patent on a chemical compound. The current authoritative rationalization of the Patent Office practice is *Application of Papesch.*[14] In this case the Patent Office had rejected an application for a patent on a chemical alleged to have anti-inflammatory properties on the ground that the chemical was structurally obvious given certain other compounds known to the art. Reversing, the court said:

> [W]e think that . . . [the decision of the Patent Office in this case] rests on one fundamental error of law, namely, the failure to take into consideration the biological or pharmaceutical property of the compounds as anti-inflammatory agents on the ground that to chemists the structure of the compounds would be *so* obvious as to be beyond doubt, and that a showing of such properties is to be used only to resolve doubt.
>
> From the standpoint of patent law, a compound and all of its properties are inseparable; they are one and the same thing. The graphic formulae, the chemical nomenclature, the systems of classification and study such as the concepts of homology, isomerism, etc., are mere symbols by which compounds can be identified, classified, and compared. But a formula is not a compound and while it may serve in a claim to *identify* what is being patented, as the metes and bounds of a deed identify a plot of land, the *thing* that is patented is not the formula but the compound identified by it. And the patentability of the thing does not depend on the similarity of its formula to that of another compound but of the similarity of the former compound to the latter. There is no basis in law for ignoring any property in making such a comparison. An assumed similarity based on a comparison of formulae must give way to evidence that the assumption is erroneous.
>
> The argument has been made that patentability is here being asserted only on the basis of *one* property, the anti-inflammatory activity, and that the compounds claimed and the compound of the prior art presumably have many properties in common. *Presumably* they do, but presumption is all we have here. The same is true of all of the compounds of the above cases which were held patentable over compounds of the prior art, many of which must have had more in common by way of properties than the compounds here because the relationships, structurally, were even closer than here.

14. 315 F.2d 381 (Court of Customs and Patent Appeals, 1963).

As to the examiner's view that in a case such as this the applicant should claim his invention as a process utilizing the newly discovered property, the board appears to have ignored it, properly we think. It is contrary to practically all of the above decisions wherein no fault was found with granting product claims. Such claims have well-recognized advantages to those in the business of making and selling compounds, in contrast to process-of-use claims, because competitors in the sale of compounds are not generally users.[15]

The problem with this rationalization is that it does not explain why the person who discovers the therapeutic or other property is entitled to a monopoly on the substance. It is simply an act of definition to say that the substance and its properties are inseparable. The patent system can treat them as separate if it makes sense for the patent system to do so. Moreover, to reject a process or use claim which would do precisely that on the ground that the claim on the substance has commercial advantages is to rely on a ground not to be found in the statute.

The other leading authority supporting the Patent Office is the case of *Commissioner of Patents* v. *Deutsche Gold-und-Silber-Scheideanstalt Vormals Rossler*.[16]

This case came to the Court of Appeals for the District of Columbia under an alternative review procedure available for the review of Patent Office decisions. Again, as in *Papesch*, the Patent Office had rejected an application for a patent on a compound as structurally obvious. The applicant had shown utility, not in his application but by means of affidavits. Incredibly, the Court of Appeals, in an opinion by now Chief Justice (then Circuit Judge) Burger, reversed. The decision is incredible because the utility on which the court relied to support issuance of the patent was not even disclosed in the patent. This is not a trivial distinction, since in the usual, unlitigated case there will be no disclosure that affidavits exist, and a person obtaining a copy of the patent will not be informed of the utility. Thus the decision would seem to enable a person to obtain a patent on the ground that he has discovered a use for a compound while effectively concealing information about that use from the public. Aside from this unusual feature, the court confronted the arguments relating to structural utility and rejected them. The court observed that "if we are to accept a determination of structural obviousness which cannot be rebutted by evidence of

15. *Id.* at 391.
16. 397 F.2d 656 (D.C. Cir. 1968).

chemical, pharmaceutical, or biological properties, few pharmaceutical compounds will be patented, and the incentive aspect of the patent system which is basic, will be lost from an important area." [17]

The critical passage of the opinion is as follows:

> The final assertion from the Commissioner's sweeping contentions is interesting but does not compel a contrary result. He views the claim as defining by name and diagram a mental concept of a chemical compound which, to the ordinary chemist, would convey both the structure and characteristics of a family of compounds. The Commissioner would have us adopt the following logic: Since section 103 refers to "subject matter as a whole," the antecedent of which is "subject matter sought to be patented," these obviously refer only to the *claimed* compound; hence, if that claim does not specifically refer to the particular property which demonstrates non-obviousness, it does not distinctly claim the invention as required in section 112, paragraph 2, but instead claims that compound for all uses and properties, thus overclaiming and foreclosing the public from using the compound in an unrelated, but unobvious, field.[18]

This passage would appear to be dispositive of the decisive overclaiming argument if it were not for the following footnote:

> The Commissioner correctly recognizes the difficulty of patenting new but obvious chemical compounds on the basis of novel properties and new uses. This problem of overclaiming arises from the fact that the patent is given for the *entire compound*, although based on only one new property it discloses. Thus, the patent holder of compound A, with properties X and Y, is foreclosed from using newly patented, structurally obvious compound B, with obvious properties X and Y, merely because compound B also possesses new and unobvious property Z. Whether or not the solution rests in strictly limiting patentability to the *new use* alone, or to the *process* by which it is made, however, is a matter for the Commissioner, the Congress, and courts with greater technical expertise to decide in the first instance.[19]

Does the footnote mean that the court is simply affirming a "first instance" determination? If the statute is to the contrary, has not

17. *Id.* at 663.
18. *Id.* at 664.
19. *Ibid*, footnote 21.

Congress already made its determination? Is the question of statutory scope a technical question on which a court should defer to technical expertise? The footnote seems to be an effort to reserve decision on the question in case it should arise in the context of an infringement case, rather than a review of a Patent Office rejection.

The established Patent Office practice, reasonably relied on in good faith by numerous patentees, might itself be reason enough for the courts to follow *Papesch* and *Deutsche*. In infringement cases, however, the courts have seldom deferred to the Patent Office, nursing a barely disguised suspicion that the Patent Office and its specialized bar are overly protective of the monopoly system. *Papesch* and *Deutsche* were decided after the courts involved heard argument from the patentee, who desired a patent, the Patent Office, which wished to defend its own practice, and in *Deutsche*, the American Patent Law Association, speaking for the specialized bar that perpetuates the practice. Thus in *Deutsche* the Patent Office claimed that its contentions were new and revolutionary, which was something of an overstatement and practically an admission that the application had been rejected simply to generate a test case. In two recent infringement cases district courts have directly attacked the Patent Office practice.

The first case is *Monsanto Co. v. Rohm and Haas Co.*[20] involving a patent on "3',4'-dichloropropionanilide" disclosing utility as a selective post-emergent herbicide. Reflecting the difficulties just discussed, Monsanto had filed three separate applications for the compound, the first in 1957, the last in 1967, each application reflecting its own continuing research into the possible uses of the compound. The District Court held the patent invalid on the ground that the herbicidal properties of the compound were not surprising in view of the similar properties of related compounds. But the court went on to say:

> ... [E]ven if this were only a case of structural obviousness, we would be disposed to hold that this in and of itself should preclude issuance of a patent. It is basic to the grant of a patent that the scope of a patent should not exceed the scope of invention. If what makes a structurally obvious chemical substance patentable is the new and unobvious properties or uses discovered by the first person to compound the substance, the discoverer should have protection on what he discovered, *i.e.*, the new properties of the substance, but should not be entitled

20. 312 F. Supp. 778 (E.D. Pa. 1970).

to a 17-year monopoly on the substance itself. To say that a person who has discovered a new use for a structurally obvious compound, which compound would not have been entitled to any patent protection absent the new use, should receive a patent on the compound itself is to extend the patent monopoly far beyond the reason for its existence. We think that the purposes of the patent law will be adequately served if patents on compounds which are structurally obvious from the prior art are limited to method patents directed to the new and useful characteristic or property which is the essence of the discovery or invention. In this case the actual advance of the art is the discovery of 3,4-DCPA as a herbicide. This fact was neither obvious nor predictable from the prior art. To a reasonably skilled chemist, the chemical formula and structure of 3,4-DCPA was obvious from the formula and structure of 3,4-DCAA. Such a chemist would also expect both compounds to have similar properties. Both compounds can be easily produced by using known chemicals and methods of synthesis. Hence there was nothing characteristic of invention in the routine compounding of 3,4-DCPA. Dr. Huffman himself testified that 3,4-DCPA was synthesized by his assistant using old and known methods and compounds (Huffman, N.T.57). The "invention" was discovering 3,4-DCPA's peculiar characteristics as a herbicide. The question of whether Dr. Huffman is entitled to a process patent on the use of 3,4-DCPA as a herbicide is now before the patent office in an interference involving the same parties and is not before this court.[21]

These same thoughts were again expressed in *Carter-Wallace, Inc. v. Davis-Edwards Pharmacal Corp.*,[22] a case involving a patent on meprobamate disclosing its utility as an anti-convulsant. Again reflecting the difficulties under discussion, the patent application had been filed in 1950, two years before further animal testing revealed the tranquilizing properties which led to its highly successful marketing under the trade names Miltown and Equanil. The court held the patent invalid on the ground that the anti-convulsant properties were not surprising given the similar properties of related compounds. But the court went on to say that:

... [T]here seems to be basic error in here invoking the *Papesch-Stemniski* approach of according products patentability

21. *Id.* at 790–91.
22. 341 F. Supp. 1303 (E.D. N.Y. 1972).

to such a technically "new" compound as meprobamate on the ground that its "properties," viewed as indivisibly a part of the whole compound, differ markedly in kind from, or unexpectedly in superiority over the "properties" of structurally similar compounds. That approach, as applied by the patent office in the present case, and now argued in support of patentability, confuses uses with properties, the utility requirement of Section 101 with the unobviousness of the act of invention or discovery that Section 103 requires, and the "subject matter" of the "invention" or "discovery" with the identity of the "material" or "manufacture" or "composition of matter" to which the "discovery" or "invention" relates; it necessarily results in the new compositions' being examined against the wrong prior art, here the organic chemist's art rather than that of the pharmacologist. The result has been to grant a patent on a chemical composition as a patentably new composition of matter on the unsound ground that it was a surprisingly better anticonvulsant than a group of interesting but inadequate anticonvulsants, the parent diols (and mephenesin), and two groups of carbamates that had no anticonvulsant (or skeletal relaxant) "properties" at all. The patent was not granted on the ground that the three carbamates were, as compositions of matter, new and unobvious from the prior art of synthesizing chemical compounds (as required by Sections 101 and 103), and that they had sufficient utility to satisfy the requirement of Section 101 that the composition be not only patentably new but also "useful."

The evidence demonstrates that once the decision to make the carbamates of the patent was taken, they were forthwith made by a known process without reported difficulty. What their utilities would be was not then known, but, inferentially, it was in contemplation that they might have long-acting anticonvulsant action of the same quality as the parent diols.

The still undetermined utility of the products thus could not form part of the "invention" and render it an unobvious act of invention by retrospection if the products were empirically found to have properties that were unexpected or contradictory of expectation or far exceeded what the chemist or pharmacologist would have predicted. Certainly ... [some] of the cases say that the decision to make a product may be so far unmotivated by, or unsuggested by the prior art that the choice of the notional product that will be ordered into existence is an act attended by unobviousness when seen in relation to the unpredictable utilities that the new product turns out to possess. From that the transition is abruptly to the idea that, *ergo*, the composition is patentably novel. But that dissection of the process of "invention" obscures the patentable event: if the decision to make the compound was an inspired hunch that turns out to be right, how is the merit or the value to society of the fortunate or insightful decision altered by the irrelevant and fortuitous fact that the product hit upon had to be effortlessly synthesized for the first time rather than drawn from a printed list or a laboratory catalogue of extant but uninvestigated synthetic or natural substances?

The inescapable fact is that if a composition does not occur in nature and has not yet been synthesized, it nevertheless is in the public domain if it can be called into existence on bare request by known methods. It is as veritably in the public domain as any extant product. Without disparaging the chemist's complex arts, the new composition exists unassembled, and it is assembled when ordered. The fact that it had not been earlier ordered into existence is fortuitous; the synthesis, for example, of the carbamate of Claim 4 was not the solution of a theretofore unsolved chemical problem; the problem of making it had been earlier solved by patentable invention, perhaps, or by obvious logic; it was, simply, a composition that had not been but could readily be made.[23]

Since these two decisions there has been some support for the Patent Office practice. The Fifth Circuit, in the course of an opinion affirming the validity of a patent on propoxyphene hydrochloride, marketed under the trade name Darvon, has said:

In the field of drug patents today therapeutic value, not chemical composition, is the substance of all incentive to invent. Except where the state of the medical art and the state of the chemical art have been advanced and coordinated to the point that it is possible for the mind to conceive or predict with some minimal reliability a correlation between chemical analogues, homologues or isomers and their therapeutic value, reason compels us to agree that novelty, usefulness and non-obviousness inhere in the true discovery that a chemical compound exhibits a new needed medicinal capability, even though it be closely related in structure to a known or patented drug. When such a fresh, efficacious, undisclosed use is identified, its inventor deserves the full ambit of statutory protection. A limitation to "use" or process patentability, based solely on the existence of prior chemical formulations, would not accord with the basic constitutional power being exercised by the Congress to promote science and the useful

23. *Id.* at 1336–38.

arts. Such a niggardly patent reward for costly and painstaking research would discourage both the inspiration-perspiration process of the laboratory and the incentive to publicly disclose products of value to mankind.

However, where a court finds the alleged inventor's work in a field filled with formidable prior art to be no more novel or non-obvious than the conducting of a biological or physiological testing program among catalogued compounds or an easily formulated series of homologues or analogues that logically or predictably should disclose helpful uses, the grant or validation of a patent on the product would be out of keeping with the letter or spirit of the law. This conclusion would be even more compelled where the use claimed by such a tester in his application turns out to be a minor value of the drug which the patent would monopolize. See Judge Dooling's opinion on remand in *Carter-Wallace, Inc.* v. *Davis-Edwards Pharmacal Corp.*[24]

And the Second Circuit, in the course of an opinion affirming the decision holding the patent on meprobamate invalid, refused to take a position on the controversy.[25] Instead, the Second Circuit held that since the patent application disclosed only an anticonvulsant effect, the test of patentability was whether one skilled in the art would have synthesized meprobamate in order to determine if it had such properties. The court held that the prior art would have indicated such an effort. But this decision too is troubling for the validity of patents since the utility indicated in an application filed shortly after a substance has been synthesized will usually be the utilities the art would predict for it. The Second Circuit did offer one hopeful strategy, however, when it suggested that if a later filed document indicated a surprising utility—in the case of meprobamate, its tranquilizing properties—the applicant could still claim as the date of his invention the date of the first filing. In truth, this suggestion only illustrates the conceptual quagmire in which drug patents may have become hopelessly immersed, since the only logical implication of this position is that one can file for a patent on an invention that has not yet been made!

**3. The therapeutic claim.** These difficulties are solved if a patent is issued which claims the therapeutic use that has in fact been discovered by the inventor. Under the statute, however, there is doubt

24. *Eli Lilly & Co.* v. *General Drug Sales, Inc.* (5th Cir. 1972).
25. *Carter-Wallace, Inc.* v. *Otte*, No. 72–1406 (2d Cir. November 14, 1972), Petition for rehearing denied January 16, 1973.

whether a therapeutic claim is valid. Such claims have been granted by the Patent Office, upheld by the Court of Customs and Patent Appeals, and defended by patent practitioners. The difficulty with a therapeutic claim is the definition of patentable subject matter in section 101 of the patent statute. That section provides: "Whoever invents or discovers any new and useful process, machine, manufacture, or composition of matter, or any new and useful improvement thereof, may obtain a patent therefor, subject to the conditions and requirements of this title." [26] Since a therapeutic use is not a machine, a manufacture, or a composition of matter, it must be a process if it is to be patentable. The difficulty with the construction of a therapeutic use as a process is that a series of nineteenth-century cases equated the term process with industrial process. In 1952 an additional section was added to the statute defining process as "process, art, or method, and includes a new use of a known process, machine, manufacture, composition of matter, or material." [27] Unfortunately, this section has been treated by the courts as if it only codified the existing law. It is one of the ironies of patent law that although it is concerned with advanced technology the controlling cases are for the most part almost a century old. In the case of processes, the rule of Cochran v. Deener [28] is often cited. In that case the Court said: "A process is a mode of treatment of certain materials to produce a given result. It is an act, or a series of acts, performed upon the subject matter to be transformed and reduced to a different state or thing." [29] This may be a definition appropriate for a rolling mill, but it is difficult to extend it to the actions of a therapeutic drug upon the human body.

A further difficulty for the patentability of therapeutic effects is the case of Funk Bros. Seed Co. v. Kalo Inoculant Co.[30] That case involved a claim upon a combination of bacteria of the genus Rhizobium useful for inoculating all species of leguminous plants. The critical discovery of the inventor was that it was possible to combine bacteria suitable for inoculating different species without loss of their effectiveness, as had not previously been thought possible. The discovery made it possible for the farmer to purchase one inoculant suitable for all of his legumes. The Court held the patent invalid. Mr. Justice Douglas, writing for the Court, explained:

26. 35 U.S.C. § 101.
27. 35 U.S.C. § 100(b).
28. 94 U.S. 780 (1876).
29 Id. at 787.
30. 333 U.S. 127 (1948).

There is, of course, an advantage in the combination. The farmer need not buy six different packages for six different crops. He can buy one package and use it for any or all of his crops of leguminous plants. And, as respondent says, the packages of mixed inoculants also hold advantages for the dealers and manufacturers by reducing inventory problems and the like. But a product must be more than new and useful to be patented; it must also satisfy the requirements of invention or discovery. *Cuno Engineering Corp.* v. *Automatic Devices Corp.*, 314 U.S. 84, 90, 91, and cases cited; 35 U.S.C. § 31, R.S. § 4886. The application of this newly-discovered natural principle to the problem of packaging of inoculants may well have been an important commercial advance. But once nature's secret of the non-inhibitive quality of certain strains of the species of Rhizobium was discovered, the state of the art made the production of a mixed inoculant a simple step. Even though it may have been the product of skill, it certainly was not the product of invention. There is no way in which we could call it such unless we borrowed invention from the discovery of the natural principle itself. That is to say, there is no invention here unless the discovery that certain strains of the several species of these bacteria are non-inhibitive and may thus be safely mixed is invention. But we cannot so hold without allowing a patent to issue on one of the ancient secrets of nature now disclosed. All that remains, therefore, are advantages of the mixed inoculants themselves. They are not enough.[31]

But is not the discovery that a substance has a therapeutic effect simply another discovery of a "secret of nature"? If this decision is followed, therapeutic use claims would appear to be unpatentable.

It is easy to criticize the *Funk Brothers* decision. All inventions are in fact discoveries of useful applications of the "secrets of nature." There does not seem to be any reason to exclude biological processes from the operation of the patent laws any more than there is reason to exclude any other useful technology. This issue, however, remains a very real problem, as is illustrated by the recent litigation over the patentability of computer programs. The Court of Customs and Patent Appeals had held that a computer program was patentable as a process for operating a computing machine. A newly discovered program, reasoned the court, was just like the discovery that a better steel could be produced by certain alterations in the machinery for making it. The Supreme Court reversed, rely-

31. *Id.* at 131–32.

ing upon *Cochran* v. *Deener* and its progeny. Mr. Justice Douglas, again writing for the Court, said:

> It is argued that a process patent must either be tied to a particular machine or apparatus or must operate to change articles or materials to a "different state or thing."
> We do not hold that no process patent could ever qualify if it did not meet the requirements of our prior precedents. It is said that the decision precludes a patent for any program servicing a computer. We do not so hold. It is said that we have before us a program for a digital computer but extend our holding to programs for analog computers. We have, however, made clear from the start that we deal with a program only for digital computers. It is said we freeze process patents to old technologies, leaving no room for the revelations of the new, on-rushing technology. Such is not our purpose. What we come down to in a nutshell is the following.
> It is conceded that one may not patent an idea. But in practical effect that would be the result if the formula for converting binary code to pure binary were patented in this case. The mathematical formula involved here has no substantial practical application except in connection with a digital computer, which means that if the judgment below is affirmed, the patent would wholly pre-empt the mathematical formula and in practical effect would be a patent on the algorithm itself.[32]

A patent on a therapeutic use of a compound cannot be described as a patent on an idea. Moreover, the court's concern about claims that might reach more than has in fact been invented should argue for claims upon drug uses rather than upon the drugs themselves. The continuing vitality of the limited and highly technical concept of process in patent law, however, casts a pall over the validity of claims upon a therapeutic use.

These difficulties with the patent system as an incentive for new drug research have largely emerged since World War II. Drug patent owners are not unaware of them. One of the notable features of the drug patent field is the general absence of infringement litigation. Drug patent owners seem cautious, often willing to surrender claims to damages, eager to settle, and slow to push to trial on the merits. Reported cases often involve patents close to expiration where the risk of a finding of invalidity is much reduced. These difficulties may well have reduced private investment in new drug

32. *Gottschalk* v. *Benson*, 93 Sup. Ct. 253, 257 (1972).

research. Their effect, however, has been offset by the emergence of the FDA's new drug clearance procedure as a substitute patent system.

## III. The NDA as a Patent

Section 505(a) of the Food and Drug Act provides that "no person shall introduce or deliver for introduction into interstate commerce any new drug, unless an approval of an application . . . is effective with respect to such drug." [33] A "new" drug is defined in the Act as "any drug the composition of which is such that such drug is not generally recognized, among experts qualified by scientific training and experience to evaluate the safety and effectiveness of drugs, as safe and effective for use under the conditions prescribed . . . in the labeling thereof." [34]

A commonsense reading of the section is that once "any person" has come forward and provided the information necessary to support the issuance of a new drug application or NDA, then any other person who is a registered drug manufacturer under the Act can also manufacture and sell the drug. This reading is also supported by the legislative history. One persistently repeated theme of the legislative history of the 1962 Amendments is that the requirement of generic name labeling and reinforced manufacturing inspection would increase the effectiveness of competition in the drug industry. There is no suggestion in the legislative history that the new drug application procedure, designed to prevent the marketing of unsafe or ineffective drugs, was to become a device for restricting drug industry competition, but incredibly, that is what seems to have happened.

The key to this development is the position of the FDA that a drug which it has cleared is still a new drug. To restate the position, the fact that the FDA has approved an NDA does not demonstrate that the drug is generally recognized by experts as safe and effective: it is only recognized by the FDA as safe and effective. The impact of this position, however, would be limited if a potential competitor could obtain a copy of the new drug application. He could then submit the information submitted by the first applicant and establish that he was going to manufacture a product identical to the first applicant's. It would be difficult for the FDA to deny the second application in light of its action on the first. This strategy

33. 21 U.S.C. § 355.
34. 21 U.S.C. § 321(p).

has been effectively blocked by the position of the FDA that a new drug application is a secret document. Without the NDA, a potential competitor cannot gain access to the clinical test results nor to the technical specifications of the product. Without independent proof that his product, although identical, is safe and effective, he cannot market it.

It is not difficult to construct a policy argument in support of the FDA position, although the FDA has yet to offer one. At a conference held by the FDA staff to explain the impact of the 1962 Amendments, the staff relied upon the reporting requirements imposed on the manufacture of a new drug.

*Question:* If an approved NDA cannot be used by other manufacturers because of possible differences of controls, would not a printed protocol relieve this situation? Otherwise, wouldn't the procedure give the NDA patent status?

*Mr. Rankin* [Assistant Commissioner]: As I understand the question, it is whether, by submitting a printed or mimeographed protocol describing the control features of the manufacturing establishment, it would be possible for a half-dozen, a dozen, or even more firms to get approval on the same new drug application. If that understanding is correct, the answer is "No" because there are many factors other than manufacturing controls that enter into safety of a new drug. For example, under the proposed regulations there will be the matter of maintaining continuing records of clinical experiments with the drug, and making prompt reports to the FDA of adverse effects resulting from use of the drug in medical practice. Certainly no printed form that would apply across the board can cover the various control mechanisms, record-keeping processes, and reporting requirements that each firm should set up for itself.[35]

The answer is not responsive. Each firm operating under an NDA *could* do its own reporting and keep its own records, but that does not justify keeping information in the first NDA unavailable. The argument for the FDA policy is that since the first applicant has borne the costs of getting the NDA approved, he should not be forced to compete with other firms that have not borne the same cost. This is, of course, the argument for patent protection, but in

35. U.S. Dept. of Health, Education and Welfare, Proceedings of FDA Conference on the Kefauver-Harris Drug Amendments and Proposed Regulations, February 15, 1963, p. 72.

light of the difficulties with patent protection it is understandable
that the FDA might feel the need to supply a substitute mechanism.
There are, however, difficulties with this argument. First, it is not at
all clear that the second applicant will have to bear only the same
costs as the first applicant. The drug industry has been able to enlist
a good deal of voluntary assistance from the medical profession in
the clinical testing of new drugs. Is this assistance forthcoming for
the clinical testing of a drug that is in fact medically old? Second,
the effect of the secrecy policy is to force the duplication of the first
applicant's effort, in itself economically wasteful. Third, the NDA is
apparently secret in perpetuity, conferring a perpetual advantage
that is only lost when the FDA decides that the drug is generally
recognized as safe and effective.

The FDA position that a new drug application is secret rests on
shaky legal grounds. The Food and Drug Act provides that "the
using by any person to his own advantage, or revealing, other than
to the Secretary or officers or employees of the Department . . . any
information acquired under authority of section . . . 505 (requiring
the new drug application) . . . concerning any method or process
which as a trade secret is entitled to protection" is prohibited.[36]
This would appear to protect only those parts of an application relating to methods of manufacturing the drug, and then only if the
methods are not generally known in the industry. The position that
all of a new drug application is confidential relies upon a general
criminal statute prohibiting the revelation of trade secrets by government employees.[37] But it is difficult to argue that a new
drug application is a trade secret. The statute was enacted to
protect information that was acquired by government employees in
the course of conducting examinations or inspections relating to the
enforcement of tax, health, or safety laws. A new drug application
and its predecessor documents, however, are documents that contain information required by statute. For instance, how is the public
to appraise the actions of the FDA if it has no access to new drug
applications? How can the FDA consult with the scientific community about a new drug if it is barred by criminal statute from
revealing the content of the application?

The status of the new drug application as a trade secret under
the law is particularly important because, under the Freedom of Information Act,[38] the discretion whether or not to reveal the applica-

36. 21 U.S.C. § 331(j).
37. 18 U.S.C. § 1905.
38. 5 U.S.C. § 552.

tion does not rest with the FDA. If the information is not a trade secret, then the courts can order the FDA to reveal it. The precedents are not authoritative because the law of trade secrets has developed in the context of actions between private parties, but they are not supportive of the FDA position. For instance, the Restatement of Torts defines a trade secret as "any compilation of information which is used in one's business and which gives him an opportunity to obtain an advantage over his competitors." [39] Since the parts of an NDA other than those relating to manufacturing processes are not in fact used in one's business but are used simply to obtain government approval of marketing it is difficult to argue that they are trade secrets. As a recent article written in apprehension of the impending possibility of an action under the Freedom of Information Act concluded: "A company should not have to finance its competitors' early entry into the marketplace by any FDA action in permitting piggyback new drug applications based on exposed confidential data." [40] The article, however, which reached as far afield as the Fifth Amendment for tenuous support, could find little law to buttress its policy conclusion.

Congress and the courts are now becoming aware of this new role of the NDA as an anticompetitive device. In July 1972 the Select Small Business Committee held hearings at which the FDA was criticized for delaying action on soft contact lenses that would compete with a product already approved for marketing by Bausch and Lomb. This is the first time, so far as the present author is aware, that the FDA has ever been criticized for being too slow instead of too fast. Again, in a precedent-shattering decision in the spring of 1972, the Court of Appeals for the District of Columbia upheld a complaint by a dissatisfied potential competitor under the antitrust laws against the cleared firms and an official of the FDA. [41] The decision was precedent-shattering because the plaintiff had abandoned his NDA in frustration. The complaint alleged that the defendants, Baxter Laboratories, Travenol, and an official of the FDA, had conspired to keep plaintiff's drug Cothyrobal off the interstate market and out of competition with Choloxin, a similar drug sold by the defendant firms. One result of this decision will be that any person associated with a firm having an NDA will re-

39. Restatement of Torts § 757 Comment b.

40. William R. Pendergast, "The Responsibility of the FDA to Protect Trade Secrets and Confidential Data," *Food-Drug-Cosmetic Law Journal* 27 (1972), pp. 366, 374. See generally, James M. Johnstone, "The Freedom of Information Act and the FDA," *Food-Drug-Cosmetic Law Journal* 25 (1970), p. 296.

41. *Israel* v. *Baxter Laboratories*, 1972 Trade Cases ¶ 73, 983 (D.C. Cir., May 17, 1972).

fuse to assist the FDA in evaluating any subsequently filed application for the same or similar drug, since any consultation will open the way for a treble damage antitrust charge. This result may be desirable on conflict of interest grounds, but it may well increase the difficulty for the second applicant since he will have to develop or find entirely new experts on the drug involved. Indeed, the first applicant, by involving all possible experts in the clinical investigation and evaluation leading to the submission of his NDA may be able to practically foreclose the feasibility of any other application. The unfocused possibility of personal treble damage liability should do wonders for those doctors who otherwise might be inclined to help.

The new drug application has emerged as a substitute for the faltering patent system. Since, however, it was not designed to serve that purpose, it can do so only at considerable cost. The principal cost is increased barriers to the flow of information between drug researchers. The system creates incentives for drug firms to prevent the dissemination of information that might lead drug experts to recognize a drug as generally safe and effective and to disseminate information that raises questions, however vague and unsupported, about their products. New drug status thus assured, the first applicant has a strong position vis-à-vis any potential newcomer. Whether or not drug firms take advantage of these possibilities created by the FDA's own policies, it seems unwise to maintain a system that creates incentives for them to do so.

## IV. Conclusion

The 1962 Amendments to the Food and Drug Act were designed to increase the information available about new drugs before they are marketed. This information is to be produced by an adversary process. On the one hand are the highly profitable drug companies, assumed to be eager to market new drugs. On the other hand is the newly strengthened Food and Drug Administration. Since, as a practical matter, the FDA has little to gain from the marketing of a new drug and much to lose from the marketing of an unsafe drug, it was reasonable to assume that marketing permission would be denied until the drug companies had produced satisfactory evidence of safety and effectiveness.

It is difficult to say whether the 1962 Amendments have operated in conformity with Congressional intent. It is a perfectly reasonable interpretation of the legislative history that Congress intended to reduce the flow of new drugs. On the other hand, it is clear that the legislature did not correctly evaluate the problem. It is erroneous to confuse general profitability with the profitability of introducing new products. Indeed for many firms, a decreased rate of obsolescence of old products will increase profitability. Furthermore, the evidence adduced in legislative hearings that certain manufacturers of patented drugs enjoyed high markups (500 percent for instance) did not establish, as it was assumed to establish, that drug patent protection is as a general matter strong. It is because of these errors of analysis that Congress was for the most part able to act as if the Amendments would only reduce the marketing of "bad" drugs without any impact on the availability of desirable drugs.

If the incentives for the private development and introduction of new drugs are not sufficient to offset the costs imposed by the new drug clearance procedures, then drug companies cannot be expected to challenge the essentially negative posture which the FDA is by statute and political reality required to assume. It is important to note that the effect will be most important for the marginally superior drug or the drug to be used for treating a relatively unusual condition. In the case of the dramatically effective drug the incentive for introducing it is increased and the difficulty (and hence the cost) of proving that effect is reduced. Similarly, if the condition treated affects a relatively large population, the incentive is enhanced and the difficulty of arranging controlled studies is reduced. In spite of popular belief to the contrary, however, science more often advances in small increments than in quantum leaps, and the general health of the population is as much improved by improvements in the treatment of a large number of relatively rare conditions as it is by an advance in the treatment of a more frequently experienced one.

If one concludes that the present regulatory balance unduly impedes the introduction of new drugs, there are three possible approaches to be considered: first, the costs of the present marketing clearance system can be evaluated for possible cost reductions; second, the system of incentives for private investment can be strengthened; and third, the amount of subsidy provided for the development and marketing of new drugs can be increased.

The issue of evaluating the costs of the new drug clearance procedure is a problem in weighing the costs of the present procedures against the gains that they offer. One aspect of the present regulation does, however, seem particularly worthy of examination. The institutional structure of the FDA seems designed to minimize its ability to take risks. The hard decisions fall completely on the shoulders of civil service employees of the executive branch who must face the wrath of both their superiors and Congress should they make an error of judgment. The present Act provides no device by which some of the responsibility can be transferred from the shoulders of the FDA to the scientific medical community. Perhaps the Act should specify the conditions under which the FDA is entitled to rely on the opinions of experts and the procedures for referring the issue to experts.

An increase in government financing for drug and drug-related research has been a long-term trend that is likely to continue. Government subsidy can accelerate the speed of research and make possible research not likely to lead to a commercial profit. On the other hand, the need for centralized and "responsible" administration of government research funds may cause those funds to be concentrated in orthodox approaches to fairly well understood problems. The political context may also cause an undue emphasis on those medical problems which for one reason or another acquire a high degree of political attractiveness. It may also be difficult for the government to enter the process of developing and marketing specific commercial products without undertaking far more pervasive economic regulation of the drug industry. If the government is, for instance, to subsidize the cost of obtaining an NDA for a private firm, then it may also wish to set conditions as to the price at which the product will be sold.

The existence of private incentives for drug research may provide a useful offset to the tendencies of government subsidy systems. Decision-making in a private "prize" system is decentralized, making it possible for the confident but unorthodox to proceed on their own. The steady commercial focus of a private system may offset some of the peculiar, politically-induced foci of government subsidized research. Moreover, the existence of private incentives makes it possible for the drug industry to continue to innovate without the burden of the extensive economic control that has proven both costly and ineffective elsewhere. There is serious question, however, whether the patent system is now adequate to this task without substantial legislative revision, and the emergence of the NDA as a substitute is on shaky legal ground at best.

The possible changes are numerous. On the simplest level, the present NDA practice might be legitimated by giving each NDA an exclusive but short term while also providing that the content of each NDA would be public. This change would require the creation of some sort of priority determination procedure where more than one firm desires a particular NDA. The simplest rule would be that the NDA would go to the first firm to file for human clinical testing, subject to some loss of rights if the application was not pursued with reasonable diligence. This course at least has the advantage of not opening up larger issues of patent reform which might submerge any hope for change in their own complexity. If combined with judicial receptiveness to therapeutic patent claims and some judicial sympathy for the difficulties involved in obtaining a drug patent, this change might substantially improve the private incentives for drug research. The courts can, for instance, without undue violence to the logic of the patent law, save unsupportable compound claims by reading into them the disclosure of therapeutic utility in the specification.

# Comments on The Patent System and the New Drug Application
William F. Baxter

At the outset of his paper, Professor Kitch said that he was going to pass over the possibility that we might be better off with a tort liability system than with the present licensing system. We talked about that alternative at some length this morning.

This afternoon he has suggested that we might wind up by nationalizing the entire activity of drug invention, production, and introduction so as to get the social costs of the drug industry back in closer association with the decision-making process. This suggestion reinforces my inclination to think that we might do well to go back to a liability system and abandon licensing altogether. Certainly I would regard that as preferable to the alternative possibility of nationalization.

The patent system does, I think, lie at the heart of the particular problem described by Professor Kitch. Perhaps without boring everybody, I might develop that point a little further.

It seems to me that a company or an individual who has discovered that an old substance can be employed in a new way of curing a disease should be awarded a process patent, not a product patent. Now, that does not require any great insight. The difficulty with such a process patent is that the infringer of such a patent then becomes, not the doctor, but the patient, who is the only person who actually engages in the process when he takes the pill. Needless to say, the prospects of enforcing a process patent against direct infringers under such circumstances are very slight.

One must enforce such a patent against *contributory* infringers as a practical matter; that is, against a company that manufactures the substance and, by its advertising and labeling, counsels the infringing activity. Unfortunately, an attempt to enforce against contributory infringers runs into an idiotic 1945 decision by Justice Douglas in which he substantially gutted the possibility of enforcing patents against contributory infringers in such circumstances as are involved here.[1]

Congress tried to correct the situation by adding a section to the Patent Code; but that section in itself is terribly obscure.[2] Hence there are, as Professor Kitch has suggested, serious difficulties in the way of effective enforcement of such process patents. Moreover, these practicalities of enforcement under existing patent law constitute the basic difficulty, rather than any question of whether in some technical sense such as a process patent can be issued and

1. *Mercoid Corporation* v. *Mid-Continent Investment Co.*, 320 U.S. 661 (1944).
2. U.S. Congress, 35 § 271.

would be valid. Hence, the patent office is motivated to issue product patents which are enforceable, but of doubtful validity.

I take almost no comfort whatsoever from the idea that the NDA is somehow functioning as a more or less satisfactory alternative to sound patent law; there are some very, very major differences. If one company does research and development and gets a patent, and subsequently another company wants to practice the art and makes payments to the first company for a license, the payments are a kind of income redistribution that's going on within the industry. The aggregate expenditure of the industry and the aggregate consumption of real social resources are not being multiplied by the entry of the second manufacturer. On the other hand, to view the NDA as an alternative contemplates that the second company, in order to get its application through, must repeat all the required NDA procedures, genuinely consumptive of scarce social resources, which the first one went through; and that seems to me totally unacceptable.

I do agree with Professor Kitch that the *reason* the FDA is pursuing this kind of crude concept of equity is that the FDA perceives vaguely that the patent system isn't working properly in this context; but this perception does not lead to the conclusion that the situation is satisfactory.

I have several just minor points on which to conclude. I fail to see myself that, even should the government subsidize research and development, however extensively, any case whatsoever is created for government regulation of prices. So long as there is a more or less competitively structured industry that can exploit the resultant fruits of research and development, competition between them under those circumstances should bring prices down to the now-lower-cost yielded by the government subsidy.

Finally, to criticize Professor Kitch for something he did not say rather than for the things he did, I would lay even heavier stress than he has on the delay that is involved in present procedures. Consider the investment in and the yields from new drug innovation, and focus on the extent to which those two things are being pulled apart in time as a consequence of the excessively cautious attitude on the part of the FDA. Then discount the yields by prevailing interest rates (yields which are being pushed further and further away and to some extent outside the potential 17-year period of patent protection even if there is an enforceable patent); and surely one must conclude, when comparing those discounted yields with the very, very heavy investments, that delay by itself may furnish an adequate explanation of the slowdown in the rate of innovation. One can, of course, say that that was exactly what Congress had in mind when it passed the 1962 Amendment; but I don't believe that. Its purposes were more politically transparent. Moreover, had the slowdown in innovation been foreseen, it would not have been regarded as a good thing.

I should like to finish by saying that I thought this was a very good paper and that I agreed with most of the points made by Professor Kitch; I wouldn't want my comments to disguise that fact in any way.

# The Benefits and Costs
# of New Drug Regulation
## Sam Peltzman

# I. Introduction and Summary

This paper seeks to measure the social benefits and costs of the
1962 Amendments to the Food, Drug and Cosmetic Act, in particular those provisions relating to the introduction of new prescription drugs. To place the study in context, only the barest background to the relevant parts of the Amendments will be presented
here.

From 1938 to 1962, the introduction of a new drug required approval of a new drug application (NDA) by the Food and Drug Administration (FDA). An NDA was approved unless the FDA determined within a statutory period of 180 days that the NDA did
not demonstrate adequately that the drug was "safe" for the use
suggested in the proposed labeling. The initial impetus to a change
in the law came from hearings initiated by Senator Estes Kefauver
in 1959. A major line of argument developed in the hearings was
that the prevailing regulation permitted the introduction of many
new drugs of dubious efficacy which were sold at unusually high
prices. This was said to arise from a combination of patent protection for new chemical formulas, consumer and physician ignorance,
and weak incentives for physicians to minimize patient drug costs.
A caricature of the drug market established in the hearings might
run as follows: [1] Drug companies devoted inordinate amounts of research to the development of patented new drugs which represented
only a minor modification of existing formulas. The drug companies
would then seek to capitalize on patent protection by expensive promotion campaigns in which extravagant claims for the effectiveness
of the new drug were impressed upon doctors and, sometimes,
patients. Since most doctors did not have sufficient pharmacological
expertise to evaluate new drugs, they relied heavily on information supplied by drug companies, and, at least initially, they frequently treated this information with insufficient skepticism. More-

This study was prepared under a grant from the Center for Policy Study,
University of Chicago, for presentation at the Center's Conference on the
Regulation of New Pharmaceuticals in December 1972. I am indebted to Yale
Brozen, Harold Demsetz, Milton Friedman, James Jondrow, Richard Landau,
and George Stigler for helpful comments and suggestions. The study has
benefited from diligent research assistance by Joyce Iseri. Finally, I am grate-
ful to Richard Burr of R. A. Gosselin, Inc., and to Paul de Haen of Paul de
Haen, Inc., for providing me with essential data.

1. A good popular account of the Kefauver hearings and the Congressional
debate surrounding the 1962 Amendments is provided by Harris (9). Senator
Kefauver's elaboration of the discussion that follows, may be found in
*Administered Prices, Drugs* (35), especially ch. 6–15.

over, they had little incentive to evaluate drug company claims carefully, since prescription costs were borne by their patients. Some patients who might otherwise question the cost-effectiveness of drugs prescribed for them failed to do so, because they too were impressed by the curative powers of new drugs about which they had heard. Indeed, these patients frequently pressured their doctor to prescribe new drugs against the doctor's better judgment.

Even where patent protection was weak, as, for example, for new products which were combinations or duplicates of existing chemical formulas, it was argued that the existence of consumer ignorance and weak cost-minimization incentives made product differentiation an attractive strategy. Since the patent laws provided some incentive to chemical-formula-differentiation, drug company rivalry in this dimension faced physicians with a mentally-taxing array of complex chemical names from which to choose. This induced the doctor to rely on easily remembered brand names in his prescribing practice. As a result, an important contribution to a drug company's success was the production of easily recalled, hence expensively promoted, brand names for old as well as new chemical formulas.

In summary, the Kefauver hearings characterized much drug industry innovation as socially wasteful. The waste arose from product differentiation expenditures in an imperfectly competitive market permeated by consumer ignorance. The waste was manifest in prices for new drugs which incorporated these product differentiation expenditures but which did not reflect the "true value" of the drug to the consumer. That is, only in considerable hindsight would doctors and/or patients discover that claims for new drugs were exaggerated. In light of this knowledge, consumers would have regarded themselves as better off if they had substituted lower priced old drugs (especially unpatented old drugs and most especially non-branded unpatented old drugs) for the new drugs; they would have paid less for treatment at least as effective as that which they received.

The clear implication of the Kefauver hearings was that there was readily available a cheaper method of providing valuable information about new drugs to consumers than these assertedly frequent payments for worthless information provided by the drug industry. The method lay in government regulation of manufacturers' claims for new drug effectiveness. A proposal to implement such regulation was incorporated in a bill proposed by Senator Kefauver in 1961, and the modification of his proposal that appeared in the 1962 Amendments will provide the major focus for this study.

Any account of the forces shaping the 1962 Amendments must mention the thalidomide episode of 1961 and 1962. The drug thalidomide was, in fact, kept from the U.S. market by the FDA under existing provisions of the Food, Drug and Cosmetic Act. The manufacturer, however, had distributed the drug to some physicians for experimental purposes. Under the Act such distribution could be made to those deemed by the manufacturer to be "qualified experts" as long as the drug bore a label warning the expert that it was an investigational drug. The American manufacturer of thalidomide ceased investigational distribution of the drug and withdrew its NDA after reports from Europe that deformed babies had been born to mothers using the drug during pregnancy. These well-publicized reports aroused concern that clinical testing of new drugs was insufficiently regulated. The lesson of the thalidomide episode appeared to be that, in their rush to market new drugs, producers were exposing humans to potentially harmful drugs before that potential could be adequately evaluated.

The Amendments to the 1938 Food, Drug and Cosmetic Act enacted in late 1962 and subsequent implementing regulations have two major foci relevant to our purposes. These correspond roughly to some of the concerns raised in the Kefauver hearings and those arising from the thalidomide episode, that is, to the conditions surrounding the introduction of new drugs and their pre-market testing. A brief summary of the relevant provisions follows.

**Introduction of new drugs.** In response to Senator Kefauver's concern over the value of new drugs, the Amendments added a "proof-of-efficacy" requirement to the proof-of-safety requirement of the 1938 Act, and they removed the time constraint on the FDA in disposing of an NDA. No new drug may now be marketed unless, and until, the FDA determines that there is substantial evidence not only that the drug is safe, but that it is "effective" in its intended use. An effective drug, in this context, is one which the FDA determines will meet the claims made for it by the manufacturer. Subsequent promotion of the drug can claim no more than the effects established before the FDA, and must include a summary of "side effects, contraindications, and effectiveness." [2]

2. The FDA is also permitted to order withdrawal of drugs introduced prior to 1962 if they are found ineffective. This provision is, however, largely unimplemented pending an evaluation of old drugs by the National Academy of Sciences.

**Drug testing.** The essence of the 1962 Amendments and subsequent implementing regulations was to empower the Food and Drug Administration and the Secretary of Health, Education and Welfare to specify the kind of testing procedure a manufacturer had to engage in to produce acceptable information for evaluation of a new drug application. Prior to submission of a new drug application, the manufacturer was now required, among other things, to submit a plan for investigation of the new drug in humans as well as information from preclinical testing. Periodic progress reports to the Food and Drug Administration on the investigation were required and the FDA was empowered to terminate or order modification of the investigation if the drug is deemed unsafe or ineffective at any point in the testing. In this way, it was hoped, human exposure to drugs like thalidomide would be reduced both during testing and after marketing.

If the 1962 Amendments have been at all effective, they might be expected to have reduced the flow of new drugs marketed (eliminating those deemed ineffective by the Food and Drug Administration, but not by the manufacturer) and increased the gestation period for any new drug reaching the market. The latter effect would arise from the requirement for proof of efficacy, the removal of the time constraint on FDA action on a new drug application, and the requirement for tests and evaluations that the manufacturer would not otherwise undertake. The added costs associated with the expanded information requirements of the 1962 Amendments to the Food and Drug Act would also be expected to reinforce any reduced flow of new drugs.

The realization of any of these effects would not, of course, tell us anything about the social costs and benefits of the 1962 Amendments. These would depend on the value of the particular drugs introduced or kept off the market by the Amendments and the value of the information generated by more extensive drug testing. More fundamentally, however, a reading of the 1962 Amendments can, at best, tell us the direction of change in drug innovation and its gestation period, but not its magnitude. Therefore, before we estimate the costs and benefits of the Amendments, we want to know whether their effects on drug innovation have been substantial or small. If, for example, very few drugs have been kept off the market by the operation of the Amendments, their net benefits or costs might reasonably be ignored as trivial, unless they have substantially altered the composition, that is, the average safety or efficacy, of new drugs marketed.

## Summary

In Section II, therefore, I estimate the effect of the Amendments on the flow of new drugs and their gestation period. These effects are substantial: the flow is shown to be more than halved, and the gestation period more than doubled by the Amendments.

Section III develops a method for measuring the net consumer benefits or costs of the Amendments. The operating assumption is that the more effective the new drugs are, the more durable will be the demand for them; that is, the demand for ineffective drugs tends to decline in the light of cumulative physician-patient experience with them. Consumer surplus analysis is then adapted to provide a measure of the gains and losses (arising from uninformed consumption of ineffective drugs) yielded by any set of new drugs. For empirical implementation, the losses are assumed to be eliminated by the Amendments. Although the same analysis is applicable to some aspects of drug safety, it is shown to be inadequate for either atypically unsafe or beneficial drugs.

Empirical estimates of the demand for new drugs are developed in Section IV, and the net benefits of the 1962 Amendments are calculated from the consumer surplus implied by these demand curves. These calculations yield negligible losses prior to 1962, so that the decline in new drug flows induced by the Amendments results in a net loss to consumers. The loss is estimated at between $300 and $400 million annually as of 1970, or about 7 percent of total drug expenditures. The evaluations of pre– and post–1962 new drugs by some "expert" groups are then examined for implicit differences in the incidence of ineffective drugs. In general, this incidence is found to be unaffected by the Amendments, and thus the conclusion that the decline in innovation has entailed a net loss to consumers is reinforced. An alternative measure of the annual gross waste on ineffective new drugs is derived from one expert group's evaluations (AMA Council on Drugs), and this amounts to about 2 percent of total drug expenditures.

Finally, it is shown that the barrier to entry created by the Amendments has resulted in slightly higher prices for old drugs. The annual cost of this to consumers is about 1 percent of their total drug expenditures. The conclusion of the section, therefore, is that the Amendments impose a net cost on consumers in excess of 5 percent of their drug expenditures.

Section V attempts to remedy the inadequacy of the consumer surplus analysis for unusually harmful or beneficial new drugs by

examining the effects of such drugs on the value of human capital
and costs of disease treatment. It is shown that a moderate increase
in the gestation period for beneficial drugs is far more costly than
what is saved by completely suppressing harmful drugs. This conclusion need not be modified even if it is assumed that a thalidomide type of drug would have been widely marketed in a pre–
1962 environment but suppressed under the Amendments. The
specific costs and savings attributable to the Amendments are uncertain. It is shown, however, that had the Amendments been
passed a decade or two prior to 1962, the annual net cost of delayed marketing of new drugs would be sufficient to double the
total social cost of the Amendments. Similar potential costs are
shown to be inherent in the magnitude of some health problems
currently engaging pharmacological research.

Although the Amendments appear to have hurt their intended
beneficiaries, the drug consumers, a complete accounting would
include effects on the wealth of drug producers. These are, therefore, estimated in Section VI from drug company stock prices. The
Amendments appear to have had little affect on the wealth of drug
company owners, but have reduced wealth variability. Therefore,
if owners are assumed to be risk averse, they have benefited from
the Amendments.

## II. Introduction of New Drugs

The 1962 Amendments appear, on the surface, to have greatly re-
tarded the flow of new drugs. The relevant data are in Table 1.
They show that the annual flow of new drugs since 1962 is less
than half that prior to 1962, and that there was no obvious downward trend in this flow prior to 1962.

Before these data are interpreted, a word about the nomenclature
used in Table 1 is in order. "New chemical entities" (NCEs) are
drugs containing a single chemical formula not previously marketed This category would include virtually all drugs generally regarded as significant therapeutic breakthroughs. About 80 percent
of the "other" new drug category consist of combinations of previously discovered chemical entities, and the remainder are previously introduced chemical entities marketed under a new brand
name, usually by a manufacturer different from the one who introduced it as an NCE, and sometimes for a new therapeutic indication.[3] Although all these new drug types are subject, directly

3. Table 1 omits data on new dosage forms of previously introduced chemi-

## Table 1

### Average Annual Number of New Drugs Introduced 1951-1970, Selected Subperiods

| Period | New Chemical Entities | Other New Drugs |
|--------|----------------------|-----------------|
| 1951–54 | 39.0 | 303.0 |
| 1955–58 | 42.0 | 351.5 |
| 1959–62 | 43.5 | 239.3 |
| 1963–66 | 17.0 | 120.0 |
| 1967–70 | 15.3 | 68.8 |
| 1951–62 | 41.5 | 297.9 |
| 1963–70 | 16.1 | 94.4 |
| Ratio $\dfrac{1963–70}{1951–62}$ | .389 | .317 |

Source: Paul de Haen, Inc., New York

and, as in the case of the NCE derivatives, indirectly, to the 1962 Amendments, this study will focus largely on the NCEs. The reasons for this will be elaborated subsequently. It is, however, relevant to point out here that the distinction between these types appears to be more than one of terminology or intuitive appeal. For example, one study estimates that the mean development cost of an NCE prior to the Amendments was well over triple that of a combination product (21, p. 77).*

Although the data in Table 1 show a precipitous decline in new drug introductions since 1962, they do not tell us how much of this decline, if any, can reasonably be attributed to the 1962 Amendments. One wants to allow for the possibility that some or all of this decline might be due to some fundamental change in the factors underlying the demand or supply of new drugs which is independent of the Amendments. Indeed, it might be argued that the

---

cal entities—for example, a tablet form of a liquid. The flow of new dosage forms, however, roughly parallels that of the new drugs in the Table. The annual average flow was 104.5 for 1951–62 and 26.4 for 1963–70.

* Italicized numbers refer to the references at end of article.

1962 Amendments were in the nature of a "public good" for the
drug industry which could have raised the demand for new drugs.
That is, if many inefficacious new drugs were being introduced prior
to 1962, there would presumably have been a demand for independent evaluation and certification of new drugs. A private producer of such evaluations, however, might find it difficult to recoup
his costs from direct sales to consumers due to costs of detecting
and excluding "free riders," while their value might be reduced by
public skepticism if paid for by drug producers. If the 1962 Amendments correct the resultant private underproduction of new drug
evaluations, one might expect them to have raised the price the
public is willing to pay for new drugs and thereby to have stimulated their production.[4]

I shall attempt to distinguish the effects of the 1962 Amendments
from other forces affecting the flow of new drugs by first developing a simple model for the "unregulated" introduction of new
drugs. The parameters of the model will be estimated from pre–
1962 data, and they will be used to extrapolate beyond 1962. A
comparison of these extrapolations with actual post–1962 new drug
flows will provide an estimate of the net effect of the 1962 Amendments.

I will treat each drug (specifically, each chemical entity) as a
homogeneous bit of non-depreciable therapeutic information. The
demand for these bits will, as a first approximation, be taken as
proportional to the (logarithm of the) expected size of the drug
market. Since production of these bits entails a lengthy research
and development process, producers must estimate the demand for
them by first estimating the size of the drug market in the future.
I assume that they do so by naive extrapolation from the present
output of drugs. In implementing this assumption, I make use of
Schnee's estimate that the mean development time of a (pre–1962)
NCE was about two years, with a standard deviation of one year
(21, p. 77).[5] This I take to imply that the bulk of NCE producers

4. It should be pointed out that, among others, the American Medical
Association has a continuing new drug evaluation program, predating 1962,
the results of which are widely disseminated to its membership. Although this
says nothing about whether the amount of such private evaluation is socially
optimal, the FDA itself has not noted any increase since 1962 in the number
of drugs which, by its own standards, are "important therapeutic advances."
These have declined from an annual average of 12.8 in 1951–62 to 9.1 in
1963–70. (Data are from "New Drug Development Study," unpublished, FDA,
1971.)

5. "Development time" comprehends the period from clinical testing of a
chemical entity with desirable biological activity to approval of an NDA.

are committing resources to the NCE development process based on estimates of total drug output one to three years in the future. Therefore, and in view of the limited amount of data I shall have to work with, I assume that the output base from which NCE producers extrapolate naively can be represented conveniently by a three-year moving average of drug output centered about two years prior to the year for which the demand for chemical entities is being estimated.

I shall include only one factor other than expected output in the demand for chemical entities, namely the (log of) expected output of physicians' services. I am assuming that physicians' services are complementary with drug output, so that, for example, the expectation of an unusually high output of such services will cause producers of chemical entities to expect the demand for drugs (and, thereby, chemical entities) to be unusually high as well. Once again, it will be assumed that expectations about output of physician' services are formed by naive extrapolation from a moving average of current output.

It would be desirable to incorporate factors influencing the cost as well as the demand for chemical entities into the model. Since much of the cost of developing chemical entities is labor expense for research personnel, a logical cost variable might be something like the relative price of research to existing-drug-production labor. Unfortunately, continuous data on the cost of research personnel are unavailable as far back in time as we require. The fragmentary data that are available, however, suggest that omission of this variable will not seriously bias any resulting estimate of the effects of the 1962 Amendments. That is, there appears to have been neither an upward trend nor any large increase since 1962 in the relative price of research to production labor in the drug industry.[6]

We are then left with a simple model that relies on two demand

6. The Bureau of Labor Statistics reports that from 1961 to 1970, the average annual salary of chemists (a prototypical form of research labor) rose by 50.2 percent (25). This corresponds closely to the 52.6 percent rise in average hourly earnings of drug industry production workers (24). Data from the U.S. *Census of Population* show that, from 1949 to 1959, median annual income of chemists rose by 63.8 percent while that of "natural scientists" rose 74.0 percent (26). In the same period, BLS data show a 55.8 percent increase in drug production worker average hourly earnings (24). Taken together, then, the data imply a slightly more favorable labor cost environment for research after 1962 than before. Annual earnings of research personnel could, however, have been unduly depressed by the 1949 recession, and the safest conclusion would be that no obvious labor cost inducement to substitute production for research activity can explain any of the post-1962 decline in new drug innovation.

variables to explain the behavior of producers of chemical entities. The model can be elaborated and stated more precisely in symbols as follows:

$$(1) \qquad \overset{*}{N_t} = a + b\overset{*}{X_t} + c\overset{*}{P_t}$$

$$(2) \qquad \overset{*}{X_t} = d + \overline{X}_{t-2}$$

$$(3) \qquad \overset{*}{P_t} = e + \overline{P}_{t-2}$$

where $\overset{*}{N_t}$ = total number of chemical entities which producers wish to have available for marketing in year t.

$\overset{*}{X_t}$ = log of expected output of drugs in t.

$\overset{*}{P_t}$ = log of expected output of physicians' services in t.

$\overline{X}_{t-2}$ = log of a three-year moving average of actual drug output centered about t—2.

$\overline{P}_{t-2}$ = log of a three-year moving average of actual output of physicians' services centered about t—2

a,b,c = constants

d,e = the expected biennial growth rates of X and P respectively, assumed to be constants.

When the expressions on the right-hand sides of (2) and (3) are substituted for their counterparts in (1), (1) becomes:

$$(1)' \qquad \overset{*}{N_t} = a + bd + ce + b\overline{X}_{t-2} + c\overline{P}_{t-2}$$

We must now specify how producers react to this demand for total chemical entities in supplying *new* chemical entities in a particular marketing period (one year). The annual flow of NCEs may, in this context, be regarded as an attempt by producers to close the gap between the number of entities they wish to have on the market and those already developed and marketed. I assume here that the cost of closing such a gap will rise with the rate at which it is closed, so that producers may not wish to eliminate the gap in every marketing period. This can be translated as:

$$(4) \qquad \overset{*}{n_t} = h\,(\overset{*}{N_t} - N_{t-1}),$$

where $\overset{*}{n_t}$ = number of NCEs producers wish to market in t,

$N_{t-1}$ = total number of chemical entities available for marketing at the start of t.

h = a constant coefficient of adjustment between zero and unity.

To implement (4), it is assumed that producers, on average, attain n*, and deviations from n* are random. Upon substituting the right-hand side of (1)' for $N_t^*$, (4) may then be written

$$(4)' \quad n_t = (ha + hbd + hce) + hb\overline{X}_{t-2} + hc\overline{P}_{t-2} - hN_{t-1} + u$$

where u = a random variable. I then estimate (4)' by ordinary least-squares on pre–1962 data, employing the following empirical counterparts to the variables.

$n_t$ = number of new chemical entities introduced in t. Paul de Haen, Inc., New York.

$\overline{X}_{t-2}$ = log of three-year moving average of total number of out-of-hospital prescriptions sold (millions) centered about t—2. *American Druggist* (1).

$\overline{P}_{t-2}$ = log of three-year moving average of personal consumption expenditures on physicians' services (million dollars) deflated by price index (1958 = 100) for these services and centered about t—2. U.S. Office of Business Economics (30, 31).

$N_{t-1}$ = cumulative number of NCEs introduced through t—1. Paul de Haen, Inc., New York.[7]

The estimate of (4)' is:

$$(E1) \quad n_t = -2990.016 + 471.352\,\overline{X}_{t-2} + 45.590\overline{P}_{t-2} - .672N_{t-1}$$
$$\quad\quad\quad\quad\quad\quad (75.616) \quad\quad\quad (32.142) \quad\quad (.113)$$

Coefficient determination = .800 Standard error of estimate = 4.969 Sample period: 1948–62 (15 observations), standard errors of coefficients are in parentheses. The regression implies that size of the drug market is by far the more important of the two demand

7. The cumulation is begun from 1945, so that $N_{t-1}$ is, in fact, the "true" number of chemical entities developed to t–1 minus a constant (the number developed to 1945). This difference between $N_{t-1}$ and the "true" value will affect only the intercept of the regression estimate of (4').

The cumulation procedure assumes no "depreciation" of the stock of chemical entities. In fact, old chemical entities are sometimes withdrawn from the market, but this does not imply that the knowledge embodied in them has "worn out." That knowledge is non-depreciable, and so we treat each NCE as a net addition to the stock of knowledge.

variables,[8] and that roughly two-thirds of the gap between N* and N is closed in any annual marketing period. This rather simple model is able, given the size of the coefficient of determination, to explain most of the variation in new chemical entity flows in the post-war period up to 1962. The satisfactory performance of the model is confirmed by inspection of Figure 1, where actual values

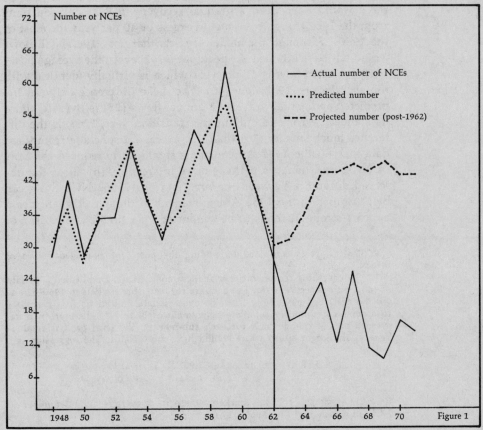

Figure 1

of n are plotted against the values predicted by E1. There were at least two major cycles (beginning 1948 and 1955) in NCE flows in the pre–1962 period, and the model "tracks" both of them closely. In particular, note that the decline from the post-war peak (63 NCEs in 1959) to the trough (27) just prior to passage of the 1962 Amendments is virtually all accounted for by the variables in E1.

The next step in the analysis is to ask our model to predict an-

8. A given percentage change in X increases the demand for chemical entities by more than ten times that of the same percentage change in P.

nual NCE flows in the post–1962 period, and to compare these predictions with actual flows. The predicted flows are estimated by plugging post–1962 values of $\overline{X}$ and $\overline{P}$ along with the implied values of N into E1;[9] they may be regarded as estimates of n in the absence of any change in the law. These estimates are also plotted in Figure 1, and they imply that, except for the 1962 Amendments, there would have been a gradual recovery in NCE introductions from the 1962 trough to a level in excess of 40 per year for most of the 1960s. Although the model predicts that post–1962 NCE flows would not have attained the peak pre–1962 levels, the average post–1962 predicted flow is 41 per year which is virtually identical with the average pre–1962 flow (40). The mean difference between the predicted and actual post–1962 annual flows (25) is over 10 times its standard error and only in the transition year, 1963, is the difference much smaller (15) than this average. I conclude from these data that (a) the 1962 Amendments significantly reduced the flow of NCEs and, what is perhaps more interesting, (b) all of the observed difference between the pre– and post–1962 NCE flows can be attributed to the 1962 Amendments.[10] Although this conclusion appears strong, it tends to be supported by a simple comparison of

9. That is, N is computed by adding the post-1962 predicted values of n to $N_{1962}$.
10. To check the reasonableness of these conclusions, I replicated a variant of (4') on cross section data. The data are for drug sub-markets in 1960–62 and will be described more fully later. Because of data limitations it is necessary to assume continuously complete adjustment of N to N*. Therefore n is regressed on the change in X for each sub-market; the level of X is retained because the larger sub-markets should have more NCEs. The regression is

$$(E1)' \qquad n_i = .394 + 1.901 \, X_{i,\,t-2} + .195 \, \overline{X}_{i,\,t-2}$$
$$(.884) \qquad\qquad (.098)$$

$R^2 = .14$, $i = 1,2 \ldots 42$ sub-markets where $n_i$ = average annual number of NCEs in sub-market i for 1960–62,

$$\dot{X} = \text{average annual change in } \overline{X}.$$

I next used (E1)' to extrapolate forward and backward in time on the aggregate data. Since the scale of the dependent variables in (E1) and (E1)' differ, it is convenient to express the results as an index. For 1948–59, (E1)' predicts an average n equal to 109 percent of the 1960–62 average. The actual average using aggregate data is identical to this. For the period 1963–70, the average predicted value for n is 106 percent of the 1960–62 average. The actual value, however, is only 43 percent. Extrapolation from the cross-section results, then, leads to the same conclusions as that from the time series: all of the large post-1962 decline in drug innovation must be attributed to extra-market forces, such as the Amendments.

U.S. and British NCE flows. Data reported by Wardell show that for 1960–61, the United States flow was 1.13 times the British; while for 1966–71 this ratio was only .52, or .46 of its pre–1962 value.[11] This last figure is already roughly comparable in magnitude to the ratio of U.S. NCEs to the number predicted by E1 for 1966–71 (.34). Simple enumeration of post–1962 U.K. NCE flows, however, probably understates the amount of innovation to be expected in a pre–1962 regulatory environment and, correspondingly, understates the effect of the Amendments in the United States. Most of the U.K. NCEs are produced by firms with substantial sales in the United States, and the U.K. NCE flow is reduced whenever one of these firms decides that the cost of complying with the U.S. law is sufficiently great to deter development of an NCE for both markets. Although a detailed study of this transnational effect of the Amendments is beyond the scope of this paper, the simple comparison of U.S. and U.K. experience lends credence to the large effects I have attributed to the Amendments.

To the extent that some of the costs of complying with the Amendments are "fixed"—that is, unrelated to the size of a new drug's market—one might expect that output of new drugs has declined less than their number. There is, however, no strong evidence that drug manufacturers have been successful in achieving larger output per NCE than prior to 1962, though there is some indication that they have tried to do so. In subsequent analysis I use a sample consisting of "important" NCEs. These are NCEs that account for 1 percent or more of prescriptions sold in a sub-market which itself typically accounts for over one million new prescriptions annually. To be sure, number of prescriptions is a rather crude output measure, and the criteria defining sub-markets (therapeutic categories) may not always correspond to relevant economic criteria. I shall, however, tolerate these imperfections in order to be able to work with disaggregated data.[12] Here I compare the fraction of all drug prescriptions accounted for by these important NCEs one year after

11. William M. Wardell, "The Drug Lag: An International Comparison," unpublished mimeo., University of Rochester School of Medicine. Wardell's definition of NCE differs slightly from that in my data.

12. The data to be used here are from R. A. Gosselin, Inc., *National Prescription Audit Therapeutic Category Report* (NPA) (20). The NPA uses a sample of prescriptions filled at a panel of pharmacies to estimate national dollar and prescription sales for each drug sold by prescription. Drugs are grouped by two, three, and four digit therapeutic categories according to either chemical similarity (for example, penicillins) and/or similarity of the symptoms for which the drugs are prescribed (for example, analgesics). Four-digit categories are employed here. The data are limited to new prescriptions,

introduction in the period just prior to (1960–62) and the period after the 1962 Amendments (1964–69, the transition year 1963 is excluded). These NCEs accounted for an annual average of 1.58 percent of all drug prescriptions in the pre–1962 period and only 0.57 percent in the post–1962 period. This difference roughly parallels the difference in number of NCEs introduced, so that each NCE captures about the same share (.1 percent) of total prescriptions in each period. These data, however, exclude two important drug categories (diuretics and oral contraceptives) which were essentially invented just prior to 1960, but where substantial post–1962 innovation took place (see footnote [12]). Their inclusion would bring the post–1962 annual NCE share up to 1.18 percent compared to 1.77 percent for the pre–1962 period. It would be risky, however, to conclude from this last comparison that there is a persistent tendency to increased output per NCE. The effect of these few major innovations is concentrated in the first triplet of the post–1962 years, which implies that they are a "spin-off" of pre-Amendment innovation. The average annual NCE share for 1967–70 is a mere 0.36 percent. More important, perhaps, no wholly new drug category has appeared since 1962 which has produced innovations that now seem capable of duplicating the impact of diuretics and oral contraceptives. The safest conclusion to draw here would be that the decline in number of new drugs has been roughly matched by a decline in their output.

Fixed costs of complying with the 1962 Amendments seem to have affected the size of the markets where innovation takes place, rather than the average size of innovation. Today, drug manufacturers appear to be concentrating innovation more on larger markets than they used to. To illustrate, the average sub-market penetrated by one or more important NCEs in a post–1962 year accounted for 3.49 percent of all drug prescriptions compared with 1.82 percent pre–1962. This difference is significant, and would be more substantial were diuretics and oral contraceptives included. If manufacturers are entering larger markets in expectation of larger

since the NPA began collecting data on refills only after 1962. I exclude from my sample of the NPA data those therapeutic categories in which the major innovation (50 percent or more of dollar or prescription sales) took place in a single year during or up to three years prior to the period being sampled. The motivation for these exclusions derives from the subsequent analysis of the relative output of new and old drugs. Where a category has, in effect, just been invented, it will not contain a reliable sample of old drugs. The categories remaining in my sample account for about 80 percent of all prescriptions sold in a typical year.

sales per NCE, the expectation has not, as we have shown, been realized. An explanation for this failure is contained in subsequent analysis of the demand for new drugs.

### The Length of the New Drug Development Process

The few pieces of evidence available imply that the proof-of-efficacy and clinical testing requirements of the 1962 Amendments have added at least two years to the gestation period for new drugs. The FDA reports that the average time between filing and approval of an NDA was 7 months in 1962 (see footnote 11). This rose steadily to 30 months by 1967, and has averaged 27.5 months for the period 1967–72.[13] These figures are roughly in the middle of the 12– and 48–month range estimated by a drug company research director (7, pp. 115–116). The Amendments have also, of course, added to the information required before an NDA is filed. The same research director estimates that total development time for an NCE is now 51 to 105 months. The mid-point of this range exceeds by about four years Schnee's previously cited estimate of two years for the same process prior to 1962. Even when generous allowance is made for the considerable variation in drug development time, it is difficult to attribute less than two years added development time to the operation of the 1962 Amendments.

## III. Costs and Benefits of the 1962 Amendments: Analytical Framework

The preceding analysis establishes only that the 1962 Amendments have had a substantial effect on the new drug market, but not whether the Amendments have succeeded or failed to serve their intended beneficiaries. Some of the 200 or so new drugs that would have been introduced in the absence of the Amendments may have been "worthwhile," and their potential consumers are made worse off by their unavailability. Others may have been "inefficacious" (or unsafe) and their potential consumers are benefited by their unavailability. I shall attempt here to outline a procedure for determining how these gains and losses, and thereby the net impact of the 1962 Amendments, can be estimated.

The procedure to be outlined here will focus largely on consumer

13. Private communication from the FDA. These data do not distinguish between NCEs and other types of new drugs. The FDA, however, informs me that there is no significant difference between types.

evaluation of drugs observed in the marketplace. This choice of focus may be controversial, and deserves explanation. One could approach the problem at hand by relying on the judgment of non-consumer "experts" to determine which drugs are worthwhile and which are not. On this approach, if expert judgment declares drug X to have no more medical effectiveness than, say, aspirin, one would say that consumers would be benefited if X was not on the market, the benefit equalling sales of X minus the cost of a med-ically-equivalent amount of aspirin. I largely eschew this approach, at least in part to maintain a sensible division of labor. It is simply not within an economist's expertise to resolve pharmacological dis-putes. A more fundamental problem with relying primarily on expert judgment to deduce consumer welfare arises, however, when expert judgment and consumer behavior persistently differ. Let us assume that before X is marketed all interested parties—the drug manufacturers, FDA, doctors, and patients, etc.—agree unanimously on who is best qualified to evaluate the drug's pharmacological prop-erties. Assume further, that the disinterested expert finds that X and aspirin are indeed pharmacologically equivalent, and, what will be important to subsequent analysis, that every interested party is in-formed of this finding. Now, suppose that, in light of this informa-tion, doctors persistently prescribe X and patients persist in buying it at a substantial premium over aspirin. In such a case, the doctor/patient consumers would, given their own informed preference for X, suffer a loss rather than benefit if X were not marketed. Exclu-sive reliance on expert judgment would then lead to inaccurate benefit-cost estimates, unless, of course, one wished to assert that any such estimate should simply exclude benefits deriving from consumer behavior that deviates from that prescribed by experts.

I am aware that many readers may, implicitly or explicitly, wish to leave out of account benefits and costs associated with what they may regard as irrational, even if fully-informed, behavior. I will not here seek to defend my taking these into account. Instead, these readers are referred to a subsequent section in which costs are imputed to the "irrational" behavior of informed consumers. For-tunately, the margin of "error" here is probably smaller than it would be in evaluating benefits and costs of some policy designed to regulate, say, smoking and diet patterns. In these cases, the behavior prescribed by experts and that of informed consumers often differ markedly. There may also be drug consumers who will respond, somatically or psychologically, to an appropriately mar-keted placebo in full knowledge of its chemical properties. It would,

however, require rather strong assumptions, which I am here un-
willing to make, about both the current state of pharmacological
science and the nature of the benefit consumers seek from medicines to expect this group to be numerous. If most consumers are
seeking improved health by their drug consumption, and if the
effect of drugs on health can be predicted well from their chemical
properties, then most of those buying placebos will simply be both
ignorant and unhealthy. If this is so, then one can avoid having to
choose between contenders for best-qualified, disinterested experts
and rely instead on the behavior of informed consumers to evaluate
the benefits and costs of various drug consumption patterns. This,
of course, will require specification of what constitutes an "informed" consumer.

Although lack of information may be the most important source
of difference between the behavior of consumers in the marketplace
and that which experts might prefer, the conceptual difference
between the approach to be used here and one that relies completely
on expert evaluation of drugs should nevertheless not be minimized.
I will therefore use expert evaluations of drugs in this study to
check the reasonableness of my conjecture about the empirical significance of this difference in the drug market.[14]

In the context of this study, the 1962 Amendments may be
viewed as an attempt to reduce the costs of information that consumers of new drugs (the doctor/patient unit) faced in the pre–
1962 environment. Some information about the safety of a new
drug was acquired when the FDA approved an NDA. Further information on safety and on efficacy were acquired from drug company promotion and actual usage. The 1962 Amendments amount
to a substitution of FDA-provided information for drug company
promotion and actual usage. That is, the NDA today restricts what
the drug company may claim, but provides the user with independent assurance about the accuracy of what is claimed. This
independent assurance is produced by preventing actual usage until
the FDA has what it considers sufficient clinical test evidence to
make the assurance valuable. I next outline the circumstances in
which this substitution of information would benefit drug consumers.

14. The reader, however, should not treat that discussion as an analysis
of the pharmacological competence of the FDA. Such an analysis would be
presumptuous and could too easily lead to the erroneous conclusion that the
effect of the Amendments on consumer welfare depends solely on who ad-
ministers them. In consequence, the relative pharmacological competence of
the FDA and other expert groups is not discussed here.

First consider a pre–1962 consumer of a drug X that has just been placed on the market. He evaluates the benefits of X in the light of the information available to him (the fact of NDA approval plus information provided by, for example, the manufacturer). This perceived evaluation is summarized by his demand curve for X, ADM in Figure 2, which shows the varying consumption rates of

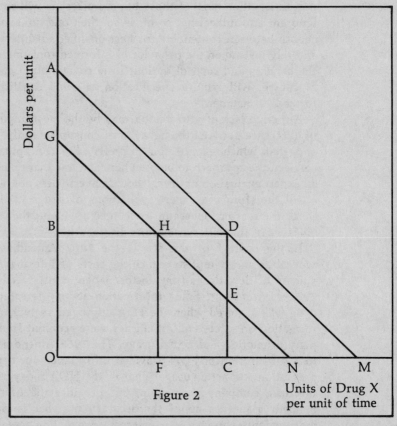

Figure 2

Units of Drug X per unit of time

X undertaken at different prices, or the value placed on increments to varying consumption rates. If the consumer is faced with a per unit price of OB, his evaluation leads him to purchase OC units. The total gross benefit he believes these OC will provide is equal to the area under ADM up to OC, or OADC dollars. He pays OBDC (= OB × OC) dollars for the OC units, leaving him with a perceived net benefit of BDA. Now suppose that, in the light of his initial experience with the drug, the consumer discovers that X was not as valuable as he had originally thought—the manufacturer's claims overstate what he discovers to be the drug's effects. At this point, the value he attaches to the drug is reduced, and his demand curve becomes GHEN. He now buys only OF units, and the genuine net benefits these provide are BHG dollars per unit time. He also discovers that, in hindsight, he wasted money. Before he discovered the genuine merits of the drug, he was consuming an extra FC units of the drug per unit time, the true value of which were HECF, but for which he paid HDCF. These extra FC units therefore entailed a net loss of HDE dollars for as long as it took the consumer to learn the drug's true value. Put differently, if an alternative information-source had from the outset provided the consumer with all the information he obtains by experience, the consumer would have been willing to pay up to HDE dollars to this source for so long as he would otherwise have consumed OC units. If the consumer could in fact have obtained this information at a cost less than the value of the stream of his HDE losses, establishment of the alternative information source would provide him with a net benefit.

The 1962 Amendments established an additional source of information. In this context, the rationale for the Amendments would be that, by relying on the information-gathering and evaluation expertise of the FDA, the consumer could frequently avoid losses like HDE. He might, to be sure, have to pay something for this information, since the costs of the added testing required of drug manufacturers might be reflected in a price above OB. This higher price would cause net benefits to be less than BHG per unit time. Nevertheless, so long as the present value of these reduced benefits fell short of that of his prospective HDE losses, the 1962 Amendments would yield the consumer a net gain. One must also remember that, in practice, the 1962 Amendments entail delay in marketing new drugs, so the consumer loses some part of the BHG benefit stream. If this delay simply equalled the time required for the consumer to fully evaluate his own market experience, then the Amendments could confer net benefits only if BHG were less than HDE (that is the benefits sacrificed by the delay induced by the Amendments fell short of the losses avoided by the Amendments). Alternatively, the delay in marketing would have to be sufficiently short so that prospective HDE losses avoided exceeded the BHG benefits sacrificed by delay.

The preceding analysis raises important problems if we try to generalize its characterization of the incompletely informed consumer in the pre–1962 environment. Specifically, what consumers have learned about some new drugs from their market experience should affect their evaluation of other new drugs. If, for example, they find that they have consistently overestimated the benefits of a particular manufacturer's new drugs, their evaluation of claims for his future new drugs will be discounted—the initial and "true" demand curves will come together. We must, however, ignore or minimize the empirical importance of this more general learning-from-experience process if we wish to entertain the possibility that the 1962 Amendments have conferred net benefits on consumers. Similarly, we must ignore or treat as empirically unimportant any other private source of information which would reduce quickly the difference between ADM and GHEN. For these purposes, I shall assume that in the pre–1962 drug market such differences may have been numerous and persistent. I will also treat the pre– and post–1962 drug markets as mutually exclusive and exhaustive states of the world.

To estimate the social gains and losses produced by the 1962 Amendments we would want in this context to compare estimates of the initial and "true" consumer evaluations of the same new drugs. We cannot, of course, know what both of these are at the time a drug is introduced since, prior to 1962 at least, the true evaluation depended to a greater extent than now on market experience. We shall, therefore, have to infer this true evaluation from consumer behavior at some time after the drug has been introduced. Moreover, to shed light on the effects of the Amendments, we would like ideally to observe evaluations by the same set of consumers (or two otherwise similar sets) of the same drugs marketed under the pre– and post–1962 regulatory environment. Such a controlled experiment is unavailable, since different drugs have been introduced within each environment. Therefore, we shall have to compare consumer evaluations of different drugs. This would pose no problem if we could assume that the only important difference between pre– and post–1962 drugs is that the latter have passed through a more extensive review process which unambiguously provides more information. The 1962 Amendments, however, try to change the composition of consumer information as well as its amount. Specifically, they regulate the amount of privately-produced information which is tied to a new drug. Although it is convenient to speak of the consumer as buying pills or prescriptions, he values these for their expected effects on his health. The consumer will typically wish to spend something to learn these expected effects, and some of this expenditure, most notably that for drug-industry-produced information, will be tied to his purchases of pills and prescriptions. The valuations manifested in the market, therefore, are those for a tied product: pill-cum-information. Because the 1962 Amendments were designed to change the information component of this package, they may have changed consumer evaluations of the package. Drug manufacturers may no longer advertise effects other than those claimed and certified by the FDA in its approval of an NDA. Although this stricture may not prevent all consumption of new drugs for non-sanctioned purposes, it will raise the cost, and presumably decrease the amount of privately-produced information sold with each new drug. Prescription for non-sanctioned uses only substitutes some costs, like increased physician experimentation, greater exposure to malpractice suits, etc., for the costs explicit in the Amendments.

The Amendments may also have unintentionally reduced the amount of information possessed by consumers about new drugs. Consumers cannot form an evaluation of products of whose existence they are ignorant, and some consumers will learn about a new type of drug when Brand A is introduced to them. If the potential seller, faced with the cost and uncertainty of complying with the Amendments, never markets Brand A, a consumer may remain ignorant about the new drug type, and he will therefore not seek out Brand B. In this way, the decision not to market A reduces information about and the demand for the new drug type generally. More to the point, perhaps, if neither Brand A nor Brand B are marketed, the consumer cannot express an evaluation of the drug type, so demand for it will be operationally non-existent. It was shown previously that essentially all of the drastic post–1962 decline in the number of new drugs can be attributed to the Amendments, so this source of reduced new drug information may well be more important than the explicit restrictions on promotion.

It cannot, however, be presumed that the reduction of privately-produced information decreases the value of the drug-information package to consumers. The consumer may learn that some privately-produced information misled him. Indeed, a motive for substituting government-produced information (FDA certification of efficacy) for other types was the implicit belief that this substitution would improve the "true" value of a new drug, since the substitution would reduce the anticipated costs of learning-from-experience. However, we will want to allow for a change in the value of the typical drug-information package in a way that does not simply presume the direction of change. The problem this raises may be seen with reference to Figure 2. Let us suppose that a drug exactly like X is marketed after 1962, but that we observe an initial demand curve for it like GHEN instead of ADM. This different initial demand could reflect the elimination of exaggerated claims for the drug by the 1962 Amendments. It could also reflect the elimination of worthwhile information because manufacturers could not demonstrate the worth of the drug to the FDA's satisfaction at an acceptable cost, or because there are fewer sellers of X. Only if one assumes an answer to the central problem of this study—the effects of the Amendments on consumer welfare—could one choose between these alternative possibilities simply by observing the lower initial demand curve.[15]

I shall attempt to choose between these alternatives by comparing the changes over time in demand curves for drugs introduced before 1962 with changes in post–1962 demand curves. My procedure can be most readily understood by assuming for simplicity, that the true demand never changes and by ignoring the superiority of present over future benefits. Assume, again for simplicity, that there are only two periods, one before (BL) and one after (AL) any learning-from-experience is completed, and that prices are unaffected by the Amendments. Now let us compare two somewhat simplistically labeled states-of-the-world: (I) Amendments are Right or (II) Amendments are Wrong. In State I, the pre–1962 BL period demand curve is ADM, but the "true" demand curve, which we observe in period AL is GHEN. The true surplus in period BL is BGH-HDE, that in the subsequent period is BGH. Total surplus is 2BGH-HDE. After 1962, in this State, consumer over-optimism is dispelled by FDA testing so the true demand is revealed instantly. True surplus is BGH in each period, and the net benefit of the Amendments is the HDE loss suffered pre–1962 in period BL. In State II, pre–1962 consumers learn from experience that their initial evaluation of the new drug was correct, so the true demand is ADM and it is observed in period BL as well as period AL. The true pre–1962 surplus is thus 2ABD. The post–1962 consumer is, in this State, simply deprived of valuable information about new drugs, so his demand for the new drug is lower than ADM—say, for expositional convenience, GHEN. The OF units purchased yield net benefits of BGH in each period. The net cost of the Amendments is then 2AGHD, or the difference between pre–1962 Amend-

15. If the initial demand curve had been above ADM, one could conclude that government-produced information is more valuable than any privately-produced information it displaces, but there would remain the question of whether this improvement in value exceeds the extra costs of obtaining it.

ments net benefits (2ABD) and post–1962 net benefits (2BGH).

Finally, consider the mixed case where the true pre–1962 demand lies above GHEN but below ADM. Here true pre–1962 benefits exceed post–1962 benefits by something less than 2AGHD, and there is a pre–1962 loss but smaller than HDE. Whether the Amendments have net benefits or costs must then be determined empirically.

To implement this approach, I shall have to estimate new drug demand curves before and after 1962. Further, for pre–1962 new drugs, I shall want to estimate the demand at the time of introduction and at a subsequent time when learning-from-experience should be complete. The preceding discussion implies that, whatever the state-of-the-world, the true post–1962 demand curve will be revealed instantly. This assumption will be carried forward to the empirical work, even though we cannot realistically expect post–1962 demand curves to remain precisely stationary. Nor for that matter do we realistically expect stationary pre–1962 demand curves if the Amendments are Wrong. Since the demand for new drugs can wax or wane for reasons unrelated to regulation, we shall as a practical matter have to distinguish between states-of-the-world on the basis of differential growth of pre– and post–1962 demand curves. If pre–1962 demand grows more slowly (declines more rapidly) than post–1962 demand, this differential growth will form the basis for calculating a loss like HDE. There is, to be sure, a pro-Amendments-are-Right bias in this procedure. More rapid post–1962 growth in demand could reflect learning-by-experience that FDA sanctioned information was too restricted. Then the initial post–1962 demand is "too low" in that it entails the sacrifice of genuine benefits. These missed benefits will be assumed non-existent, in part for procedural simplicity, but more importantly, to impart a conservative (pro status-quo) bias to the empirical results. I believe that, given the importance of the policy implications which might be suggested by the empirical results, such a conservative bias is not undesirable. In keeping with this belief, moreover, wherever a choice of procedure may entail bias, I shall try to make a pro-Amendments-are-Right choice. In the present context, for example, I will rule out the possibility that the Amendments produce slower growth in demand for drugs after initial marketing. If post–1962 growth is in fact slower, then this will be attributed to non-regulatory forces, and the initial demand curve will simply be assumed to be the true demand curve for each period.

Although the subsequent empirical work can be understood in the context of the simple two-period model outlined above, I shall in fact make use of a multi-period model that dispenses with the simplifying assumptions of zero growth in true demand, unchanged prices, and no discount on future benefits. This model can be best stated mathematically as follows: write the true demand for new drugs (GHEN in Figure 2) as

$$(5) \qquad p = f^*(q), \; p = \text{price}, \; q = \text{quantity}$$

The true net benefit or consumer surplus from consuming new drugs, s, in any year, t, is then

$$(6) \qquad s_t = \int_0^{q_t} f^*(q)dq - [p_t q_t]$$

The first term on the right-hand side of (6) would correspond to OGHEC in Figure 2, and the second to OBDC. The actual demand at t (e.g. ADM) may be written

$$(7) \qquad p = f^t(q),$$
so that (6) could be rewritten

$$(6)' \qquad s_t = \int_0^{q_t} f^*(q)dq - [f^t(q_t) \cdot q_t]$$

The assumption that $f^*$ is, in the absence of regulation, revealed by experience leads to the empirical identification of $f^*$ with $f^T$, where T is the time required for learning. I will assume further that $f^T$ is attained linearly, so that,

$$(8) \qquad \frac{\delta f^t}{\delta_t} = \frac{1}{T}(f^T - f^o),$$

and

$$(9) \qquad f^t = f^o + t\frac{\delta f^t}{\delta t} = (1 - \frac{t}{T}) \cdot f^o + \frac{t}{T} f^T$$

This permits us to rewrite (6)' as

$$(6)'' \quad s_t = \int_0^{q_t} f^T(q)dq - [(1 - \frac{t}{T}) \cdot f^o(q_t)q_t + \frac{t}{T} f^T(q_t) \cdot q_t]$$

Note that s can be negative, since $f^o \geq f^T$.

New drugs yield benefits for more than a single year, so the stream of annual benefits must be discounted to yield the present value of that drug's net benefits (S). That is

$$(10) \qquad S_t = \int_0^\infty {}_os_t \, e^{-rt} \, dt,$$

where r is an appropriate discount rate.

This procedure will be modified in light of post-Amendment experience. I will make the strong assumption that no learning-by-experience is required for $f^*$ to be revealed when the FDA approves an NDA under the Amendments. Instead

$$(11) \qquad F^* = F^o,$$

where F denotes a post-Amendment demand curve. If $F^T$ happens to be smaller than $F^o$, this will be attributed to other market forces. Thus, for the post–1962 period, $(6)''$ would be simply

$$(12) \qquad s_t = \int_0^{q_t} F^t(q)dq - [F^t(q_t) \cdot q_t]$$

If $F^T \neq F^o$, that fact along with any associated price changes will be used to compute the "normal" growth or decline (g) in s:

$$(13) \qquad g = \frac{1}{T} \ln(\frac{s_T}{s_0}),$$

so that (10) would be, simply,

$$(14) \qquad S_t = s_0 \int_0^\infty e^{-(r-g)t} \, dt = \frac{s_0}{r-g}$$

Since $s_0 \geq O$, (14) can never be negative.

If $F^T \neq F^o$ and $F^o = F^*$, then this implies modification of the identification of $f^*$ with $f^T$. The modification to be employed will be

$$(15) \qquad f^* = \min\{[\frac{f^T}{f^o}/\frac{F^T}{F^o}] \cdot f^o, f^o\}$$

That is, the differential growth in demand between the pre- and post-Amendment period will be used to find f\*, if demand did in fact grow more slowly (fall more rapidly) prior to the Amendments. The f\* of (15) will then be substituted for $f^T$ in (6)". Since f\* also grows by g, (10) could then be written, for the pre-Amendment period

$$(10)' \qquad S_t = \int_0^T s_{t}e^{-rt}dt + e^{-rT}\frac{s_T}{r-g}$$

The 1962 Amendments would then have positive net benefits if the value of S in (14) exceeded that in (10)'. This could occur if, for example, there were great losses due to inefficacy, so that the first term on the right-hand side of (10)' is very small or negative. If, on the other hand, the Amendments' restriction of privately produced information reduces $s_0$ in (14) substantially compared with, say, $s_T$ in (10)', then S in (10)' would exceed that in (14), and there would be a net social cost to the Amendments.

**Drug prices.** The preceding discussion has focused on shifts in the demand curve for new drugs. The net consumer benefits associated with any demand curve, however, depend on the price facing the consumer, and shifts in demand may induce sellers to change price. Such demand-induced price changes would tend to increase the net consumer benefits (reduce losses) of the Amendments in either State I or State II. If, for example, OB is the seller's profit-maximizing price when the demand curve is GHEN, a higher demand would under appropriate supply conditions cause sellers to charge more than OB. Therefore, even if the Amendments are "wrong," the consumer would, in their absence, have received a net benefit less than ABD and his loss due to their error is less than AGHD. Similarly, in State I, the high ex-Amendments initial demand would engender a price above OB, and, therefore, the losses of learning-from-experience would exceed HDE.

The Amendments have, however, also affected the cost of developing and marketing new drugs, and the effects of these costs on prices render the overall impact of the Amendments on new drug prices ambiguous. The quantitative limit on seller-provided information would, standing alone, lower marketing costs. The associated price effects would complement those just discussed, again, independently of whether the extra information would have been "good" or "bad." [16] However, the important proof-of-efficacy and clinical testing provisions of the Amendments work to increase new drug development costs and prices. These provisions serve to increase direct expenditures for research and development expenditure, increase the uncertainty of their payoff, and, by delaying the payoff, increase the capital costs of the investment in new drug development. These costs appear to be substantial.[17] We cannot then know *a priori* the net effect of the Amendments on new drug prices.

There is a similar ambiguity in connection with the effects of the Amendments on competition. The proof-of-efficacy requirements and the associated restrictions on drug advertising were designed in part to stimulate price rivalry. If the seller could not "artificially" differentiate his new product, the price he could get for it would be more sensitive to those of close substitutes. The other side of this, however, is that if the product never gets to the market, a source of new competition for existing sellers is removed. Since the Amendments have proved an effective barrier to entry, there is at least the possibility that they have weakened rather than promoted price competition in the drug market. I shall therefore investigate the effects of the Amendments on the prices and net consumer benefits of old as well as new drugs.

16. Where the extra information would have been worthwhile the price of a properly defined drug-information bundle is increased by the quantitative restriction, but the price-per-pill falls. Consumers simply pay a little less for a much inferior product package.

17. The effects on R&D cost may be estimated from a time series of real R&D (using the GNP deflator) per "NCE equivalent." An NCE equivalent is defined as 1 NCE + .30 new combination product + .16 new dosage form; the weights are Schnee's estimates of the relative R&D cost of different new drug types (21, p. 77). Following Schnee's estimates of development time for these types of new drugs, the number of NCE equivalents appropriate to any year's R&D is a three-year moving average centered about one (new combinations and dosage forms) or two (NCEs) years later. Prior to 1960, real R&D per NCE equivalent was increasing at 14.8 percent per year (the correlation coefficient with time is + .96). When this rate of increase is extrapolated forward, however, post-1962 values are consistently under-predicted. For 1965–69, the extrapolated values average about half the actual values: that is, the Amendments appear to have doubled the R&D costs per NCE. Even with only five observations, this average difference is over ten times its standard error. These extra R&D costs come to between $5 and $10 million per NCE equivalent, or roughly a year's sales for a fairly successful NCE. This then implies an increase in the unit-cost of a new drug at least equal to the cost of capital, and each year of delayed payoff to the R&D would inflate that increase by one plus the cost of capital.

## Drug Safety and Important Medical Advances

The procedure of estimating and comparing the temporal behavior of demand curves for new drugs will be relied on extensively in this study, but it will provide an inadequate measure of the costs and benefits of the 1962 Amendments for some specific cases. Consider first the case of a drug which is found, only after being marketed, to damage the health of some users by far more than it improves the health of others. Even if this drug disappears from the market, the maximum loss to consumers which will be estimated by the previously outlined procedure will be all consumer expenditures on the drug. This will clearly be an egregious underestimate, since, apart from drug expenditures, consumers will be suffering medical expenses, lost income, and even death. If extended testing keeps a drug of this type off the market or reveals its toxic effects before introduction, data derived solely from the drug market will have to be supplemented to arrive at a reasonable estimate of the benefits of the 1962 Amendments. The requisite supplementary data are, however, too skimpy to permit more than an estimate of the order of magnitude of this benefit. The derivation of this estimate is left for subsequent discussion.

Our procedure will also hide some important costs of the 1962 Amendments for some drugs that are kept off the market or are delayed in introduction. For effective drugs that the Amendments keep off the market for some time, we want to know the maximum amount that consumers would have been willing to pay rather than go without the drug for that time. The procedure I have outlined gets at this by examining consumer reaction to drug prices: at higher new drug prices, consumers substitute more attractive alternatives (old drugs, no drugs, etc.), and the more extensive this substitution, the less presumably would be lost if the new drugs were not introduced. We can, however, never directly observe the evaluations of a consumer for a drug that is not marketed, even if the consumer knows that such a drug exists. In practice, these evaluations will be estimated by extrapolation from observable data, and this will sometimes yield serious underestimates. An extreme example will illuminate the reason for this. Suppose that the market for a new drug consists of two individuals, neither of whom would pay anything for more than one unit of drug X. Individual I has a malady that could be as well treated by 1 unit of drug Y, which sells for $1.01, while II would perish without X, and he would part with all his wealth of $1 million rather than forgo 1 unit of X.

If the market price of X were $1.00, both I and II would purchase 1 unit, and the total amount demanded would be 2 units, as illustrated in Figure 3. Now suppose that the price rises to $1.10, and, since I now switches to Y, we observe only 1 unit of X sold. If we (erroneously in this case) deduce from this market behavior that the smooth line BA is a segment of the demand for X, we would estimate a loss to consumers of 15¢ (= $1.10 BA $1.00) from this price increase. (The actual loss is only 11¢—the 10¢ more paid by II for X and the 1¢ more paid by I for Y). Now suppose X were not

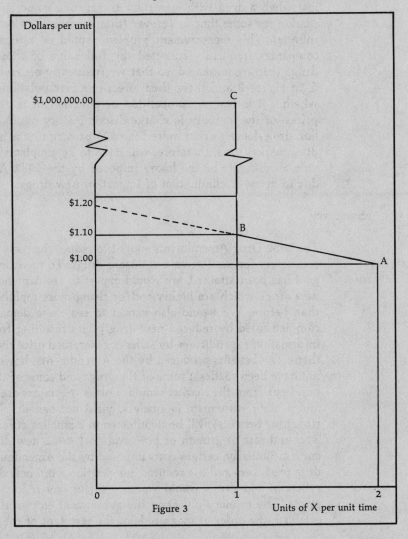

Figure 3

marketed, and we ask what the loss from this event is. Since II perishes in this event the correct answer, of course, is about $1 million. Unfortunately, no data in the drug market will tell us that the actual demand curve looks like $1 million CB above $1.10. Instead, we would naively extrapolate AB and obtain $1.20 as the maximum value placed on the smallest consumption rate of X, and this would imply an estimated consumer loss of 5¢ (= $1.20 B $1.10).

The example is extreme, but it illustrates that drug market data alone cannot be relied on to provide accurate estimates of what is lost when a drug with important therapeutic value is kept off the market for some time or forever (that is when the effective price is infinite). This measurement problem would be mitigated if drug companies frequently collected the full value of those important drugs that are marketed, so that we frequently observe points like C in Figure 3 and these then affect our extrapolations. However, whether it is fear of competition or government reaction to such prices, or the inability to charge discriminatory prices, the $1 million drug doesn't exist; indeed the $25 prescription is a rarity. The drug market data, therefore, will have to be supplemented to provide an estimate of the losses imposed by the 1962 Amendments due to delay or elimination of important new drugs.

## Summary

The 1962 Drug Amendments sought to reduce the costs incurred by consumers for ineffective and unsafe drugs. To the extent that this goal has been attained, we would expect to see demand curves for new drugs which are higher and/or rising more rapidly after 1962 than before. We would also expect to see these demand changes complemented by reduced new drug prices resulting from reduced information expenditures by sellers or increased price rivalry among them. The benefits produced by the Amendments, however, should not have been costless: some of the drugs and some of the information kept from the market would, unless regulators are omniscient and dealing with them is costless, yield net benefits. These costs (foregone benefits) will be manifested in a smaller difference in the level and rate of growth of pre– and post–1962 new drug demand curves. Similarly, certain costs imposed by the Amendments on new drug producers and the reduced competition from new drugs facing sellers of old drugs would work to offset any reduction of drug prices. The primary object of the subsequent empirical work is to establish the order of magnitude of the resultant of these forces.

# IV. Estimates of the Costs and Benefits of the 1962 Amendments

## A. Consumer Evaluations in the Drug Market

This section derives demand curves for new drugs, and uses them to draw inferences about changes in the consumer surplus generated by new drugs since passage of the Amendments.

**Data.** Most of the data used in this section are taken from the National Prescription Audit (NPA). The data have been described previously [18] but some of their shortcomings (for present purposes) deserve mention. The output measure to be used will be number of prescriptions sold and the corresponding price will be average receipts per prescription. Further, since penicillin may be a poor substitute for tranquilizers, the unit of observation is not "the" drug market. The relevant sub-markets ("therapeutic categories") are, however, defined technologically by similarity of the chemical properties of the members. The potential for measurement-error in these data is, of course, substantial. The more expensive prescription may be the cheaper mode of therapy; some members of one category may be closer substitutes for those in another rather than the same category, etc. Much of the measurement error will simply have to be accepted for the sake of empirical implementation. Prescriptions for existing members of a therapeutic category will be treated as perfect substitutes for each other, but as imperfect substitutes for those for new members. The cross-elasticity of demand and supply for drugs in different categories is assumed to be zero. The potential measurement error will be taken into account in interpreting the results, and in designing the relevant sample.[19]

18. Supra., n. 12.
19. To minimize the effect of errors in categorization, minor therapeutic categories (fewer than one million prescriptions in most years sampled), and minor new drugs (fewer than 1 percent of all category prescriptions or sales) are excluded from the sample. This is done because we wish to examine the behavior of the "typical" new drug within the typical category. Where a new drug gets an unusually small share of a category, it is presumed to be related in demand to only a part of the category, so, for this drug, the category is too comprehensive. If the new drug is related in demand to drugs outside its defined category, the resulting exaggeration of its importance will be most serious if the defined category is small. I also exclude categories where new drugs account for half of prescriptions or sales in the current or any of the three preceding years. This kind of innovation essentially creates a new category, and the new drugs are presumed to have no good substitute or none that are really "old" drugs.

The data are sampled from a period spanning the 1962 Amendments. The Amendments are presumed to have affected the markets for new drugs beginning in 1964, and data on post-Amendment new drugs are sampled for 1964–70. Since new drug introductions declined after 1962, a similar-sized sample of pre-Amendment new drugs is drawn from only the three years, 1960–1962, just prior to the Amendments. (The innovation rate for these three years was about 10 percent below the pre–1962 average, so the resulting estimate of pre–1962 demand will be conservative.)

**Model.** We wish to estimate a demand curve for new drugs from which estimates of consumer surplus can be derived. To do this, it will be assumed that new-drug prescriptions within a therapeutic category are perfect substitutes.[20] Then, the demand for new drugs may be written

$$(16) \qquad q_{nt} = f(p_{nt}, p_{ot}, X_t),$$

where t denotes a particular year and

$q_n$ = number of prescriptions for new drugs in a therapeutic category per unit time,

$p_n$ = the price per $q_n$,

$p_o$ = the price of imperfect substitutes for new prescriptions,

$X$ = a vector of all other factors affecting the demand for new drugs.

For simplicity, $p_o$ is identified with the average price of prescriptions for old drugs in the same category. The vector $X$ is composed of two elements: (1) all of the systematic non-regulatory factors apart from $p_n$ and $p_o$ that might affect the demand for new drugs (for example, prices of complements, income, "tastes") are assumed to be reflected in total output of prescriptions in the therapeutic category $(Q_T)$; (2) since the 1962 Amendments may have changed the demand for new drugs, and since our data will span the Amendments, the presence or absence of the Amendments $(A)$ is included in $X$. It is assumed that (16) is homogeneous of first degree in all non-regulatory arguments and that there are random components of $q_n$, so (16) may be rewritten:

20. The prescription priced above (below) average is simply more (less) than a "standard" prescription.

$(16)'$ $\dfrac{q_{nt}}{Q_{Tt}} = f(\dfrac{P_{nt}}{P_{ot}}, A_t, u_t)$ where $u_t$ is a random variable.[21]

In the subsequent empirical work $(16)'$ is assumed to have the linear form:

$$(17) \qquad \frac{q_{nt}}{Q_{Tt}} = a + b\frac{P_{nt}}{P_{ot}} + cA_t + u_t$$

with a, b and c constants; $a > O$, $b < O$, and the sign of c is uncertain. It is assumed here that sellers set $P_n/P_o$ in each period, and offer to sell indefinitely large amounts at that price during the period. Variation in $P_n/P_o$ is assumed to be determined largely by non-demand-related factors, such as costs, so that any empirical estimate of $(16)'$ will largely reflect demand relationships.[22]

**Empirical estimates.** Before (17) is estimated, it is instructive to examine some of the underlying data. It has been pointed out previously that the post-Amendment period has witnessed a substantial decline in new drug output. At the same time, there is no strong evidence that this decline has been associated with a rise in the relative price of new to old drugs. Table 2 presents data on the mean relative prices and market shares of new chemical entities in the year following introduction for those therapeutic catagories that are in our sample and where NCEs were marketed. There is a perceptible decline in NCE market shares from 1960–62 to 1964–

21. The size-of-market deflator could have been chosen as the output of old drugs in a therapeutic category $(Q_T - q_n)$. The choice of $Q_T$ is made for subsequent computational convenience, and to minimize the variance in empirical counterparts to the dependent variable arising from random output shifts between new and old drugs. Since $q_n/Q_T$ and $q_n/(Q_T - q_n)$ are positively and monotonically related, there is no sacrifice of generality with $(16)'$.

On the basis of preliminary empirical work, I have not included in $(16)'$ a variable for growth of total category demand, though such a variable is suggested by the previous analysis of new drug introductions. The preliminary work included past growth of category output as a demand-growth proxy. Although this variable had the expected positive relationship to $q_n/Q_T$, the effect was insignificant and none of the results derived from the simpler formulation of $(16)'$ was materially altered.

22. Since the Amendments may have affected both demand and costs, there is a potential problem in interpreting estimates of c. For example, suppose the Amendments have caused $P_n/P_0$ to rise, and $q_n/Q_T$ has at the same time fallen partly because of an Amendment-induced fall in demand. An empirical estimate of (17) might mistakenly attribute all of the decline in $q_n/Q_T$ to the price increase. I shall argue below, however, that this potential problem is empirically unimportant.

## Table 2

### Average Market Share and Relative Price for NCEs in Year After Introduction

| Years NCEs Introduced | Annual Average Number of Therapeutic Categories with NCEs | Average NCE Share of Category Output | Ratio: Price of NCEs / Price of Other Drugs in Category |
|---|---|---|---|
| 1956–57 | 11.0 | .132 (.033) | 1.223 (.063) |
| 1960–62 | 10.3 | .107 (.019) | 1.263 (.104) |
| 1964–69 | 5.4 | .064 (.012) | 1.165 (.050) |

Note: There are 50 therapeutic categories in the sample. Column (1) indicates the average number of these in which one or more important NCEs were introduced each year per period. Column (2) is the average number of new prescriptions accounted for by NCEs per year as a fraction of total category prescriptions for categories where NCEs were marketed. Column (3) is mean dollar value per NCE prescription divided by dollar value of other prescriptions in category. Standard errors are in parentheses.

Data are from R. A. Gosselin, Inc. (20). (The 1956–57 category classification differs slightly from the later years and the coverage is less comprehensive.)

70, and a decline in the number of markets penetrated by NCEs. At the same time, the mean relative price of NCEs has in fact fallen, though the decrease is insignificant. It is possible that the essentially unchanged relative price of NCEs marks a departure from some trend, but this is unlikely. Table 2 contains data for 1956–57, which had levels of NCE introduction and output comparable to 1960–62; the NCE relative price then is virtually the same as that for both later periods.[23]

23. Prices of other new drugs (combinations of NCEs and old NCEs marketed under a new trademark) also remain substantially unchanged after 1962. The 1964–69 average price relative is 1.14 v. 1.07 for 1960–62. The small difference is insignificant.

These data appear to rule out an increase in the supply price of new drugs as an important effect of the 1962 Amendments, but they are potentially consistent with several demand effects and demand characteristics that are relevant to this study. For example, such data would be generated in a world where new drugs are essentially no more than high-priced perfect substitutes for existing drugs—where the demand curve for new drugs is essentially infinitely elastic—since varying quantities are purchased at roughly the same price. In such a world there would be essentially no costs (no consumer surplus lost) offsetting the benefits of the Amendments. If the demand for new drugs is not infinitely elastic, then the data imply a post–1962 decline in demand. The apparent decline, however, might mean that the "true" demand for drugs is unchanged, and merely reveals itself without a long and costly learning-by-experience process. Alternatively, the decline is "real," and reflects the reduced information content associated with new drugs under the Amendments. The data do permit us to rule out the possibility that the Amendments have increased the initial demand for new drugs, since that would imply a rise in post–1962 sales at the essentially unchanged price. An empirical estimate of (17) and of its temporal behavior, however, is required to distinguish among the potentially valid interpretations of the data.[24]

Estimates of (17) are in Table 3, and they rule out an infinitely elastic new drug demand curve. The estimates employ data on therapeutic category market shares and relative prices of NCEs in the year following their introduction for NCEs introduced 1960–62 and 1964–69. The variable A is unity for each post-Amendment observation and zero otherwise. Only those observations where significant NCE market penetration (1 percent or more of category prescriptions and sales) occurred are employed in the estimates. The categories are of widely varying size, and preliminary estimates revealed heteroskedastic residuals: as might be expected, residual variance decreased with category size. To restore homoskedasticity, Table 3 shows weighted regression estimates of (17), with the ratio of total category prescriptions to total prescriptions for all drugs in the year of observation as the weight. Equation E2 reveals a significant negative relationship between market shares attained by NCEs and their relative price, and a significant post–1962 de-

24. The unchanged post-Amendment new drug price relative is not necessarily inconsistent with a net increase in new drug production costs. If new drug production is subject to diminishing returns, a fall in new drug demand would have produced a decline in price in the absence of an increase in costs (a leftward shift of supply).

**Table 3**
**Estimated Demand Curve for New Chemical Entities**
**(NCEs Introduced 1960-62, 1964-69)**

**Coefficients and Standard Errors of:**

| Equation and Dependent Variable | Constant | $P_n/P_0$ | $Q_n/Q_T$ | A | $R^2$ | S.e. |
|---|---|---|---|---|---|---|
| E2 $q_n/Q_T$ | .1188 | −.0304 | | −.0510 | .2885 | .0687 |
| | .0232 | .0132 | | .0147 | | |
| E3 $P_n/P_0$ | 1.6922 | | −2.9084 | −0.3772 | .8360 | .6721 |
| | .1543 | | 1.2588 | .1501 | | |
| E4 $q_n/Q_T$ | .3503 | −.1871 | | −.0903 | | |
| | .1550 | .0810 | | .0519 | | |

Note: Sample consists of 58 therapeutic categories; 31 in 1960–62 and 27 in 1964–69.
*Variable definitions:*
$q_n/Q_T$ = number of new prescriptions for NCEs divided by total number of new prescriptions for all drugs in therapeutic category in year following introduction of NCEs.
$P_n/P_0$ = average price per prescription for NCEs divided by average price per prescription for other drugs in category in year following introduction of NCEs. Average price = dollar sales divided by number of prescriptions.
A = unity for 1965–70, zero otherwise.
Standard errors are below coefficients.
$R^2$ = coefficient of determination,
S.e. = standard error of estimate (both for weighted data).
Coefficients of E4 are simple averages of those in E2 and those implied by E3, and their standard errors are approximate upper bounds.

Source: R. A. Gosselin & Company (20).

cline in the level of demand. The elasticity of market share with respect to price (at sample means) implied by E2 is only .7, which indicates that consumers treat new and old drugs as rather poor substitutes. The perceived consumer surplus from new drugs will be larger the less elastic the demand for new drugs, and so too would the perceived loss of surplus due to the post-Amendment decline in demand. However, in light of the measurement error in the price and quantity variables, it is risky to accept the estimates in E2 at face value. In particular measurement error in $P_n/P_0$ will lead to downward bias in the estimated demand elasticity. It is possible, however, to obtain an upper bound to this elasticity by regressing price on quantity instead of vice versa. This is done in E3, which implies an elasticity fully ten times that of E2. It must be noted that the form of E3 contains the implausible implicit assumption that sellers of new drugs predetermine output and then find a price which clears the market of this output, so E2 is probably closer to the "truth" than E3. However, to keep the relevant estimates of consumer surplus conservative, I will assume that the true values of the demand parameters lie exactly half-way between those in E2 and those implied by E3. The resulting parameter estimates are shown in E4.

Equation (17) was also estimated for new drugs other than NCEs. The counterpart to (E2) was

$$(E5) \qquad \frac{q_n'}{Q_T} = \underset{(.0357)}{.0515} - \underset{(.0299)}{.0049} \frac{P_n'}{P_o} - \underset{(.0095)}{.0251} A,$$

where the prime refers to "other new drugs." The coefficients imply a virtually inelastic demand curve which decreased after the Amendments. Taken literally, this would imply a far more substantial perceived net benefit loss due to the Amendments for "other new" drugs than for NCEs. However, reversing the dependence of quantity on price generates an almost perfectly elastic demand curve which increased after the Amendments. This would mean that consumers perceive no net benefits from "other new" drugs (they treat them as perfect substitutes for old drugs at prevailing prices), and that all of the value of the post–1962 increased demand for other new drugs is simply appropriated by price increases. These conflicting interpretations regarding the shape and location of the "other new" drug demand curve, which may be derived from the same data, imply rather substantial measurement error. Although the true demand curve is surely neither perfectly elastic or inelastic, the risk of error in using the regression data to estimate demand parameters is much larger here than for NCEs.[25] In light of this risk, I will make what is here the most conservative assumption, namely, that the true demand is perfectly elastic. This amounts to asserting that there is no perceived net benefit to con-

25. The standard error of the average of the two estimated price coefficients is so large that it fails to rule out either essentially perfectly elastic or inelastic demand.

sumers from a class of new drugs with total annual sales comparable to those of NCEs. I leave open the possibility that the 1962 Amendments have produced net benefits for consumers of "other new" drugs; demand may have grown more slowly before 1962. However, in view of the extreme assumptions being made here, the reader should be wary of any estimate of these benefits. Given the poor results obtained from the data on "other new" drugs, the most reasonable procedure might be to simply leave these drugs out of the account entirely, and evaluate the Amendment on their effects on NCEs. Most of the subsequent work is therefore limited to NCE data.

**The perceived loss of consumer surplus due to the Amendments.** The first ingredient in our estimate of the net benefits due to the 1962 Amendments will be a gross cost: the decline in consumer surplus perceived by consumers upon their initial evaluation of information about new drugs. The higher pre–1962 evaluation of this information may, of course, reflect ignorance, so this gross cost of the Amendments will have to be set off against gross benefits arising from reduced costs of learning-from-experience. At this stage, I am naively treating the initial demand, estimated by E4, as the "true" demand.

The general formula for calculating consumer surplus (an area like ABD or GBH in Figure 2) with linear demand is

$$(18) \qquad s = 1/2 (P_n{}^a - P_n)(q_n),$$

where the a superscript refers to the vertical intercept of the demand curve. In terms of the variables in E4, (18) would be:

$$(18)' \quad s = 1/2 \left[ \left( \frac{P_n}{P_o} \right)^a - \left( \frac{P_n}{P_o} \right) \right] \left[ \frac{q_n}{Q_T} \right] \cdot P_o \, Q_T$$

An approximation to the total of (18)' over the whole drug market can then be obtained from the parameters and the appropriate sample means of E4 and the value of $P_o Q_T$ for categories with NCEs.[26] To provide comparable dollar values, $P_o Q_T$ is measured in

26. The appropriate sample means are the root mean square of $q_n/Q_T$ and its associated $P_n/P_o$. Use of the simple average of $q_n/Q_T$ understates aggregate surplus; surplus for below average $q_n/Q_T$ is overvalued by less than the undervaluation of surplus for above average $q_n/Q_T$.

terms of the 1970 drug market. Specifically, the aggregate of $P_oQ_T$ for all categories with NCEs is divided by the aggregate for all sample categories in each year, and the sub-period averages of this ratio (.235 before and .231 after the Amendments) are multiplied by the 1970 value of $P_oQ_T$ for the whole drug market ($5.2 billion).[27] This permits (18)' to be evaluated as $51.9 million per year prior to the Amendments and $9.9 million per year subsequently; the perceived loss in consumer surplus due to the Amendments is thus $420 million annually for any year's flow of NCEs.[28] Now, since any year's NCEs will yield benefits over many years, the stream of these annual benefits must be converted to present values. For the moment, I will treat the stream of benefits as a perpetuity with an unchanged average annual return. The return is, however, uncertain, since the (growth of) future demand for any set of new drugs and its competitors will fluctuate. The appropriate discount rate for the stream of expected NCE benefits will therefore be the annual rate of return in activities with similarly risky rewards. I will use a 10 percent rate of return, which roughly corresponds to

27. This is essentially the value of prescription sales at retail outlets as estimated from NPA data (20). The NPA reports estimated sales at the manufacturers level, which they estimate average .48 of retail value. I have excluded drug sales to hospitals, since these data are not used to estimate the relevant demand curve. Such sales are roughly one-third those of manufacturer sales to the retail market, so our surplus estimates may be considerably understated.

28. The data underlying these estimates are as follows:

| Variable | Pre-Amendment Period | Post-Amendment Period |
|---|---|---|
| $(P_n/P_o)^a$ | 1.872 | 1.390 |
| $(P_n/P_o)$ | 1.199 | 1.094 |
| $(q_n/Q_T)$ | .1259 | .0554 |

These data assume that only the height and not the slope, of the demand curve has changed. When E4 was reestimated to allow for change in slope, the resulting difference in surplus estimates increased. Since, however, the change in slope is insignificant, it is ignored here.

To check the sensitivity of the calculations to use of weighted regressions I recomputed surplus from the unweighted analogue to E4:

$$\frac{q_n}{Q_T} = \frac{.5353}{(.2213)} - \frac{.3399}{(.1385)} \frac{P_n}{P_o} - \frac{.0785}{(.0502)} D$$

The demand schedule implies annual surplus of $42.1 million pre-1962 and $14.8 million post-1962. The difference remains substantial, but about one-third less than the estimates from weighted regressions.

the long-run average rate of return on investment in equities. This discount rate then implies a perceived net loss to consumers of $420 million in each year that the Amendments have been effective, or about 8 percent of total annual drug sales.[29]

It is possible to assess this somewhat arbitrary procedure for capitalizing the net benefit streams against observable capital values. One such value is the R&D investment in a new drug, which I have shown previously (Supra., n. 17) has been increased by the Amendments. If one assumes that the higher R&D investment in new drugs post–1962 will be fully recovered by producers (and, notwithstanding the failure of relative new drug prices to rise, the last section of this paper does not conflict with this assumption) and, generously, that neither any other cost nor the demand for new drugs has been changed by the Amendments, then the initial consumer loss (L) from the decline in R&D productivity can be approximated:

$$(19) \qquad \overset{\bullet}{L} = [C - C^*] \, [n + 1/2 \, (n^* - n)], \qquad \text{where}$$

29. The reader should keep clear the distinction between two benefit streams affected by the Amendments: (1) benefits derived from the stream of NCEs, and (2) the stream of benefits derived from any one year's NCEs. The reduction in (2) is $420 million, and this is repeated every year.

This calculation assumes that the decline in new drug demand leaves unchanged the price and quantity of old drugs for each $q_n$. However, if the reduced value of information about new drugs leads sellers to increase information provided at each old drug price-quantity combination, part of the $420 million gross loss on new drugs will be offset. It will be shown subsequently that the Amendments have had small effects on prices of old drugs, so a higher old-drug demand should show up in higher old drug output for a given output of new drugs. To see whether this has occurred, I regressed the annual growth in old drug prescriptions ($\dot{q}_0$) from the year prior to the year subsequent to introduction of NCEs on the annual growth of category prescriptions ($\dot{Q}_T$) in the four years prior to introduction of NCEs, the ratio $q_n$ to $\dot{Q}_{T,t-2}$ ($q_n'$) and the dummy variable A, of Table 3. (Experimentation with a price-change variable for old drugs proved unsuccessful.) This regression is meant to determine whether, holding constant the expected growth in $q_0$ ($Q_T$ is a proxy for this) and the encroachment of new drugs ($q_n'$), the growth of old drug sales has accelerated post-1962. The result of the weighted regression for the therapeutic categories of Table 3 is

$$\dot{q}_0 = \underset{(.0135)}{.0035} + \underset{(.0948)}{.3590} \; \dot{Q}_T - \underset{(.1007)}{.8636} \; q_n' - \underset{(.0133)}{.0104} \; A$$

The regression implies that, after accounting for the normal effect of new drugs on old drug sales—an 86 percent replacement of the latter by the former—there has been no acceleration of old drug sales following the Amendments. This, in turn, implies that there is no gain in consumers' surplus on old drugs to offset the loss on new drugs.

C = actual post–1962 R&D investment per NCE (n), and the asterisk (*) denotes values expected in the absence of the Amendments. This formulation treats producers as "selling" NCEs at a "price," collected over time, but equal in present value to the R&D investment. The post–1962 decline in n is attributed to the post–1962 rise in this price. If this implied demand for NCEs is linear, the present value of consumer loss in any year is the rise in R&D cost for that year's NCEs (n(C–C*)) plus the surplus foregone on NCEs that are not produced because of the cost increase 1/2 (C–C*) (n*–n). To evaluate L, I used the predicted post–1962 values of the R&D cost regression in n.17 Supra as estimates of C*. Since C is measured per "NCE equivalent," I then multiplied the predicted post–1962 values of E1 by 3.03, the pre–1962 average ratio of NCE equivalents to NCEs, to generate n*. Further, for consistency with C and C*, n and n* are three-year moving averages centered two years subsequent to the year in which R&D funds are spent. The 1963–69 averages of these variables are n = 36.1, n* = 129.9, C = $13.4 million, C* = $6.9 million (1970 dollars). When L is estimated for each year, 1963–69, the average is $523.0 million (1970 dollars), or about $100 million more than the loss I have estimated from new drug demand curves.

## The Reduction in Waste of Inefficacious Drugs

The Amendments would be imposing an annual net burden of $420 million on drug consumers only if they never helped to save consumers money on drugs which consumers only later realized were ineffective. But it is precisely such savings that the Amendments are designed to produce. To estimate the magnitude of these savings we must examine the behavior of new drug demand over time. If the Amendments have been dealing effectively with what once was an important problem, we should see the difference between pre- and post-Amendment new drug demand narrowing over time, since the pre-Amendment consumers would have been abandoning the ineffective drugs that the Amendments now screen out. Some relevant data are presented in Table 4. I am assuming that four years experience with a new drug is sufficient to reveal its true value. Although choice of this period is somewhat arbitrary, it is in part forced by the data. A longer period would have left an unreliably small sample of post–1962 drug data.

These data reveal a remarkable stability in the demand for new drugs over time, and, what is most important here, there is no

## Table 4

### Weighted Average Market Shares and Relative Prices for New Drugs One and Four Years After Introduction

| Drugs and Subperiod | Market Share ($q_n/Q_T$) | | Relative Price ($P_n/P_o$) | |
|---|---|---|---|---|
| | Year After Introduction | Fourth Year After Introduction | Year After Introduction | Fourth Year After Introduction |
| Year NCEs Introduced | | | | |
| 1960–62 | .083 (.017) | .083 (.020) | 1.414 (.144) | 1.327 (.124) |
| 1964–69 | .039 (.008) | — | 1.209 (.045) | — |
| 1964–66 | .049 (.012) | .038 (.013) | 1.184 (.061) | 1.221 (.051) |
| Year Other New Drugs Introduced | | | | |
| 1960–62 | .064 (.011) | .077 (.014) | 1.133 (0.026) | 1.130 (.023) |
| 1964–69 | .024 (.005) | — | 1.206 (.029) | — |
| 1964–66 | .025 (.004) | .023 (.004) | 1.231 (0.042) | 1.192 (.040) |

Note: Data are averages for those categories where new drugs were introduced, weighted by category share of total drug prescriptions.
Standard errors are in parentheses.
Source: R. A. Gosselin, Inc. (20).

substantial difference in this respect between pre- and post-Amendment new drugs. None of the intertemporal differences in NCE relative price or market shares is significant for either sub-period. We shall, however, have to accept the substantial risk of error in identifying the small differences that are present with changes in population means to attribute any benefits to the 1962 Amendments. First, I assume that any intertemporal change in demand is one of intercept rather than slope.[30] It will then be seen that both pre- and post-Amendment NCE demand fall slightly over time. In the pre-Amendment period there is a fall in price with no increase in quantity, while the post-Amendment decrease in quantity exceeds that expected from the small rise in price.[31] The post–1962 NCE demand curve, however, falls by less than its pre–1962 counterpart. The data imply that the vertical intercept of the former falls by .026 v. .087 for the latter. This .061 difference can be interpreted as the difference in intercept between the initial and true demand curve for NCEs prior to 1962, since it is assumed that all of the difference is due to the greater incidence of inefficacious drugs prior to 1962. The implied true demand curve can then be used to estimate the true consumer surplus for NCEs (GHB in Figure 2) and the waste due to initial ignorance of their true value (HDE in Figure 2). Since the difference between initial and true demand is so small, it is not surprising that the difference between perceived and true surplus is small and that the waste is trivial. The estimated true surplus for pre–1962 NCEs in the first year after introduction is in fact $43.0 million, and the estimated waste only $0.4 million. The conclusion to which these data point is that the foregone consumer benefits for NCEs kept from the market by the Amendments substantially exceed the waste avoided on inefficacious drugs.

Since ignorance is assumed here to be dispelled by experience, this conclusion can only be strengthened by extending the relevant benefit and cost estimate beyond the first year in which any set of NCEs is marketed. Such estimates were made on the assumption that both the true demand and the pre–1962 gap between initial and true demand decreased linearly for the four years after NCEs were introduced. Similarly, prices and quantities for intermediate

30. This assumption was tested by reestimating E4 on year-after introduction and four-year-after introduction data for the relevant subset of data. The resulting difference in the coefficient of price was less than its standard error.

31. From E4, a (1.221 − 1.184) rise in price should have produced only a .007 fall in quantity rather than the .011 observed fall.

years were estimated by linear interpolation of the terminal values. The resulting estimates are in Table 5. The pre-Amendment surplus, net of waste, actually increases in spite of the small decline in true demand. This increase is due to an increased dispersion of market shares which is not repeated for the post–1962 sample.[32] There is, consequently, a small decline over time in the surplus from post–1962 drugs.

## Table 5

### Estimated "True" Net Consumer Surplus for One Year's NCEs in Years Following Introduction
#### (million dollars)

| Years After Introduction | Pre-Amendment NCEs | Post-Amendment NCEs |
|:---:|:---:|:---:|
| 1 | $ 42.6 | $ 9.9 |
| 2 | 49.1 | 9.7 |
| 3 | 55.9 | 9.6 |
| 4 | 63.2 | 9.4 |
| Present Value of Surplus Stream for: | | |
| (a) Perpetual Stream | 491.0 | 82.4 |
| (b) 15-Year Stream | 397.3 | 67.3 |

Note: True net consumer surplus is the estimated consumer surplus for the true demand curve less any waste for ineffective drugs. Waste is assumed zero for post-Amendment NCEs. See text for method of calculation.

Table 5 also provides estimates of (10)' and (14). These are derived by assuming that the pre–1962 growth in $s_t$ ends abruptly at $t = 4$, and that the permanent subsequent growth in s is that of the post–1962 series (about −2 percent per year). If the benefits streams are perpetual, the Amendments are imposing a net loss on consumers of roughly $400 million ($491.0 — $82.4 million) per year. If it is assumed that benefit streams from new drugs last for

32. The increased dispersion raises the root-mean-square market share, which is the quantity at which surplus is evaluated, even though average market share is unchanged.

only 15 years, the estimated net loss is about $330 million an-
nually.[33]

The reader is cautioned against a too literal interpretation of
these estimates. They are best regarded as indicators of relevant
orders of magnitude. Treated this way, the estimates imply either
that the magnitude of the problem of ineffective new drugs prior
to 1962 was trivial or that the ability of FDA regulation to reduce
the problem is small. At the same time, the reduced flow of new
drugs due to the Amendments is imposing net losses on consumers which are the rough equivalent of a 5 to 10 percent excise
tax on all prescriptions sold. The general thrust of this conclusion

33. The reduced variability of post-1962 drug demand does confer a benefit,
which is left out of account in Table 5 because it is difficult to measure
precisely. The benefit arises because inability to perceive true demand immediately imposes a cost regardless of the error of the initial forecast. In
the case of an over-optimistic forecast, the consumer buys too much initially,
and, as we have seen, his loss is the area HDE in Figure 2. There is also a
similar loss if the initial forecast is too pessimistic. Suppose, for example, that
the true demand is in fact ADM but that the initial demand is only GHEN.
In this case the consumer buys too little. With full information he would buy
OC instead of OF, and he therefore sacrifices the surplus of FC units until
he learns the true value of the drug. This sacrifice is also equal to HDE.
Since HDE increases with the gap between initial and true demand, the consumer will be better off the smaller this gap regardless of its sign. Now,
while we have seen that, on the average, initial demand is an essentially
unbiased predictor of true demand both before and after 1962, the dispersion
about the average (that is the average absolute error) is apparently greater
before 1962. For pre-1962 NCEs, the standard deviation of the change in
market share over the four years following introduction is 4.3 percent compared to 3.7 percent after 1962. This difference is statistically insignificant,
and factors other than initial consumer ignorance affect both of these dis-
persions (for example, discovery of new applications for a drug). We must
assume, however, that none of these other factors is operative to estimate the
value of the reduced post-1962 variability. This estimate entails evaluating
HDE with HD set equal to the standard deviation of market share changes
in each period. I assume that the initial error of prediction is revealed and
adapted to gradually so that the fourth-year error is zero. The resulting
estimate is that the four-year cost of variability for a year's NCEs was
$10 million prior to 1962 and $7 million subsequently, or a difference under
$1 million annually.

It is surprising in this context that, relative to the smaller average market
share, variability of post-1962 market share changes exceeds, though insignificantly, its pre-1962 counterpart. If consumers are made cautious toward
all new drugs by the introduction of many ineffective drugs, one might
conjecture that the temporal instability of pre-1962 market shares is the resultant of growing use of the effective drugs by cautious buyers and declining
use of ineffective drugs. On this argument the 1962 Amendments, by removing
uncertainty about product quality, would reduce the need both for caution
and gradual discovery of the ineffective drugs. This argument, however,
implies a smaller relative variability in post-1962 market share changes,
which we do not observe.

holds up when data on new drugs other than NCEs are examined. Table 4 shows the same temporal stability in relative price and output for these drugs both pre- and post–1962 as for NCEs.[34] These data imply then that any savings on inefficacious drugs due to the Amendments would, as with NCEs, not compensate for foregone benefits from drugs kept from the market. Given our conservative assumption that net benefits from other new drugs are zero, these data should strengthen confidence that the estimated net loss from the Amendments is not exaggerated.

The conclusion that the 1962 Drug Amendments have taxed rather than benefited drug consumers is sufficiently startling to ask for corroboration. I have thus far relied completely on the consumers' own evaluations of drugs to measure benefits and costs. I will next examine evaluations of presumably more sophisticated (non-FDA) "experts." The purpose here will not be to develop an alternative "paternalist" measure of costs and benefits. Nevertheless, the working assumption will be that "expertise" entails the ability to discover the "true" consumer interest. Thus, if there are pervasive differences between expert and consumer evaluations and these are reduced by FDA supervention for consumers, some doubt will be cast on the magnitude of the net costs we have adduced to the Amendments.

## B. Expert Drug Evaluations

The effectiveness of new drugs, or their superiority over old drugs, is uncertain. Therefore, in addition to the explicit cost of the drug, the buyer bears a risk-cost related to the probability that the drug will be ineffective. This cost is the product of the loss if a new drug is ineffective and the probability that a new drug will be ineffective. I am here going to test the null hypothesis that this probability, which is a proxy for the expected cost of inefficacy per new drug unit, has declined since 1962. It should be noted that in light of the decline in drug innovation, truth of this hypothesis is necessary, but not sufficient, for the Amendments to yield net benefits. Indeed, the preceding analysis assumed the truth of the hypothesis, and still imputed net costs to the Amendments. The Amendments yield net benefits only if they have reduced total inefficacy costs by more than the gross benefits they have foreclosed. Our estimate of the

34. If anything, pre-1962 other-new-drug demand increases (quantity rises with price unchanged) while post-1962 demand falls (price and quantity fall) over time. However, given the relevant standard errors, the most prudent conclusion would be that demand is unchanged over time in both periods.

magnitude of reduced inefficacy costs, however
confidence in it should be weakened by strong e
hypothesis.

To test the null hypothesis I will examine its implications for
the behavior of three groups who are presumably more knowledgeable about new drugs than the ordinary consumer: hospitals, expert
panels employed by state public assistance agencies, and the American Medical Association's Council on Drugs.

**1. Hospital drug purchases.** Hospitals account for about one quar-
ter of the value of manufacturer drug shipments. In many cases
their drug purchase decisions will reflect the prescribing habits of
the same physicians who are prescribing for the out-of-hospital
market. However, to take advantage of large-scale purchase econ-
omies, many larger hospitals limit the bulk of their inventory to a
standardized drug list (formulary) developed by a specialized committee. Doctors are then encouraged or required to prescribe from
the formulary (13, pp. 99–100). There is then enough difference in
the putative sophistication underlying hospital and non-hospital
drug purchase decisions to make a comparison of the two meaningful. To be sure, that difference might be larger in some cases—for
example, hospitals affiliated with teaching or research programs.
Comprehensive data, however, are available only for the hospital
universe. These data are dollar sales to hospitals of drugs, classified into the same therapeutic categories employed for the out-of-
hospital market.

If sophisticated hospital purchasers have always been able to
discern ineffective drugs better than over-optimistic, unsophisti-
cated ordinary buyers were prior to 1962, then we should observe:
(1) prior to the Amendments, new drugs took a substantially
greater share of the non-hospital than the hospital market; (2) after
the Amendments, this difference narrows or disappears; (3) there
is no change in the pre- and post-Amendment hospital market
share of new drugs. A glance at columns (1) and (2) of Table 6
shows that all three implications are amply fulfilled. The same
pre–1962 new drugs took over twice their hospital market share in
the non-hospital market (column (1)); that difference is substantially
eliminated for post–1962 drugs (column (2)); and there is virtually
no difference between pre- and post–1962 hospital market shares
(line 1., columns (1) and (2)).

Before one accepts these data as conclusive support for the hypothesis of a significant Amendment-induced decline in the incidence

## Table 6

### Weighted Average Percentage of Therapeutic Category Sales Accounted for by NCEs, Hospital and Non-Hospital Markets by Years After Introduction

| Market | 1 Year After Introduction | | 4 Years After Introduction | |
|---|---|---|---|---|
| | (1) Pre-1962 | (2) Post-1962 | (3) Pre-1962 | (4) Post-1962 |
| 1. Hospital | 5.59% | 4.87% | 11.78% | 6.47% |
| | .85 | 1.10 | 2.06 | 3.73 |
| 2. Out-of-Hospital | 14.02 | 4.67 | 13.60 | 4.14 |
| | 2.11 | .81 | 2.56 | 1.21 |
| 3. t-ratio, line 1-line 2 | −4.67 | .31 | −1.03 | .59 |

Note: Sample comprises NCEs with sales to both markets (a few NCEs are sold only in one market).

Percentages are weighted averages of (NCE Sales/Total Sales in Category) × 100 in each market. The weight is the ratio of Category to total drug sales in each market. Standard errors are below percentages.

Line 3 is the ratio of the average difference between hospital and non-hospital sales in category (weighted by ratio of Category to total drug sales in both markets) to its standard error.

Columns (1) and (3) employ NCEs introduced 1960–62, column (2) those introduced 1964–69 and column (4) those introduced 1964–67. The column (2) values for drugs in column (4) are 5.45, 5.06, and 0.24 for lines 1–3 respectively.

Out-of-hospital data are from R. A. Gosselin Inc. (20); hospital data from R. A. Gosselin Inc., (19).

of inefficacious drugs, one must, however, examine the implications of consumer learning-by-experience. If the core of efficacious drugs commands the 4 to 6 percent share characteristic of the hospital market in both periods (and the non-hospital market after 1962), then we would expect: (1) the non-hospital market share will gravitate toward this figure over time, as consumers learn from experience; (2) the hospital market share will remain stable over time since the initial judgments by hospital buyers are accurate. The data in columns (3) and (4) of Table 6, however, reveal a startlingly different pattern. It is the hospitals rather than the ordinary buyers

who are the "slow learners." With the passage of time, pre–1962
NCEs maintained their share of the non-hospital market, but fully
doubled their share of the hospital market. The net result is that,
after 4 years, hospitals were just as enthusiastic buyers of pre–1962
NCEs as ordinary buyers had been all along (the column (3) difference in market shares is insignificant). In spite of a small increase
over time in the hospital market share of post–1962 NCEs, hospitals ultimately find themselves about as restricted as ordinary
buyers by the Amendments—without the Amendments, they would
apparently buy twice as many NCEs as they do with them (cf.
columns (3) and (4)).

These remarkable results are difficult to understand. Perhaps they
reflect risk aversion by large institutions where one wrong decision
will inevitably affect many patients and so be widely publicized or,
perhaps, they reflect only the slowness of committee decision-making. In any case, they surely provide no support for the hypothesis
that the Amendments have selectively kept inefficacious drugs from
the market. Indeed, a most intriguing aspect of the Table 6 data is
the rather close agreement between the permanent effects of the
Amendments and the temporary effects of over-cautious hospital
purchases. In both cases, half the effective new drug sales are kept
from the relevant market.

**2. State public assistance program formularies.** In recent years there
has been a substantial increase in prescription drug sales which are
financed from public funds. Under various state and local general
public assistance and medical assistance programs, pharmacies are
reimbursed for prescriptions provided at no, or small, charge to
the program clients. In an effort to control drug expenditures under
these programs, several states have developed formularies listing
drugs eligible for reimbursement. Reimbursement for drugs not in
the formulary is allowed only in unusual circumstances and/or requires extra effort by the physician.[35] Although the method by
which these formularies are compiled varies considerably, some of
the larger states delegate the task to specialized committees employing consultants with pharmacological expertise. Two formularies so compiled, those of California and Illinois, will be used
here. Their general intent is to provide a list of least-cost, effective
remedies for the range of symptoms likely to be encountered by

35. For example, Illinois will not grant reimbursal for a non-formulary
drug unless the prescriber has secured approval of a written request to the
Illinois State Medical Society.

prescribers. As such, they might be expected to screen out Senator Kefauver's *bête noir*, the high-priced therapeutic equivalent to what is already on the market.

If many drugs introduced before the Amendments and few of those introduced subsequently are ineffective, the former should have disproportionately sparse representation in the state formularies. That is, when drugs in the formularies are classified by date of introduction, the pre-Amendment set should constitute a smaller fraction of all pre-Amendment drugs than its post-Amendment counterpart. (Many drugs introduced in either period will not appear in a formulary because, for example, they treat uncommon conditions.) This hypothesis was tested by a conventional chi-square test for independence of classification. The question asked is: does the likelihood of an NCE's appearance in the state formulary depend on its date of introduction? The data in Table 7 reveal that in one case (Illinois) the answer is "no"; in the other case (California) it is "yes," but it is the pre-Amendment drugs that are more likely to appear. To see how much of the "poor" performance of post–1962 NCEs might be attributable to bureaucratic inertia toward the newest NCEs, I replicated the chi-square test using only 1964–67 NCEs. The results are basically unchanged: chi-square for Illinois remains insignificant, that for California declines to only marginal insignificance. The implication of these data seems to be that one set of experts (formulary committees) is about as likely to judge effective a drug that has been defined effective by other experts (FDA) as it is any other drug.[36] This inability of independent expert groups to improve on the consistency of a random number table might imply that inefficacy is unmanageably difficult to define or that it is empirically trivial. Neither circumstance would be conducive to a major reduction in the incidence of inefficacious drugs, and the data in Table 7 are inconsistent with any such reduction.

**3. American Medical Association, Council on Drugs, drug evaluations.** Since 1905, the AMA has conducted evaluations of drugs for its membership. This is today the largest such program outside government. The evaluations published in *AMA Drug Evaluations* (*DE*), summarize the existing pharmacological literature on each

36. Replication of these tests in the future may show more consistency among experts. The National Academy of Sciences is reviewing the efficacy of all pre-1962 drugs, and the FDA is empowered to remove inefficacious old drugs from the market. Illinois, however, alerts physicians that drugs deemed ineffective by the NAS review may be deleted from the formulary prior to any FDA action (10).

## Table 7

### NCEs Classified by Date of Introduction and Appearance in State Formularies, California and Illinois

| Date of Introduction and State | Listed in Formulary | Number of NCEs Not Listed in Formulary | Total |
|---|---|---|---|
| **Illinois** | | | |
| 1946–62 | 158 (155) | 358 (361) | 516 |
| 1964–70 | 31 (34) | 82 (79) | 113 |
| **Illinois Total** | 189 | 440 | 629 |
| **California** | | | |
| 1946–62 | 221 (208) | 295 (308) | 516 |
| 1964–70 | 33 (46) | 80 (67) | 113 |
| **California Total** | 254 | 375 | 629 |

| Summary Statistics | Illinois | California |
|---|---|---|
| Chi-Square | 0.46 | 7.56 |
| Approximate risk of error, d.f. = 1 | 0.50 | .006 |

Source: *NCEs by Date of Introduction:* Paul de Haen, Inc. (*16*).
Illinois: Illinois Department of Public Aid (*10*).
California: California Department of Health Care Services (*6*).
  Figures in parentheses are expected number of NCEs with independence of classification. "Risk of error" is the risk associated with accepting the hypothesis that the number of NCEs in each cell is dependent on classification by date of introduction.

drug reviewed and make some judgment about the likely effectiveness of a drug in its various indications (2). I attempted to extract
from DE some measure of the incidence of ineffective drugs by date
of drug introduction. The evaluations in DE are frequently guarded
and qualified, so some arbitrary judgments were required. I attempted to compile, for NCEs introduced in 1960–62 and 1964–70,
the longest list of drugs of questionable efficacy. Evaluations were
found in DE for 80 of the 111 NCEs introduced in 1960–62 and 94
of the 113 introduced 1964–70. Whenever DE suggested that a drug
could be ineffective, it was classified into one of two groups: Group
I, Not Effective; or Group II, Equally or Less Effective than other
drugs. There are relatively few drugs that DE will label "not effective" unqualifiedly, therefore, in addition to these, any drug
where, for example, clinical data had not yet established effectiveness or were inconclusive, was placed in Group I. Group I is surely
too large, since for many of its members, DE is willing to recom-
mend use for certain indications.[37] The bias, however, is deliberate,
since we want here to establish some upper limit to the incidence of
inefficacy. A drug was placed in Group II if a less expensive alternative seems to be available for any important indication.[38] This
Group is also too large, since it contains drugs that are effective in
some indications. I make the pessimistic assumption that doctors
prescribe these drugs mainly when a cheaper alternative is available. Table 8 summarizes the resulting classification, and contains
the results of a chi-square test for independence of the classification
from time. This test does show that ineffective drugs appeared
more frequently before 1962. To be sure, the risk of error in accepting the hypothesis of dependence on time is moderately high.

37. The following description of a Group I drug will illustrate the kind
of judgment made. "Results of clinical studies to date indicate that [drug]
may be useful in treating [list of conditions], but data are insufficient to
permit comparison of its effectiveness with that of recommended doses of
other [drugs]. The usefulness of [drug] in [list of other conditions] has not
been proved."
A generous interpretation of this might be that the drug is clearly effective
for some conditions and possibly others. I made the pessimistic assumption
that doctors are prescribing the drug only for those conditions where usefulness has not been proved, or that the apparently incomplete clinical data
are too optimistic.
38. There are two sub-classes in Group II: (1) Those labeled "as effective"
as some other specified drug or any other drug in the therapeutic category;
(2) those "less effective" than some other drug or group of drugs. A drug
labeled "as effective" in DE is in Group II if the average cost of a prescription
in the year following its introduction exceeds that of the specified alternative;
all "less effective" drugs are in Group II.

**Table 8**

**NCEs Classified by AMA Evaluation and Date of Introduction**

| Date of Introduction | Number of NCEs Evaluated as | | | |
| --- | --- | --- | --- | --- |
| | Group I | Group II | Effective | Total |
| 1960–62 | 8 (4.6) | 8 (6.9) | 64 (68.5) | 80 |
| 1964–70 | 2 (5.4) | 7 (8.1) | 85 (80.5) | 94 |
| Total | 10 | 15 | 149 | 174 |

Summary statistics :
Chi-square: 5.53
Approximate risk of error, d.f. = 2: .067
Note: See text for definition of Group I and Group II, and see Note to Table 7.
Source: American Medical Association (2).

The data, however, are worth further investigation, because we have not previously encountered any evidence so suggestive of an Amendment—induced reduction in the incidence of inefficacy.

In consequence, I next estimated the dollar value of the "waste" entailed by purchase of drugs in Groups I and II in the year following their introduction. All Group I drugs were assumed to have no therapeutic value, therefore all consumer expenditures on them are pure waste. For those Group II drugs that are as effective as cheaper alternatives, waste is the difference in per-prescription price times the number of prescriptions of the Group II drug purchased. Where a Group II drug is less effective than an alternative, I arbitrarily assumed that equal therapeutic value could have been obtained for the cost of half of a prescription for the alternative, and the resulting waste per-prescription is then multiplied by number of prescriptions. The resulting average annual bill for waste, adjusted to 1970 drug sales, is $17.3 million for pre-Amendment NCEs and $3.4 million for post-Amendment NCEs.[39] If one assumes that these

39. Waste each year was divided by total drug sales that year and the quotient multiplied by total drug sales for 1970 to obtain these figures.

payments continue perpetually and discounts the resulting stream at 10 percent per year, the present value of waste on each year's NCEs is ten times each figure. These present values may then be compared with the counterpart estimate of surplus in Table 5. The result is that, on an exaggerated estimate, about one third of surplus is eroded by waste, but, what is relevant for our purposes, this fraction is roughly the same for pre- and post-Amendment NCEs. Thus, although the Amendments seem to have reduced waste, they have not, in spite of the suggestiveness of the Table 8 data, reduced its incidence. Therefore, they leave consumers with a net loss. Indeed, the amount of pre–1962 waste is sufficiently small for this last conclusion to have held even if post–1962 waste were eliminated.[40]

If consumers learn from experience, it may, moreover, be unreasonable to suppose that even this small waste continues unabated perpetually. Given the crudeness of the waste calculation, any derivative data should be treated cautiously. It is nevertheless interesting to find some agreement between pharmacological experts and the judgment of the market place. The market share of the 16 pre-Amendment drugs in Groups I and II declined an average of 12.9 percent per year from the first to the fourth year after introduction, and this is twice its standard error. Only 4 of the 16 drugs show increased market shares. Since relative price also declined (by a statistically significant average of 2.4 percent per year), the market share performance implies a rather substantial decline in demand for ineffective drugs. The drug consumers' ignorance thus seems something less than invincible.[41]

The last result, as tentative as it must be, may provide a clue to our difficulty in finding a large effect of the Amendments on the incidence of inefficacious drugs. Simply put, the effective new drug will be more profitable. The ineffective new drug, to be sure, takes

40. Limitation of our sample to NCEs may, however, be important here. DE is extensively critical of combination drugs, typically on the ground that only one component affects a given symptom and that "rational" prescribing requires the physician to select the appropriate component. Any waste calculation for combination products based on DE's conclusions would be extremely difficult. The difference between the cost of the appropriate NCE bought separately and as part of a combination would have to be set off against the cost of more extensive diagnosis and the added cost of separate prescribing where each part of a combination has some expected benefit.

41. If $17.3 million of waste decreases by something like the 15 percent per year implied here, the present value of the waste issuing from one year's NCEs is $69 million ($17.3/(.10 + .15)$) rather than $173 million, and the improvement due to the Amendments is $56 million rather than $139 million.

an initial market share and sells at a price roughly equal to that of other new drugs.[42] The effective drugs do not, however, experience the substantial and fairly prompt loss of market share that we find for ineffective drugs. Thus, everything else being the same, the likelihood that a seller can recapture his investment in a new drug will increase with its effectiveness. These penalties imposed by the marketplace on sellers of ineffective drugs prior to 1962 seem to have been enough of a deterrent to have left little room for improvement by a regulatory agency. The only important reduction of sales of inefficacious new drugs brought about by the Amendments has come simply as a by-product of their reduction of the flow of all new drugs. Therefore, none of the data we have examined, whether obtained from the evaluations of ordinary consumers or experts, would have been very much different if instead of detailed regulation an arbitrary marketing quota had been placed on new drugs in 1962.

The conclusions to which this examination of expert drug evaluation seem to point are:

1. The null hypothesis of a decline in the incidence of inefficacious drugs cannot be accepted with tolerable risk of error; this incidence appears to be about the same today as it was before 1962.

2. To the extent that data permit measurement of its size, the costs of inefficacy seem to be small. This is implied by the similarity of new drug market shares in sales to buyers of varying pharmacological expertise (hospital versus non-hospital). The implication is confined by a direct estimate of what, by the lights of pharmacological experts, consumers are wasting on ineffective new drugs; this is consistently substantially less than half the consumers' surplus generated by new drugs.

3. These conclusions are similar to those implied by the previous analysis of ordinary consumer behavior, where we found both a trivial decline in demand for new drugs as they became more familiar, and a trivial difference in the rate of decline between pre- and post-Amendment new drugs.

4. That analysis assumed a gradual learning process that eliminates waste on inefficacious drugs. The market behavior of a sample of new drugs deemed ineffective by experts seems to confirm the usefulness of that assumption. Their decrease in demand

42. The 16 "ineffective" pre-1962 drugs in our sample had an average initial market share of 8.7 percent and their average relative price was 1.16. For all pre-Amendment NCEs in our sample, these figures are 7.5 percent and 1.26.

and the generally stable demand for new drugs render the losses from inefficacious drugs trivial compared to the surplus generated by other new drugs.

**The overall effect of drug innovation on prescription drug prices.** Perhaps the most extreme interpretation of the rationale underlying the 1962 Amendments would be that most, if not all, new drugs bring no therapeutic improvement over existing drugs. The bulk of the preceding data—on market shares and prices of new drugs over time, expert drug evaluations, etc—belies this view, but, for present purposes, I want to accept it. If the consumer "should" but doesn't treat old and new drugs as identical, his presumed gains and losses from regulation of drug innovation will turn completely on the impact of regulation on the prices he pays for drugs. That is, if he pays $1.50 for a new drug rather than $1.00 for a presumably equivalent old drug, he would be saved 50¢ if the new drug was never marketed.

This view might rationalize even the most arbitrary restriction of drug innovation, since we have seen that new drugs sell at a premium over old drugs in the same therapeutic class (see Tables 2 and 4). The Amendments have not increased this premium, and may even have reduced it.[43] Simple arithmetic, therefore, would seem to indicate that the Amendments, simply by reducing drug innovation, have saved money for consumers.

Such arithmetic would however ignore the effects of competition between producers of new and old drugs. If the latter face a decline in demand, because new substitutes become available, they may be expected to respond by reducing prices so that the new drug price premium becomes unattractively large for some customers. Thus, even if all of some initial price premium for new drugs is regarded as a waste, the overall effect of reduced drug innovation on consumer drug costs is ambiguous. The corresponding removal of a source of competition for established producers may preempt sufficient price rivalry to offset any savings on high-priced new drugs.

To resolve this ambiguity, I will here treat old and new drugs in the same therapeutic category as perfect substitutes and focus on the average price of all drugs in the category. I then seek to measure

43. Table 4 shows a 20 percentage point decline in the premium after 1962. This is only barely insignificant. However, the weighted average price relative for the 1956–57 NCEs in Table 2 is only 1.13. Since this is less than its post-1962 counterpoint, it is risky to believe that the premium has been reduced.

the net impact of drug innovation on this average. The reader should understand that, in the absence of price rivalry engendered by it, more innovation will increase this average. I first regress a time series of the annual percentage change in average price per drug prescription ($\dot{p}_t$) in the pre-Amendment period on the number of NCEs introduced in each of the two preceding years ($n_{t-1, t-2}$). Since major initial sales of any of the $n_{t-1}$ are typically attained in t, the coefficient of $n_{t-1}$ will reflect most of the inflationary impact of the new drug price premium. If there is a lag in response of old drug producers, the coefficient of $n_{t-2}$ will capture the major deflationary impact of price rivalry. The regression is:

$$\text{(E6)} \qquad \dot{p}_t = 8.652 - .003 n_{t-1} - .125 n_{t-2}$$
$$(.006) \qquad (.058)$$
$$R^2 = .388, 11 \text{ observations } (1952\text{--}62)[44]$$

Since the coefficient of $n_{t-1}$ is insignificant and that of $n_{t-2}$ is significantly negative, the regression implies that the dominant effect of reduced drug innovation is reduced price rivalry. Specifically (E6) predicts that a permanent annual decline of 20 NCEs would accelerate the change in drug prices by 2.5 percent per year. However, while that magnitude of NCE decline has been experienced since 1962, the predicted price effect has not. Instead, there has been a deceleration from the pre-1962 average of over 1 percent per year. This might mean that the relationship in (E6) is aberrant, or that factors exogenous to that relationship have been holding drug prices down since 1962.

To distinguish among these possibilities, I next examine cross-section data for the three years preceding the Amendments. Exogenous forces are assumed to affect all sub-markets equally at any moment, and the dependent variable is redefined as the deviation of the price change for a category from the average price change for all categories in the same time period ($\dot{p}'$). Instead of the number of NCEs, I use $q_n/Q_T$, as well as the market share of "other" new drugs ($q_n'/Q_T$), as independent variables. The dependent variable is measured over two years spanning the years subsequent to drug innovations, which is the year used to measure the independent variables.

---

44. Standard errors are in parentheses. The dependent variable is derived from a series on the average retail price of drug prescriptions from *American Druggist* (1). When the series was deflated by the GNP deflator, the same general result was obtained, though with some loss of explanatory power. This may reflect inaccuracy of the deflator.

In this way, the coefficients of the independent variable reflect both any immediate inflationary impact of the associated innovation and any lagged competitive reaction. The resulting regression is

$$(E7) \qquad p' = .329 - 13.230 \underset{(5.625)}{} \frac{q_n}{Q_T} - 1.216 \underset{(5.015)}{} \frac{q'_n}{Q_T}$$

$R^2 = .036$, 153 observations
(51 therapeutic categories, for 1960–62 innovations).

While it is weak, the negative overall effect of NCEs on drug prices persists in the cross-section data, and the effect remains significant (non-NCE innovation has a neutral effect on drug prices). The magnitude of the predicted effect of reduced innovation on drug prices is however much smaller here than in (E6). The average NCE share of category output has declined by roughly 1.5 percentage points, and in (E7) this translates into an approximate .1 percentage point annual acceleration of average drug prices.

The safest conclusions from these data are, I believe:

1. It is difficult to conclude that drug innovation has a net inflationary impact on drug prices, even when innovation is regarded as producing no improvement in drug quality.[45]

2. If innovation has any impact on prices, it is probably deflationary, though the magnitude may be small.

3. Specifically, our estimate of a .1 percent annual acceleration of drug prices due to the 1962 Amendments translates into a permanent annual cost to drug consumers of about $50 million.[46]

## Summary

The 1962 Drug Amendments sought to reduce consumer waste on ineffective new drugs. Although this goal appears to have been attained, the costs imposed on consumers in the process seem clearly

---

45. Such a conclusion would be difficult even on simple arithmetic. The data in Table 4 imply that, for 1960–62, the average price of all drugs is 1 percent more than the average price of all old drugs, and the deceleration of average prescription price has exceeded that amount since 1962.

46. A permanent .1 percent increase in drug prices this year costs consumers $5 million this year. Since the price increase is presumably permanent, there will be a perpetual stream of such costs whose present value is $50 million at 10 percent. A similar $50 million stream of costs is engendered every year that innovation is retarded.

to outweigh the benefits. The reason for this is that the benefits are largely a by-product of the Amendments having reduced consumer exposure to all types of new drugs. The incidence of ineffective new drugs has not been materially reduced, and, even if it had, the pre–1962 waste on ineffective new drugs seems to have been too small to compensate for the benefits consumers have had to forego since 1962 because of reduced drug innovation. The largest estimate of this annual waste-saving, based on ungenerous interpretations of the drug evaluations of the AMA Council on Drugs and pessimistic assumptions about consumer behavior, is $100–$150 million, and this has to be reduced by more than half to take account of the loss of market share of ineffective drugs over time.

In the context of this study, these foregone benefits show up as a decline in the demand for (and, consequently, the consumer surplus generated by) new drugs. In a previous section, it was shown that essentially all of the post-1962 decline in drug innovation—a reduction of over half in the number and output of new drugs—can be attributed to the 1962 Amendments. This, combined with the absence of any increase in the relative price of new drugs, implies a lower demand for new drugs. The decline in demand has been attributed to the reduced value of information supplied with new drugs, which I have in turn attributed both to the explicit restrictions on seller promotion of new drugs in the Amendments and to the reduced number of sellers who are typically informing consumers about new drug types.

The bulk of the evidence indicates that the post-1962 decline in demand does not reflect a substantially more realistic appraisal by consumers of the genuine worth of new drugs. The pre-1962 demand did not fall after consumers had time to learn the worth of new drugs from experience, as it would have done if consumers were initially over-optimistic. Since consumers did not act as if they "regretted" their initial evaluations of pre-Amendment drugs, the lower post-1962 demand for new drugs resolves largely into reduced net benefits ($300–$400 million) to drug consumers from a reduced flow of new drugs and information about them. That conclusion is verified by assessments of experts and sophisticated drug buyers. The probability that they will assess a new drug as ineffective is about the same for the pre- and post-1962 sets of new drugs and any reduced losses from ineffective post-1962 drugs merely offset a part of the foregone benefits.

Finally, one should mention the direct budgetary cost of implementing the Amendments. This is relatively trivial. Of the total

1970 FDA budget ($66 million) it is unlikely that more than $15 million is attributable to the requirements added by the Amendments.[47]

# V. The Value of Drug Safety and of Important Therapeutic Advances

I previously pointed out the inadequacy of empirical demand analysis in accounting for the costs of unsafe drugs or the benefits of unusually successful drugs. Briefly, the victim of the former loses more than his drug expenditure, and the beneficiary of the latter gains more than the cost of the most expensive drug. It will not be possible here to measure these particular gains and losses in any systematic way. However, I hope to convey some idea of the magnitude of those components affected by the 1962 Amendments.

This will entail placing money values on lives saved and spent and on illness suffered and avoided. There is no universal agreement on how this should be done, and the reader should not be misled by the seeming precision of any specific number.[48] For example, I will identify the value of a death or illness avoided with the present worth of the added earnings thereby engendered. The earnings lost through death and illness are surely an important component of "society's" loss, but are not comprehensive. They leave out of account such losses as the bereavement of relatives, the pain of illness, and foregone non-pecuniary income (for example, some leisure activities). At the same time, alternative methods of valuing life would include deductions from earnings.[49] Any conclusion ought to be regarded as risky if it cannot survive doubling or halving of the cost estimate on which it is based. In the last analysis, though, I cannot here hope to surmount either the controversy or inaccuracy attending any mode of valuing life. I will, therefore, wherever possible provide physical counterparts to the economic costs and benefits.

The questions I ask here are: (1) Have the 1962 Drug Amend-

47. From 1947 to 1962, the FDA budget, deflated by the price index for general government output rose 6.6 percent per year. In the two subsequent years, this accelerated to 18.0 percent. The 1964–70 growth rate was 4.4 percent. If we assume that the pre-1962 growth rate would have been maintained if the Amendments had not been enacted, the 1970 budget would have been about $59 million, or $7 million lower than the actual 1970 budget. Alternatively, if we compound the 1962 budget at the slower post-1964 growth rate, the estimated 1970 budget is $15 million below the actual.

48. Some of the relevant issues are discussed by Mishan (15).

49. For example, the monetary loss of death to a "society" of everyone but the victim is his expected future wealth contribution—earnings minus consumption.

ments improved drug safety enough to "pay" for the tax they have imposed on consumers? (2) Has any substantial additional tax been imposed by restricted or delayed introduction of unusually beneficial drugs?

**Drug safety.** Information on drug toxicity is never, of course, complete, and some of it may be discovered only after widespread human use. The additional testing requirements of the 1962 Amendments enforce a trade—more clinical testing and, incidentally, more time for less widespread human use—in the production of some toxicity information. Much of the cost and benefit of this trade is comprehended by the previous analysis: the presumably reduced risk of human use will make the demand for new drugs higher than otherwise and the cost of added testing will similarly increase their price. The Amendments, however, presume that the risk of some unusual harm, such as might have been inflicted had thalidomide been marketed, was not completely reflected in either the demand or costs facing producers of new drugs. We want therefore to estimate separately the cost of such unusual harm prior to the Amendments.

The marketing of the thalidomide-type of product does not appear to have been common prior to 1962, and where such products were marketed systematic data on their health effects are rare. I shall therefore have to rely on but one case where such data are available, and where adverse health effects of the type that the Amendments might reasonably have been expected to reduce were present.[50] The case concerns the drug chloramphenicol, marketed under the trade name Chloromycetin.

This antibiotic was introduced in 1949 and met with immediate market success. Within the next three years, however, the drug became implicated as a cause of a sometimes fatal blood disease, aplastic anemia. In 1952, the FDA temporarily halted sales of the drug, but later permitted their resumption, with its indications limited to a few infections such as typhoid fever. It is reasonable to suppose that, had the 1962 Amendments been law in 1949, the relationship between chloramphenicol and aplastic anemia would have been discovered prior to marketing. It may be less reasonable to suppose that all users of chloramphenicol who perished in ignorance of its relationship to aplastic anemia would have been spared

50. Since the Amendments add a few years time and clinical testing, they cannot, for example, be expected to reduce adverse health effects of long-term use.

by such a discovery. After a precipitous decline in sales to 1954, chloramphenicol sales—and aplastic anemia deaths—more than recovered their pre-1952 levels by 1960. Users of the drug, knowing the risks, found them outweighed by prospective benefits. This seems to imply that the initial market reaction to knowledge of chloramphenicol's adverse effects might have been smaller had the knowledge been conveyed in a less dramatic fashion that it was in 1952. I will, however, assume that had the Amendments been in force, the death rate from aplastic anemia would have been, from 1949 onward, at the nadir it attained after the 1952 disclosure of chloramphenicol's link to the disease. And I will ignore any benefits sacrificed by the exaggerated decline in chloramphenicol use which permitted this low rate.

These assumptions are employed in Table 9 to estimate the bene-

### Table 9

### Estimated Benefits from Amendments for Chloramphenicol-Type Drug Introduced in 1970

| Years after Intro- duction | (1) Death Rate without Amendments (per 100,000) | (2) Deaths Avoided with Amendments | (3) Present Value of Deaths Avoided ($ million) |
|---|---|---|---|
| 1 | .43 | 81 | 3.1 |
| 2 | .40 | 20 | .7 |
| 3 | .44 | 102 | 3.3 |
| 4 | .53 | 285 | 8.3 |
| 5 | .49 | 204 | 5.4 |
| 6 | .42 | 61 | 1.5 |
| 7 | .39 | 0 | 0 |
| Total | | 753 | 22.3 |

Note: Column (1): Death rate for aplastic anemia, U.S., 1949–55, as reported in Smick, Condit, Proctor and Sutcher, (22).
Column (2): (column (1) − .39) × 10 × U.S. population in 1970, 203 million.
Column (3): $38,565 × column (2) discounted to year 1 at 10 percent. $38,565 is the present worth of 45 years of 1970 U.S. average personal income, $3,910, discounted at 10 percent.

fits that would be produced by the Amendments were a drug exactly like chloramphenicol marketed today. The first column of Table 9 shows the U.S. death rate from aplastic anemia from 1949 (year 1) to 1955, the post-chloramphenicol low. Assume next that, with the information generated by the extended clinical testing required by the Amendments, the higher pre-1955 death rates could have been avoided. That is, all of the difference between the 1955 and any pre-1955 death rate is assumed attributable to mistaken use of chloramphenicol. This difference, multiplied by the current population, is an estimate (column (2)) of the lives that would be saved if the chloramphenicol twin were introduced today. I next assume that each person saved would earn the U.S. average personal income for 45 years, and discount this stream at 10 percent to get the monetary value of a life saved. In column (3), the aggregate value of lives saved is again discounted to get the present worth of lives saved in each future year. The $22.3 million total is the present value of the added earnings produced by the 753 people spared from death by aplastic anemia. It should be noted that I am using a 10 percent discount rate for symmetry with previous and subsequent work, and that this rate understates the saving. An appropriate discount factor would be lower by the expected annual growth of population and per capita income. In this case, the understatement is mitigated by the fact that the highest incidence of aplastic anemia is among the very young and very old, who have a lower present value of earnings than any appropriate national average.

The conclusions that may be drawn from the chloramphenicol experience are not, however, substantially modified by doubling or trebling the estimated saving. The anecdotal evidence nowhere suggests that drugs with the unknown lethal side-effects of the magnitude of chloramphenicol were being introduced regularly prior to 1962.[51] Indeed, that magnitude appears unique for the U.S. drug market. It would therefore risk exaggeration to attribute to the 1962 Amendments savings much in excess of the magnitude in Table 9 once or twice in each decade. An annual saving on the order of 100 lives is an impressive achievement standing alone. At the same time, the associated monetary value is only a tiny fraction of the loss otherwise imposed by the Amendments on consumers. It would therefore require a very large valuation—several million dollars per individual—for the non-quantifiable benefits of reduced mortality to offset the loss to consumers.

51. See M. Mintz (14) for an extremely critical review of drug safety.

## The Delay of Important Innovations

As is the case with drug safety, the mundane costs and benefits associated with a longer gestation period for new drugs are subsumed in previous calculations. One of the costs associated with the proof-of-efficacy and testing requirements of the Amendments is the loss of something like two years' return on the capital invested in new drug development. Part of this cost is presumably reflected in higher new drug prices, fewer new drugs, and, therefore, reduced net benefits to consumers. The cases I deal with here are those where even an exceptionally high price would not exhaust net benefits, but where the price of the drug is effectively infinite, temporarily or permanently, because it lacks NDA approval.[52] For these cases, the previous consumer surplus analysis will understate foregone benefits, since the demand schedule underlying it implies zero net benefits when the price of any new drug is less than twice that of existing drugs.

There are at least two problems in remedying the inadequacy: identifying the specific effect of the Amendments and quantifying the foregone benefits. The latter problem may be illustrated by something like aspirin. This was an innovation whose substantial delay would very likely have denied consumers benefits many times the cost of the drug. But most of these benefits would consist of increased comfort rather than any easily measured increase in productivity. As a practical matter, I will have to limit this investigation to drugs with measurable productivity effects, that is, drugs which can be directly related to reduced morbidity, mortality, or treatment costs. It should be understood, however, that these do not exhaust the class for which the previous consumer surplus analysis is inadequate.

Establishing the link between important innovations and the Amendments poses more formidable problems. There has been no innovation in the United States since 1962 even remotely comparable to, say, penicillin or the sulfonamides, in its effects on morbidity or mortality. But this is also true of countries with regulatory systems comparable to that of the United States prior to 1962. It would be dangerous to conclude from either fact that the costs of the Amendments have been either enormous or trivial. The American drug market and drug research establishment are each too large a fraction of the world total for the transnational cross-elasticity of

52. Or because the manufacturer does not believe he can appropriate enough of the benefits to make pursuing an NDA worthwhile.

supply of innovation to be plausibly infinite, and too small for it to be zero.

In the absence of any obvious effect of the Amendments on major drug innovation in the past decade, I make the conservative assumption that there have been none. This means that any estimate of unusual foregone benefits are prospective and unavoidably conjectural. I will also assume that no major innovation will be permanently kept from the market by the Amendments, even though this may be overly optimistic in light of previous evidence, and I will assume that the Amendments do not inhibit the research process sufficiently to delay the date of the innovation's discovery. Unusual foregone benefits will then accrue only in the extra time it takes to satisfy the testing and proof-of-efficacy requirements prior to marketing. Given some previous data, I take this time to be two years. While this time is already a conservative estimate of the effect of the Amendments, it might be shorter still for highly beneficial innovations. However, such a conjecture cannot be tested with available data. The analysis then focuses on the following question: how much benefit would be lost if a major therapeutic advance came on the market two years later than otherwise? The data will permit the reader to answer this question with any different delay he wishes to assume.

To answer this question, I will first quantify some of the benefits of a few major innovations. These innovations cannot of course be duplicated, and the purpose of this exercise is simply to establish the magnitude of foregone benefits in delaying a "typical" major innovation. Next, I examine two major health problems—cancer and heart disease—which are the focus of much current research, and try to establish the magnitude of the cost of delaying the introduction of the obviously hypothetical drug(s) which can substantially mitigate these problems. To provide comparability, each innovation is treated as if it occurred in 1970, so that, for example, mortality reduction is evaluated for 1970 incomes and population. These evaluations are deliberately kept conservative, most notably but not exclusively, by failure to allow for population and per capita income growth.

## Benefits of Past Innovations

**1. Tuberculosis therapy.** Some historical data on tuberculosis are presented in Table 10. The fragmentary data in the last two columns of the table compared with those in column (1) indicate the

## Table 10
### Tuberculosis Mortality, Morbidity, and Hospital Admissions Rates
### Selected Periods

| Period or Year | (1) Mortality Rate (per 100,000 per year) | (2) Average Annual Decrease of Mortality Rate from Preceding Period (%) | (3) Morbidity Rate (cases per 100,000 per year) | (4) Hospital Admissions (per 100,000 per year) |
|---|---|---|---|---|
| 1901–05 | 181.9 | — | — | — |
| 1906–10 | 164.4 | 2.0 | — | — |
| 1911–15 | 145.2 | 2.5 | — | — |
| 1916–20 | 134.1 | 1.6 | — | — |
| 1921–25 | 91.5 | 8.0 | — | — |
| 1926–30 | 78.0 | 3.2 | — | — |
| 1931–35 | 60.3 | 5.3 | — | 67.8 |
| 1936–40 | 50.4 | 3.6 | — | 74.5 |
| 1941–44 | 42.8 | 3.7 | 87.4 | 71.7 |
| 1945–47 | 36.6 | 4.6 | 88.1 | 68.5 |
| 1948–53 | 21.2 | 12.9 | 79.7 | 71.9 |
| 1954–57 | 8.9 | 19.0 | 56.6 | 66.7E |
| 1969 | 2.6 | 9.6 | 25.4E | 27.6E |

Note: E indicates "estimate" obtained by splicing a later to an earlier series.
Sources: Column (1): U.S. Bureau of the Census (28, 29).
  Column (2): Annual percentage change of column (1) between midpoints of periods.
  Column (3): 1941–50, U.S. Public Health Service (34); 1951–57, U.S. Public Health Service (33); 1969, U.S. Bureau of the Census (29).
  Column (4): U.S. Bureau of the Census (28, 29). Pre- and post-1954 data derived from reports of the American Hospital Association and American Medical Association, respectively, on number of admissions to tuberculosis hospitals.

high proportion of cases which were terminal prior to about 1947. The gradual decline in TB mortality in this period is in large part associated with control of its communication through such measures as improved sanitation and, especially, early isolation of victims. In the mid-1940s, two drugs, streptomycin and PAS, were discovered which acted directly against the tuberculosis bacillus. Their wide distribution, beginning about 1947, and the introduction of isoniazid in 1952, markedly accelerated the decline in the TB mortality rate. More victims were cured early and this in turn reduced communication of the disease.

To evaluate the benefits of these drugs, one must first account for the mortality and morbidity reduction that could have been expected without them. I will assume that the mortality rate would have declined by 4.5 percent per year after 1947 had streptomycin and PAS never been introduced. This is roughly the 1920–47 average annual decline, so that the slower pre-1920 decline is treated as completely atypical of any other period. Thus, the mortality saving attributable to the new TB drugs in any year is the 1947 rate compounded at $(1 - .045)$ per year minus the actual rate. I assume further that this saving reaches a maximum a decade after introduction of streptomycin and PAS. Although the abnormally high rate of decline in mortality has persisted, I will attribute the more recent portion of the decline to some potential non-drug-related medical advance so that any error understates the importance of drugs. Similarly, I assume that drug-related savings from reduced morbidity reach a maximum in 1957.

Morbidity savings would consist both of increased earnings and reduced medical costs. I assume, however, that the latter is zero. Table 10 indicates that hospital admissions for TB remained basically unchanged from the mid-1940s to 1957. I ignore the possibility that this more complete hospitalization for TB victims entailed substitution of lower cost treatment modes for out-of-hospital alternatives. The only morbidity savings, therefore, are the earnings of those who would have been expected to contract TB had streptomycin, isoniazid, and PAS not been introduced. Since the fragmentary data indicate no pre-1947 trend in morbidity or hospital admissions, the expected non-drug morbidity rate is taken to be 87.4, the 1941–44 average, for each year 1948–57.

The resulting estimates of the mortality and morbidity savings attributable to streptomycin, isoniazid, and PAS are in columns (2) and (5) of Table 11. By 1957, annual mortality and morbidity were reduced by 29,000 and 56,000 (1970 population base) respectively, or to about 40 and 60 percent of their expected levels. These savings can then be converted to money values as follows: each life saved is evaluated at the average discounted value of (1970) median earnings for the estimated 1956 age-sex distribution of lives saved. This is done to account for the disproportionate number of working males saved, and results in an estimated value per life saved about 20 percent higher than the simple capitalization of per capita income. Each TB case prevented is assumed to gain an additional

## Table 11

### Estimated Cost of Two-Year Delay in Introducing Drugs for Tuberculosis Therapy Values as of 1970

| Years after Intro-duction | Mortality Savings of Drugs | | | Morbidity Savings of Drugs | | |
|---|---|---|---|---|---|---|
| | (1) Death Rate Reduction (per 100,000) | (2) Number of Lives Saved (thousands) | (3) Discounted Value of Lives Saved ($ million) | (4) Reduction of Incidence (per 100,000) | (5) Number of Victims Spared (thousands) | (6) Discounted Value of Earnings for Victims Spared ($ million) |
| 1 | 2.1 | 4.3 | $ 185 | 0 | 0 | $ 0 |
| 2 | 4.4 | 9.0 | 351 | 0 | 0 | 0 |
| 3 | 4.9 | 10.0 | 355 | 5.3 | 10.8 | 47 |
| 4 | 8.0 | 16.3 | 528 | 7.5 | 15.3 | 60 |
| 5 | 11.1 | 22.6 | 665 | 12.9 | 26.3 | 93 |
| 6 | 13.4 | 27.3 | 730 | 15.2 | 31.0 | 100 |
| 7 | 14.4 | 29.3 | 714 | 19.1 | 38.9 | 114 |
| 8 | 14.5 | 29.5 | 653 | 20.8 | 42.4 | 113 |
| 9 | 14.1 | 28.7 | 577 | 25.4 | 51.7 | 126 |
| 10 to ∞ | 14.1 | 28.7 | 5,241 | 27.7 | 56.4 | 1,245 |
| Total | | | $9,999 | | | $1,898 |
| Total for Two-Year Delay | 57.4 | | 8,259 | 112.8 | | 1,568 |
| Cost of Delay | | | $1,740 | | | $330 |

Note: Column (1): Calculated as 1947 death rate × (.955)$^t$ − actual death rate, 1948–56.

Column (2): Column (1) × 203.7 million, the 1970 population.

Column (3): Column (2) × Average present value of life saved. The latter is computed by first estimating the number of lives saved in each age-sex cohort for 1956. To estimate this, the 1920–47 decline in the cohort death rate is extrapolated to 1956; the actual 1956 death rate is subtracted and the difference multiplied by cohort population. These numbers are then used as weights to compute a weighted average of cohort lifetime earnings. This average is $47,400. The data in column (3) are thus the present value of $47,400 × column (2).

Cohort lifetime earnings are derived from 1970 earnings data. The typical cohort member's age is assumed to be halfway between end points, and he is assumed to earn the median income of his and older cohorts for his expected lifetime. This earning stream is discounted at 10 percent.

Column (4): Calculated as (87.4 − actual incidence) × .726. The most recent incidence data are for "newly reported active cases," and, for years of overlap with earlier data, these were .726 of total reported cases. For the first two years, this figure is negative, so zero saving is assumed.

Column (5): Column (4) × 1970 population.

Column (6): Column (5) × Present value of one year's average earnings of victim spared. Morbidity is assumed proportional to mortality in each age-sex cohort. Therefore the weights for column (3) are applied to 1970 median earnings in each cohort to compute one year's earnings of victim spared ($5,739). Column (6) is thus the present value of $5,739 × column (5) at 10 percent.

Sources: Morbidity and Mortality: See Table 10.
Earnings: U.S. Bureau of the Census (27).

year's earnings, one year being a rough estimate of the term of the typical TB case reported to Weisbrod (38).[53] The present value of reduced TB morbidity and mortality (1970 income and population bases) is reported in columns (3) and (6) of Table 11. Their sum is about $12 billion. The Table also shows the present value of the same streams of benefits commencing two years later than otherwise; their sum is about $10 billion. The $2 billion difference represents the loss, in 1970 values, that would have been incurred had streptomycin, isoniazid, and PAS been kept from widespread introduction for two years more testing and evaluation than they in fact were.[54] The most obvious loss would have been that incurred by the 13,300 or so who would have died in those two years. But the less obvious losses—the excess death and morbidity from delayed diffusion and favorable communicable disease effects of the drugs—are quantitatively more important: these amount to a further 44,100 lives lost and 112,800 extra TB victims.

**2. Tranquilizers.** The first of the modern tranquilizers, chlorpromazine, was introduced in 1954. Since then, over 40 other tranquilizers have been introduced, and the group now accounts for more than 10 percent of all prescription drug sales. Many purchasers of these drugs are seeking relief from tension and anxiety symptoms that do not have any easily measurable effects on their productivity. The drugs have, however, been used for treatment of severe psychoses, and it is on the unusual benefits of the drugs in this use that I will concentrate.

Prior to the introduction of tranquilizers, severe psychotic disorders often entailed lengthy confinement in a mental hospital. The tranquilizers have not reduced the incidence of such disorders, but rather the average length of confinement. That is, the drugs help some psychotics to function in a non-institutional environment, so that their hospital confinement can be terminated early (8, p. 176). The net effect of the tranquilizers, then, has been a substantial reduction in the average length of confinement, and a less substantial reduction in total patient-days at mental hospitals.

The basic data are in Table 12. The absence of any change in the

53. In addition, the average length of stay in TB hospitals in the late 1940s was about 8 months. Since hospital admittees could be expected to have had the disease for some time prior to admission, Weisbrod's estimate seems reasonable.

54. This loss should be netted against savings on purchase of the drugs, but these are trivial. The earliest data I have are for 1955, during which manufacturer shipments of all TB drugs were under $10 million.

## Table 12

### Annual Admissions, Patient-Days, and
### Average Length of Stay, Mental Hospitals
### Selected Periods

| Period or Year | (1) Admissions (per 1,000) | (2) Patient-Days (per 1,000) | (3) Average Length of Stay (days per patient) |
|---|---|---|---|
| 1932–35 | 1.4 | 1,394 | 1,025 |
| 1936–40 | 1.5 | 1,573 | 1,063 |
| 1941–45 | 1.7 | 1,673 | 1,014 |
| 1946–50 | 2.0 | 1,651 | 817 |
| 1951–54 | 2.0 | 1,648 | 817 |
| 1955–58 | 2.2 | 1,520 | 697 |
| 1959–61 | 2.3 | 1,458 | 626 |
| 1962–64 | 2.6 | 1,373 | 522 |
| 1969 | 3.1 | 958 | 309 |

Sources: Columns (1) and (2): U.S. Bureau of the Census (28, 29). Column (2) is average daily census at mental hospital times number of days in year divided by population. Column (3): Column (2)/Column (1). This is an approximation, since many patients were admitted in prior years.

incidence of disabling psychotic disorders is evident in column (1). Both the pre- and post-tranquilizer growth rate in hospital admission rates is around 2.25 to 2.5 percent per year. The average period of confinement was about three years until 1943. This declined to 2 years, 3 months by 1947, but stayed at that level until chlorpromazine was introduced, when the decline that has continued largely uninterrupted to the present level of less than one year commenced The length of this period of decline seems attributable both to a succession of drug innovations and to their gradual acceptance by the medical profession. Although most NCEs in the chlorpromazine family (the phenothiazines) were introduced by 1959, one was introduced as recently as 1970. There was also much initial skepticism about the effectiveness of the phenothiazines, and the major clinical evidence supporting their effectiveness was completed only in the mid-1960s (8, p. 163, p. 177).

This history raises two problems for estimating the benefits of tranquilizers, both of which I resolve on the side of underestimating benefits. First, the failure of the World War II decline in average length of stay at mental hospitals to persist beyond 1947 implies that the post-1954 rise in admissions would have been accompanied by a rise in patient-days in the absence of the tranquilizers. There is, however, no important trend in patient-days (column (2), Table 12) from 1936–54. I will assume that the same would have been true after 1954, so that, in the absence of the tranquilizers, the immediate pre-1954 average of 1.65 patient-days per capita would have been experienced in each post-1954 year. Second, it seems plausible that the full benefits from tranquilizers have not yet been attained. However, the further one extrapolates from 1954, the greater the likelihood that, were chlorpromazine not introduced, some non-tranquilizer treatment mode would have been discovered which produced some of the same benefits. I will, therefore, assume arbitrarily that benefits attributable solely to the tranquilizers reached a maximum a decade after chlorpromazine was introduced. The subsequent incremental benefits are assumed attainable by a conjectural alternative.

The benefits from tranquilizers consist of savings in mental hospital expenditures and earnings for those who would have been confined if tranquilizers were unavailable. These savings are presented in Table 13 for 1970 data. Each mental hospital patient-day saved is assumed to allow earnings of $10.70 (1970 per capita personal income per day) and savings of $16.67 (1970 daily expenses per patient at mental hospitals) in hospital costs. Although it seems surprising, the value of the savings from tranquilizers is virtually identical to that of the TB drugs, and so, of course, would have been the cost of a two-year delay in their introduction. Unlike TB drugs, however, tranquilizer costs are not negligible, since patients must frequently use them for long periods following hospital confinement, and the drugs are fairly expensive. A generous estimate of the magnitude of these drug costs can be made as follows: assume that, following their introduction, each patient admitted to a mental hospital, whether or not he is susceptible to tranquilizer treatment, becomes committed to lifetime maintenance on phenothiazine therapy. I take $600 as the present value of the cost of this commitment.[55] For the 1955 hospital admission rate and 1970 popula-

---

55. I assume lifetime consumption of something over ten phenothiazine prescriptions per year at 1970 retail prescription prices. (The latter cannot be disclosed here.) The $600 estimate does not allow for any impact of the 1971 expiration of the patent on chlorpromazine on drug prices.

**Table 13**

**Estimated Savings Due to Tranquilizers
Values as of 1970**

| Years after Introduction | (1) Patient-days Saved (millions) | (2) Present Value of Savings ($ million) |
|---|---|---|
| 1 | 1.02 | $    25.3 |
| 2 | 13.44 | 303.3 |
| 3 | 42.17 | 865.4 |
| 4 | 49.70 | 927.6 |
| 5 | 40.13 | 680.0 |
| 6 | 32.39 | 499.3 |
| 7 | 44.61 | 625.4 |
| 8 | 51.13 | 651.2 |
| 9 | 52.35 | 606.5 |
| 10 to ∞ | 66.00 per year | 6,944.2 |
| Total | | $12,128.2 |
| Total for Two-Year Delay | | 10,017.8 |
| Cost of Delay        132.10 | | $  2,110.4 |

Note: Column (1): (1.650 − patient-days in mental hospitals per capita in years 1955–64) × 1970 population.

Column (2): $27.33 × column (1) discounted to present at 10 percent. $27.33 = 1970 daily personal income per capita ($10.70) + 1970 daily per patient expenditures at mental hospitals ($16.63).

Source: U.S. Bureau of the Census (29).

tion, this would entail a cost of $268.8 million in the first year following introduction of tranquilizers. Discounting this at 7.5 percent (10 percent minus a 2.5 percent annual increase in hospital admissions per capita) in perpetuity yields a present value of $3,584 million. A slightly smaller figure is obtained by discounting at 7.5 percent the total 1970 retail value of in and out-of-hospital sales of all tranquilizers used as antipsychotics.[56] This assumes, hyperbolically, that all these tranquilizers are prescribed exclusively for present and former mental patients. When this crude cost estimate is deducted from gross tranquilizer savings, we are left with net benefits of about $8 billion and a net cost of delay-in-introduction of about $1.4 billion.[57] This would correspond to 132.1 million extra patient-days in mental hospitals, or an average of 25 extra days for each patient admitted over a period of 12 years.

**3. Poliomyelitis vaccines.** The Salk vaccine has permitted the virtual eradication of poliomyelitis. For this reason, this innovation is commonly regarded as among the most important of modern medicine. The economic value of polio vaccine, however, does not come close to that of either innovation previously discussed. I rely for this conclusion first on Weisbrod's recent study of the costs and benefits of polio vaccines (37), and will only summarize his results here.

Weisbrod estimates that the internal rate of return to research and development on polio vaccine is about 11 percent per year. This is the rate which equates the cost of pre–1956 R&D to the value of post–1956 benefits. Given Weisbrod's estimates of annual pre–1956 R&D expenses, the present value of post–1956 benefits which is implied by this rate of return is about $60 million, or about twice this for 1970 incomes and prices. Had a 1962–type of drug law delayed introduction of Salk vaccine by two years, about $20 million of these benefits woud have been lost.

This is clearly a trivial sum compared to those derived for TB drugs and tranquilizers, and it is useful to explore the important reasons for this difference in order of magnitude.

(a) *Incidence and mortality.* Weisbrod estimates a no-vaccine incidence of 36,000 polio cases per year, which is roughly the average incidence for the decade prior to 1956. By contrast, there were over 100,000 TB cases per year and over 300,000 admissions to mental hospital per year at the time of the relevant drug innovations. Something like 5 percent of all polio cases terminated in death, as compared with more than one-third of TB cases. Moreover, a large fraction of polio deaths occurred among the very young, whose dis-

---

56. This retail value is slightly under $250 million. The drugs are all phenothiazines plus any others mentioned as antipsychotic agents in *AMA Drug Evaluation* (2, Ch. 29).

57. This may still overstate the hypothetical cost of the 1962 Amendments. Some of the overall tranquilizer benefits are attributable to the variants of chlorpromazine. The information produced for the chlorpromazine NDA might be expected to reduce the time required for approval of the NDAs for the variants.

counted future earnings are relatively low. Thus, the aggregate mortality cost of polio was far lower than that of TB prior to introduction of drugs.

(b) *Morbidity cost.* The high incidence of polio among the young entails a substantially smaller sacrifice of earnings per day of disability than for either TB or psychotic disorders. At the same time, many polio cases were non-paralytic and these involved relatively low treatment costs. Weisbrod estimates the average treatment cost per case as $550 at 1950 prices. By contrast, each 1950 mental hospital admission cost about $2,000 (800 days of confinement at about $2.50 per day) and each 1950 TB hospital admission cost about $1,750 (250 days at $7 per day).

(c) *Drug application cost.* Eradication of polio was achieved by vaccinating first the bulk of the population alive in the mid 1950s, and then the bulk of subsequent newborn. The capital outlay for this massive initial vaccination (Weisbrod estimates this at $350–$625 million) is then amortized by benefits to a small fraction of those immunized which accrue over a long period. This ubiquitous and immediate expenditure offsets most of the benefits of the Salk vaccine. The interest cost of the initial mass vaccination is about $1,000 per polio case prevented at a 10 percent rate, while Weisbrod estimates a gross benefit of $1,350 per case prevented. Neither TB nor psychotic disorders entail this kind of capital outlay to implement drug therapy.

I have independently calculated the net benefits of polio vaccine according to the methods I used for TB drugs and tranquilizers. Many of the data for the calculation were drawn from an AMA study that employs substantially higher treatment cost estimates than does Weisbrod (3, pp. 29–46). When allowance is made for the prodigious secular increase in hospital costs, these data yield 1970 net benefit estimates considerably above Weisbrod's, though they do not obviate the conclusions one can draw from his data. I will here only outline the procedure I used.[58] The AMA study provides estimates of the number of polio cases prevented by age from 1955 through 1961. Since the disease was virtually eradicated by 1961, I simply assumed subsequent benefits and costs equal to those for 1961. The benefits for each case prevented consist of treatment costs saved and earnings permitted. For that portion of cases in which death could have been expected, the latter is taken as the present value of age-cohort lifetime earnings. (Weisbrod employs

58. The detailed calculations are available on request.

earnings less consumption.) For the remainder of cases, I assumed that earnings would have been lost only over the period of hospital confinement, thereby understating savings for cases that involve long-term impairment of productivity. The AMA data on the vaccination status of the population from 1957 to 1961 and on total 1955–61 vaccination cost are used to estimate vaccination costs in each year to 1961, and post–1961 costs are assumed equal to .018 (the current birth rate) of the 1955–61 total each year. I impute arbitrarily a value of $1.50 to the working time foregone by adults to obtain each vaccination. The present value of benefits minus vaccination costs is slightly under $900 million, and the cost of a two-year delay in introduction is about $150 million spread over about 70,000 additional polio cases. Although this is a much larger dollar-cost estimate than Weisbrod's data permit, it is still much smaller than the cost of delaying introduction of something like TB drugs or tranquilizers.

Some general conclusions are implied by the preceding analysis of three important drug innovations. First, technological and economic importance can differ substantially. Salk vaccine ranked higher than either streptomycin or chlorpromazine (the ranks were 3, 5, and 7 respectively) on a medical experts' list of the 30 most important drugs introduced between 1934 and 1962 (3, pp. 13–14), but the latter two are substantially more important economically. Second, we can give some empirical content to the rather obvious criteria for an economically important innovation, namely that it successfully treats a malady with widespread incidence which leads to high mortality or long disability. Given current earnings and hospital costs, any malady that disables more than, say, 50,000 for more than a year annually, or kills more than 5,000 each year will have an annual dollar cost running into the hundreds of millions.[59] A drug that can materially reduce these magnitudes is bound to generate net benefits far in excess of those we would be able to measure from an empirical demand curve, unless it entailed continual and not merely one-shot mass application of the Salk type. Finally, if the 1962 Drug Amendments delay introduction of any such drug for anything like two years, the cost will be substantial.

59. To put these figures in perspective, about 750,000 succumb annually to the leading cause of death (heart disease) and 30,000 to the tenth leading cause (cirrhosis of the liver). Among common sources of disability, some diseases that cost over 100,000 man-years of productivity annually and are not leading causes of death are psychoses, bone diseases (arthritis, for example) and digestive system disorders (ulcers, appendicitis, etc.). See U.S. Public Health Service (32).

For example, had introduction of the three drugs analyzed here been delayed so long, the current annual equivalent social cost [60] would be over $300 million, a sum sufficient to roughly double the previously estimated cost of the 1962 Amendments.

This last point may be illuminated further by some data on the two leading causes of death—heart disease and cancer. Both are the subject of extensive pharmacological research, but have so far proved resistant to major medical advances. The best that has been accomplished is a slowing or halt to secularly rising death rates.[61] The two diseases alone account for more than half of all deaths, and it is thus hardly surprising that their economic cost is enormous. A recent study estimates their cost for the single year 1962 at over $40 billion (17). Given subsequent inflation, the equivalent today would exceed $50 billion. I have, for this study, made independent estimates (discussed below) of the present value of future costs of these diseases. These employ the conservative estimates of the value of lifetime earnings I have used previously, but the 1970 annual equivalent cost of these illnesses is still $34 billion.

It is, of course, absurd to believe that any pharmaceutical innovation will instantly abolish these diseases, but clearly, any innovation that makes any noticeable inroad will generate substantial benefits, and any material delay in introduction will be extremely costly. The actual costs and benefits must, of course, be conjectural, but some notion of the magnitudes involved should be useful.

To obtain these magnitudes, I first estimate the present expected value of the costs of these diseases if no major therapeutic advance occurs.[62] The estimates assume that, if there is no significant medical advance, the post–1950 trend in the death rate for each disease in each age-sex cohort will be maintained until 1980, after which the death rate will remain constant.[63] The number of deaths expected in each age-sex cohort each year is then computed for the 1970 cohort population, multiplied by the estimated cost per death and discounted to 1970. The cost per death has both a mortality and

60. That is, the annual return on the more than $3 billion capital value loss due to delay.
61. This has occurred since 1950 for both diseases. From 1900–1950, the death rate from cancer was increasing at about 1.5 percent per year and that from heart disease at about .75 percent per year. Since 1950, the heart disease death rate has stopped rising, while the rate of increase for cancer has been halved.
62. I am indebted to Scott Dittrich for assistance with these computations.
63. This procedure produces a virtually constant total death rate for both diseases, which, for cancer, may be somewhat optimistic.

morbidity component. The former is the same discounted value of lifetime earnings for a cohort member which was used in the TB calculations. Morbidity costs consist of current earnings losses and treatment costs for those currently disabled by the disease.[64] The resulting estimates are on line 1 of Table 14, and they show a total expected cost of about $340 billion for both diseases with about two-thirds of the total attributable to heart disease. Next, I suppose that new drugs are discovered which can begin to reduce these costs in 1970. I assume that any hypothetical drug will reduce the mortality rate (and associated mortality and morbidity costs) gradually (linearly) over time and achieve maximum effectiveness in 1980. The savings associated with hypothetical drugs of varying maximum effectiveness are estimated on lines 2 through 5 of Table 14. Thus, a 1970 cancer drug that gradually reduces mortality so that the 1980 rate is 25 percent less than expected saves $19.5 billion (line 3). To put these figures in some context, the $12 billion estimated savings from TB drugs (Table 11) was associated with a tenth year reduction in the mortality rate of about two-thirds from the expected rate. Table 14 indicates that a similarly potent heart disease or cancer drug would produce savings of well over $71 or $39 billion respectively (gross of drug costs).

Finally, we may estimate the costs associated with delaying the introduction of any hypothetical innovation by two years. The relevant estimates are on lines 2'–5' of Table 14, and they are based on the assumption that the streams of annual benefits are all pushed forward two years. These indicate that delay in introducing even a moderately effective innovation will have costs of several billion dollars and upwards of 100,000 lives. Moreover, one can have greater confidence in these delay-cost estimates than in the total savings estimates from which they are derived. No charge is made against the latter for costs of developing the innovation, so they overstate total benefits. By the time an innovation is developed, however, the development costs have already been incurred, and

64. According to a 1965 study, for each cancer and heart disease death, approximately one man-year of earnings was lost due to absence from the labor force of those alive but disabled by the disease (17). Therefore, on the assumption of an unchanged ratio of morbidity to mortality, one year's cohort median income is used as one component of the morbidity cost per death. The same study reports total 1962 expenditures for hospitals, nursing and physician services for each disease (17, pp. 449ff). For each expenditure category, I divide these totals by the number of 1962 deaths and multiply the quotient by the ratio of the 1970 to 1962 price index. The sum of these figures for each disease is an estimate of 1970 disease treatment costs per death. These are $4,897 for heart disease and $6,639 for cancer, and are the second component of morbidity cost per death in each cohort.

# Table 14

## Costs from Heart Disease and Cancer and Potential Benefits from Reduction of their Incidence
### (in millions of dollars)

| Source of Cost or Benefit (Present Values, 1970) | Heart Disease | | Cancer | |
|---|---|---|---|---|
| | | Lives (thousands) | | Lives (thousands) |
| 1. Expected Costs, no innovation | $222,379 | | $118,820 | |
| Expected Savings due to innovations which reduce mortality rate k percent in 1980, k equals: | | | | |
| 2. 10 | 14,237 | 153.0 | 7,799 | 66.5 |
| 3. 25 | 35,694 | 382.6 | 19,498 | 166.3 |
| 4. 50 | 71,188 | 765.2 | 38,996 | 332.6 |
| 5. 75 | 106,782 | 1,147.7 | 58,494 | 499.0 |
| Expected Costs, 2-year delay in introduction of innovations, lines 2–5 | | | | |
| 2'. | 2,478 | | 1,357 | |
| 3'. | 6,193 | | 3,393 | |
| 4'. | 12,388 | | 6,786 | |
| 5'. | 18,580 | | 10,179 | |

Note: See text for sources and description. Innovations on lines 2–5 are assumed to be introduced in 1970, and the indicated reduction in 1980 is assumed to be attained linearly. For example, in the case of the innovations on line 2, it is assumed that the mortality rate reduction in 1970 is 10/11 percent of the expected 1980 mortality rate, in 1971 20/11 percent, etc. The calculations assume an unchanged ratio of mortality to incidence.

the true costs of delay are simply the gross (of R&D amortization) benefits sacrificed by not using the drug. Lines 2′–5′ overstate this only by the direct cost of applying the innovation, and if the TB experience is indicative, such costs are likely to be comparatively minor.

## Summary and Conclusions

The effect of the 1962 Amendments on drug safety and on major drug innovations is peculiarly difficult to ascertain, and it would be misleading to assign single values to the associated costs and benefits. There have been no new-drug disasters in the decade since the Amendments were passed, but the one obvious candidate for that title occurred fully a decade before 1962. There have been no major therapeutic innovations since 1962 either, but this is not unique to the United States and its regulatory environment. The safest conclusion that can be drawn is that the Amendments have so far produced neither significant safety benefits nor have they foreclosed or delayed significant therapeutic advance. Since the relevant costs and benefits are therefore prospective, we are limited to estimating some plausible magnitudes for these when (if) they are realized. I have done this first by assuming that future innovations will repeat the past, not of course in their pharmacology, but in the number of people they will affect. Second, I have tried to put plausible bounds on the potential effect of the Amendments on innovation in two major current research areas.

Although none of the resulting estimates involves an innovation directly affected by the Amendments, a fairly clear pattern emerges which seems distinctly important to any evaluation of their costs and benefits. The 1962 Amendments assume implicitly that it is "worth" sacrificing some potential return from an innovation for reduced risk. Our estimates imply that if any trade would be profitable, it would be toward more risk. One of the three innovations I have examined (Salk vaccine) turns out to have had small net economic benefits, but both of the others have benefits very much larger than those captured by the developers. In the one case (tranquilizers) where drug manufacturers have reaped substantial profits, annual sales at retail—which of course exceed profits—do not come close to exhausting half the measurable benefits. If the prospective failure to reap a substantial part of the benefits delayed even briefly the introduction of these drugs, the benefits thereby foregone could easily have been on the order of several hundred million dollars. It is equally true that, given corporate limited liability and the costs of using the courts, innovators may not bear all the costs of a drug disaster, but in fact, disasters are neither so frequent nor so severe as to begin to offset the gains from major innovations. To put the matter rather baldly in terms of lives, if generally greater risk-taking had hastened the marketing of TB drugs by, say, six months, the number of lives saved directly (excluding the effects of reduced communication of TB and hastier diffusion of the drug) would have been two or three times as great as all those lost to the delayed discovery of the lethal effects of chloramphenicol.[65]

I am unaware of any data that shed light on the question of whether the benefits from greater haste might in fact have been purchased at a cost smaller than a tripled incidence of major drug disasters. If, however, empirical support for the proposition that risk was underproduced prior to 1962 is lacking, the data then available emphatically fail to support the contrary proposition embodied in the Amendments. The Amendments have produced less haste, and even if the future number of major therapeutic advances is unaffected, this change will prove costly. It will, for example, require the prevention of more than one chloramphenicol incident annually to offset the direct cost in lives lost due to a two-year delay of a once-per-decade innovation like the TB drugs. A similar comparison of something like the tranquilizers and chloramphenicol cannot be so direct, since a tradeoff between lives and disability is involved. Nevertheless, the more than fifty-fold difference between the cost of a two-year delay in introducing something like tranquilizers and the total cost of excess chloramphenicol deaths indicates how great either the pessimism about unregulated drug safety or the non-measurable value of life must be for the prospective benefits of the Amendments to offset its costs.

Some of these points may be illustrated by supposing that the United States had failed to escape the thalidomide tragedy in 1961. This strange supposition only gives recognition to the forces shaping the 1962 Amendments. That is, the framers of the Amendments could not have regarded the foreign experience with thalidomide as unique and either unthinkable or unavoidable in the United States. Instead, the Amendments seem to presume that it was the U.S. "near miss" that was unique, and that something similar to the foreign thalidomide experience was bound to occur in the United

65. My estimate for the first year mortality reduction for TB drugs is about 4,300, compared with the six-year total of 753 deaths due to chloramphenicol (Table 9), both on a 1970 population base.

States unless the Amendments were adopted. This presumption—
which implies that it is worth delaying the introduction of all new
drugs to weed out the occasional thalidomides—is difficult to sus-
tain, given the actual data on thalidomide and those on the benefits
of drug innovation.

Thalidomide was marketed first and most extensively in West
Germany and then in most industrialized countries outside North
America. The incidence of the birth malformation induced by the
drug (phocomelia) was on the order of 10 times greater in West
Germany than elsewhere (36, pp. 1515–54; 5). Had the thalidomide
tragedy spread to the United States, it would be reasonable to expect this to have been characterized by the lower incidence. Since,
however, we are dealing with the type of conjectural tragedy that
may have influenced Congress, it may be useful to extrapolate the
unusual West German experience to the United States. The total
West German incidence of phocomelia due to thalidomide was
about 4 per 1,000 live 1961 births. Given the 1961 U.S. live birth
rate and 1970 U.S. population, this would translate into about
19,000 cases (compared to the 4,000 West German and over 7,000
world-wide cases attributable to thalidomide).

It is, of course, peculiarly difficult to compare the cost of phocomelia with, say, that of TB or mental illness. But even if one is
willing to treat phocomelia as the equivalent of death, the cost of
any material delay in marketing only one innovation with the life-
saving potential of something like TB drugs would substantially
outweigh the gains of avoiding a thalidomide tragedy. A more
precise statement than this requires evaluation of the loss from such
a tragedy. If one makes the extreme assumption that phocomelia is
inconsistent with any productivity,[66] then the malady can for these
purposes be equated with death, and the total cost of a thalidomide
tragedy in the United States would be about $150 million. Since
the value of lifetime earnings for infants is much lower than for
most adults, this straightforward application of previous methodology might not be useful here. Another way of looking at something like phocomelia is to ignore completely the utility of the victim's consumption, and then, still assuming zero lifetime
productivity, take the discounted value of the victim's future consumption as the social cost. For 1970 U.S. per capita consumption,
this cost would amount to about $550 million. Neither of these
magnitudes would be the equal of a one-year delay in marketing

66. See (18) which indicates that this assumption is indeed extreme.

something like either the TB drugs or the tranquilizers. At the same time it should be remembered that those innovations do not nearly exhaust the major innovations of the pre–1962 period, and it would be difficult to expect anything like a thalidomide tragedy more than once per decade. It is therefore interesting in this connection that the high estimate of the cost of a hypothetical phocomelia outbreak is roughly equal to the benefit of a three-month speed-up in introduction of the three beneficial innovations previously covered. If one views the former as the likely consequence of any relaxed pre–1962 safety regulation which permits the latter to be attained for all drugs, there was almost surely too little risk-taking before 1962.

At some risk of overgeneralizing the results of this section, we can estimate the cost of delaying introduction of a "typical" major innovation by two years at around one billion dollars, and the benefit of preventing a "typical" drug disaster by two years added testing at under $100 million. Before 1962 the major innovation occurred more frequently than the disaster, and our estimates of the prospective costs of heart disease and cancer indicate that the demand for innovation is far from saturated. These data then indicate that the cost of reduced risk built into the Amendments is extravagant, and if something like a moderately successful heart disease or cancer innovation should come within their ambit, our estimate that the cost of the Amendments is something like a 5 or 10 percent drug excise tax will prove egregiously low.

## VI. The Effect of the 1962 Amendments on the Wealth of Drug Producers

The effects we have so far traced to the 1962 Amendments have conflicting implications for the wealth of drug producers. On the one hand, the cost of innovation has been increased while the demand for it has been reduced. On the other hand, a barrier to new competition for producers of established drugs has been erected, and so the demand for their output is higher than otherwise. The owner of resources highly specialized to producing new or old drugs will be hurt or helped respectively. The typical drug firm, however, owns resources which, at least in the short run, are committed to producing both types of drugs, so the net effect of the Amendments on it is ambiguous.

I will here try to resolve the ambiguity empirically. My procedure will be to compare the fortunes, as recorded in the capital market, of an investor in a representative group of drug producers since the

Amendments with what could be expected in their absence. Unfortunately, for this purpose, the typical drug producer is not restricted to the U.S. prescription drug market, so the effect of the Amendments will inevitably be obscured by wealth changes arising from changes in foreign or non-drug markets. The best that we can do is to distinguish those firms that have a significant fraction of their resources affected by the Amendments in the hope that any strong effect will show up in this subset.

There have, of course, been changes in the domestic drug market apart from the Amendments which have affected the wealth of drug producers, and these too must be accounted for. For example, no one familiar with the stock market will be surprised to learn that drug stocks have outperformed the market since 1962. An investor in the group of drug stocks I will use here would have been about 50 percent wealthier in 1971 than if he had invested an equal amount in other industrial stocks in 1962 and reinvested all subsequent dividends. Since drug stocks also generally outperformed the market prior to 1962, their post–1962 performance alone cannot yield conclusive implications for the effect of the Amendments.

It would be over-ambitious here, or perhaps anywhere, to attempt a detailed explanation for the stock market's continual surprise at the favorable prospects for drug producers. Consequently, I will employ a rather naive model in which, apart from reacting to changes in innovation, the market is presumed to revise its evaluation of drug producers in light of the actual growth in demand for drugs. Since this growth has typically been greater than that for other goods, I am asserting that one source of the superior performance of drug stocks has been persistent prior under-estimation of this growth by the market. Specifically, the model I will work with can be expressed in linear form:

$$(20) \qquad (\dot{w}_{dt} - \dot{w}_{mt}) = a(g_{dt} - g_{mt}) + u_t,$$

where $w$ = rate of change of owner wealth, i.e., capital gains plus dividends divided by initial wealth

$g$ = change in the expected growth in demand for output

$u$ = random variable

$a$ = positive constant, and

the subscripts $d$, $m$ denote the drug industry and the aggregate of all industries (the "market") respectively.

I then assume that $g$ can be expressed

(21) $\qquad g_i = b_i(\dot{D}_i - \dot{D}_i^*) + c_i(n_i - n_i^*),$ $\qquad$ where

$\dot{D}, \dot{D}^* =$ actual and expected rate of change in real output respectively

$n, n^* =$ actual and expected rate of innovation respectively

$b, c =$ constants

$i = d, m,$ and all variables

are contemporaneous. That is, g is zero unless there is unanticipated output growth or innovation. For simplicity, and to conserve degrees of freedom, I assume that $\dot{D}^*$ is a constant for both d and m, that $n_m = n_m^*$, and $b_m = b_d$.[67] Further, I assume that $n_d^*$ is constant within any subperiod. These assumptions permit (20) to be written

(20)' $\quad (\dot{w}_{dt} - \dot{w}_{mt}) = aA + ab(\dot{D}_{dt} - \dot{D}_{mt}) + ac\, n_{dt} + u_t$

$\quad$ where $\quad A = b(\dot{D}_M^* - \dot{D}_D^*) - cn_d^*,$ a

constant in any subperiod.

We expect b to be positive, but are uncertain about the sign of c. Indeed resolution of this uncertainty is the main task of this section, since the sign of c is crucial to determining the effect of the Amendments.

Therefore, the first question I ask is whether c was positive or negative prior to the Amendments. The answer requires an estimate of (20)' on pre–1962 data, and this is shown as E8 in Table 15. Growth of real drug output (including non-prescription items) and growth of real gross national product are used as demand-change proxies, while $n_d$ is measured by the number of NCEs.[68] In view of the small number of drug companies for which wealth data are available (see Note to Table 15), considerable averaging is used to

67. Preliminary empirical work relaxing the last assumption yielded no change in any of the subsequent conclusions.

68. This use of real variables sidesteps the problem of the effect of inflation on owner wealth. However, none of the conclusions that will be drawn would be changed by use of nominal variables. It is sufficient to note here that the superior secular growth of drug industry profits has not been inconsistent with a secular decline in the relative price of drugs. This is especially true for the post-1965 inflation, where the decline in relative price has accelerated and drug industry profit margins have widened relative to all manufacturing industries. Apparently, the relative decline in drug prices has been dominated by superior productivity improvement, part of which is being retained by owners.

## Table 15

### Regression Estimates of Effect of Drug Innovation on Owner Wealth

| Estimate and Period | (1) Constant | (2) Coefficients of $\dot{D}_d - \dot{D}_m$ | (3) n | (4) $R^2$ | (5) S.E. | (6) Mean of Extrapolations to 1962–71 for $(\dot{w}_d - \dot{w}_m)$ Estimated Values | (7) Actual-Estimated |
|---|---|---|---|---|---|---|---|
| E8: 1949–61 | −.1648 .1298 | 2.8331 .9027 | .0034 .0031 | .5307 | .0899 | −.0380 .0167 | .0803 .0256 |
| E9: 1949–61 | −.0270 .0334 | 2.8672 .9106 | | .4741 | .0907 | .0378 .0181 | .0044 .0220 |
| E10: 1962–71 | .1041 .0892 | 1.9338 1.2323 | −.0058 .0040 | .5078 | .0688 | | |
| E11: 1962–71 | −.0163 .0361 | 2.5901 1.2252 | | .3584 | .0734 | | |

Note: Dependent variable is $(\dot{w}_d - \dot{w}_m)$, where $\dot{w}_d$ is the log of simple average of current year's stock price plus dividends divided by last year's stock price for a sample of drug stocks (see below), and $\dot{w}_m$ is the log of current year's value for Standard and Poor's 425 Industrial plus dividends divided by last year's value.

$\dot{D}_d$ is the change in the log of real personal consumption expenditures on drugs.

$\dot{D}_m$ is change in the log of real gross national product.

n is average of current and previous year's NCEs (to center series about year end).

$R^2$ is coefficient of determination, and S.E. is standard error of estimate.

Column (6) is the estimated value of dependent variable for 1962–71 using 1949–61 regression coefficients and 1962–71 actual values of independent variables.

Column (7) is the difference between actual 1962–71 values of dependent variable and those estimated for column (6).

Standard errors are below coefficients and means.

Sources: $\dot{w}_d$: Arnold Bernhard & Co. (4). The drug stocks used in computing $\dot{w}_d$ were (initial year of appearance other than 1949 in parentheses) : Abbott, American Home Products, Eli Lilly (1956), Merck, Parke-Davis (to 1969) Pfizer, Schering (1951), Smith, Kline and French, Upjohn (1960).

$\dot{w}_m$: Standard and Poor's Corp. (23).

$\dot{D}_d$, $D_m$: U.S. Office of Business Economics (30, 31).

n: Paul de Haen, Inc., New York.

reduce the variance of wealth change measures. The wealth changes are measured from annual average market prices and yearly dividends (all assumed paid on June 30). Further, to prevent dominance of $\dot{w}_d$ by one or two unusually successful firms, it is assumed that an investor sells his holdings each year and then reinvests equal amounts in each drug company in the sample; $w_m$ is simply the wealth change for Standard and Poor's 425 Industrial Stock Price Index. The regression, in which the coefficient of the relative demand growth variable is significantly positive, indicates that increased drug innovation was associated with increased wealth for drug owners prior to 1962. The coefficient is, however, insignificant, so we cannot rule out a neutral or even slightly negative effect of innovation on wealth with tolerable risk of error.

It becomes more difficult, though not impossible, to accept the hypothesis that the coefficient of n is positive when pre–1962 estimates of (20)' are used to predict post–1962 wealth changes. If we assume that the coefficient is zero, in which case E9 is appropriate, and it is in fact positive, then extrapolation to the post–1962 period will over-predict wealth changes; we shall fail to account for the decline in wealth due to reduced innovation. However, this extrapolation (columns (6) and (7) of Table 15) yields wealth changes that are almost the same as the actual wealth changes. When the extrapolation is carried out accepting the positive coefficient of n, significant under-prediction of actual wealth changes occurs. Part of this under-prediction is no doubt due to the naive implicit assumption that n* does not decline after 1962. However, E8 is no less inaccurate (nor E9 less accurate) in predicting the immediate post–1962 wealth changes, when that assumption was less naive and most of the capital market's adjustment to the Amendments should have been accomplished.[69] The positive pre–1962 value of c can be made consistent with post–1962 data only by assuming perfect foresight. If the expected flow of NCEs (n*) is reduced by around 25 (the average difference between the pre- and post–1962 value of n) immediately in 1962, the intercept of E8 is increased sufficiently for that equation to essentially duplicate the average post–1962 prediction of E9. Even here, however, the correlation of the latter's predicted values with actual values (.60) exceeds that of E8 (.40). The general impression left by these results is that innovation makes no net contribution to owner wealth, and this is strengthened when E9 is replicated on post–1962 data (E11 in Table 15). Apart

69. For 1962 to 1965, the E8 and E9 extrapolations for column (7), Table 15, are .0758 and .0156, respectively.

from some loss of explanatory power, the pre–1962 results are virtually duplicated. That is, the Amendments have not restricted the ability of owners to share in any growth in drug demand.

One possible explanation for the failure of a positive wealth effect of innovation to be reflected in post–1962 data is provided in E10, which replicates E8 on the later data. Here, the coefficient of n is negative, and, though it is again insignificant, one can only barely reject the hypothesis that it has declined from pre–1962. That is, if a pre–1962 innovation made a net addition to owner wealth, the constraints in the Amendments make for a net reduction today. The added costs of an innovation reduce the positive contribution to the wealth of the innovating firm, so that the losses of competitors dominate in the aggregate. However, the mean of the dependent variable is virtually the same in both sub-periods, and its failure to decline with the coefficient of n might reflect a smaller annual loss to competitors from innovation. Seen in this light, the absence of any overall wealth effect of the Amendments is really the resultant of offsetting effects. The increased cost of each innovation has reduced wealth, but this has been partly offset by reduced innovation and then completely offset by the resulting reduction of competition in markets affected by innovation. This interpretation is generally consistent with some previous findings, namely that increased costs of innovation have not been reflected in either higher new drug prices or larger new drug market shares, and that reduced innovation has tended to inflate prices of existing drugs.

Another aspect of owner welfare which may have been affected by the Amendments is the variability of wealth. A concomitant of reduced innovation is reduced opportunity for one firm to experience unusually large gains or obsolescence losses. We should, therefore, expect to observe a smaller variability in returns among firms at any one time and reduced variability of individual firm returns over time in the aftermath of the Amendments. This expectation is borne out by the data. Wealth data for the whole 1949–71 period are available for five companies. For this group, the cross-company standard deviation of annual wealth changes averages 19.3 percent prior to 1962 and 14.5 percent after 1962, and the difference is about twice its standard error. Similarly, for a group of four other stocks with wealth data covering 1956–69, the inter-company standard deviation of annual returns declines by over 6 percent after 1962. With the smaller sample, however, the decline is not significant. A cursory inspection of the data will

indicate that these differences would have been considerably nar-
rower. without the impact of a few major pre–1962 innovations
(for example, Smith, Kline, and French's success in tranquilizers,
Pfizer's in antibiotics, Searle's in oral contraceptives). The temporal
variability of company returns has also decreased pervasively since
1962. For each of the nine stocks with data spanning that year, I
computed the standard deviation of annual returns, less the "market" return, for the years before and after 1962. In every case, the
post–1962 returns are the more stable, with standard deviations
ranging between 50 and 80 percent of their pre–1962 counterparts.
In spite of the small sample sizes, four of the nine differences in
standard deviation are significant. Thus, the capital market is now
tending to treat different drug companies more uniformly, and the
reduced importance of company-specific events renders each of
their returns more stable over time.

It is typically assumed that investors are risk-averse, so that
they will accept a lower return for reduced variability. It therefore
appears that drug company owners have been made better off by the
Amendments, since they have led to reduced risk without reducing
returns. The continued superior performance of drug stocks, however, must temper this conclusion. If investors indeed value the increased stability of individual drug companies, one would expect
the market to have adjusted its evaluation of them upward soon
after the Amendments, so that subsequent returns were in fact
lower. We have noted previously, however, that there are no such
differences in return among post–1962 sub-periods. It is also difficult to argue that the superior post–1962 performance of drug
stocks simply reflects a slow market adjustment to reduced risk,
since that performance seems fully rationalized by the same reaction to superior growth in drug demand which characterized the
pre–1962 period. The number of risk-seeking investors is apparently sufficiently large (or the opportunities for diversification so
great) that the implications of changed risk for "owner welfare" in
a single company or small group are ambiguous. With this caveat
understood, we can provide some measure of the improved welfare of presumedly risk-averse owners by use of portfolio choice
theory. To do this, I treat the five firms for which we have continuous data as typical of the whole industry. If an investor had
concentrated his assets in the drug industry either prior or subsequent to the Amendments, his returns would have been superior to
the market but he would have sacrificed the gains of portfolio
diversification. The relevant questions here are: (1) Given knowl-

edge of the market return and its variability, how much better off would the drug industry investor have been in light of the increased risk he incurs by not diversifying? (2) Is his gain greater after 1962? To answer these, I use the following expression for the ex-post "efficiency" (E) of the strategy of concentrating one's portfolio in the drug industry:

$$(22) \qquad E = [D - N] - [(M - N) \cdot \frac{S_D}{S_M}],$$

where
D, M, N = rate of return on drug stocks (D), the general market (M), and a risk-free asset (N)
$S_{D,M}$ = standard deviation of D, M, and

M, N, $S_M$ are assumed known at the start of a multi-year investment period. A detailed rationale for (22) may be found elsewhere (for example, 12). However, heuristically, the second term on the right-hand side of (22) represents the return (net of the non-risky return) available to an investor willing to incur the variability of drug stocks if he merely holds an appropriate combination of other stocks and the non-risky asset. The appropriate combination may entail borrowing or selling short the non-risky asset. Thus, if drug stock are twice as variable as the market, and the investor is willing to accept this degree of variability, he can attain a net return of 2 (M–N) on his equity by selling short an equal amount of the non-risky asset and investing the proceeds in a diversified portfolio of stocks. Now, if D–N exceeds 2 (M–N), the investor is clearly better off precisely by this excess if he concentrates his equity in drug stocks; this excess is a bonus which he receives without incurring added variability, and he would not have earned it if the market correctly anticipated drug industry prospects when he made his investment.[70]

70. One might wish to assume that investors do not concentrate on drug stocks, but merely hold them as part of a diversified portfolio. Equation (22) will then be inappropriate, since diversification can reduce some of the risk implied by a high $S_D$. The term $(S_D/S_M)$ can be expressed as (B/r), where B is the "systematic" risk of drug stocks and r is their correlation with the market. The B component is the average change in drug stock returns for each percentage point change in the "market" return, and it is B rather than the total $(S_D/S_M)$ which is of interest to the fully diversified investor.

His diversification eliminates that risk due to the fact that r is less than one. Thus, for fully diversified investors, the discussion would focus on a form of (22) with B substituted for $(S_D/S_M)$. It turns out, however, that r is the same (.63) for both sub-periods, so that the reduction of $S_D$ without loss of

For five drug stocks in the 1948–61 period, there was such a positive bonus; E was evaluated at + 2.3 percent per year.[71] This increased to + 4.3 percent per year in 1962–71, and all of the increase is due to reduced riskiness of drug stocks: $S_D/S_M$ is actually less than unity after 1962. If one attributes all of the 2 percent annual improvement to the Amendments, drug company investors have been made about 20 percent wealthier than efficient investors in comparably risky assets. Converting this to a dollar magnitude presents formidable problems in view of the diversification of drug companies. We proceed, however, on the conservative assumption that the 20 percent bonus would apply to a "pure" domestic prescription drug company.[72] The average 1971 price-earnings ratio for drug stocks for which we have data was 30, and their total 1971 profits were 12 percent of total sales. I assume here that these ratios are applicable to the domestic prescription drug activities of these firms. Since 1971 manufacturer level sales of prescription drugs were about $3.5 billion, this assumption implies that the owner wealth of the prescription drug industry was about $12.5 billion and that the Amendment-induced bonus is about $2 billion. This bonus is equivalent to a perpetuity of $200 million per year at 10 percent. It should be emphasized, however, that this estimate is unreliable unless reduced riskiness of the drug industry is accompanied by commensurate reduced return in the future. The estimate also implies a considerably larger effect on prices of old drugs than that estimated previously, so either that estimate is too small or the bonus includes effects of other unanticipated post–1962 factors, such as the advent of Medicare.

## VI. Conclusions

I will here only reiterate, briefly and with substantial rounding of dollar magnitudes, the estimated costs and benefits of the 1962 Amendments which have been derived at length previously. I then

return has the same favorable implications for the welfare of fully-diversified and specialized drug stockholders.

71. D, M, $S_D$, $S_M$ are computed from the continuously compounded annual wealth changes in the five-drug stock series and Standard and Poor's 425 Industrials. The drug companies used are: Abbott, American Home Products, Merck, Pfizer, Smith, Kline, and French. N is set equal to 2.2 percent, the approximate 1948 yield of a 13-year U.S. Treasury Bond. For 1961–71, N = 3.9 percent, the approximate 1961 yield of a 10-year Treasury Bond.

72. Since there is presumably no bonus on non-prescription drug activities, the bonus would have to exceed 20 percent on the value of prescription drug activities for a diversified company's value to rise 20 percent.

proceed to some conclusions for public policy.

Treated as a group, consumers seem clearly to have lost on balance from the Amendments. Their annual-equivalent gains and losses break down as follows:

1. Foregone benefits (consumer surplus) due to the reduced flow of new drugs: a $300–$400 million loss.

2. Reduced waste on purchases of ineffective new drugs: a gain under $100 million.

3. Higher prices for existing drugs due to reduced competition from new drugs: a loss of $50 million.

These measurable effects sum to a net loss of $250+–$350+ million, or about 6 percent of total drug sales. There are additional gains from the screening, through added testing, of especially unsafe new drugs from the market and losses due to delay in marketing especially beneficial innovations. Since neither type has been marketed since 1962 and their ex-Amendment incidence is difficult to measure, the associated gains and losses must be prospective and conjectural. If an ex-Amendment incidence of one of each type per decade is assumed, the gain is well under $50 million and the loss about $200 million annually. The latter figure is conservative, given the pre–1962 innovation rate and the magnitude of existing major health problems.

Drug producers as a group seem neither to have been helped nor hurt by the Amendments, the gains of reduced competition having been roughly balanced by the added costs of innovation. The Amendments, however, appear to have reduced the variability of the growth of their wealth. If it is assumed that drug company owners are risk-averse, the highly tentative value of the resulting gain is $200 million.

If the Food, Drug and Cosmetics Act was intended to benefit consumers, the inescapable conclusion to which this study points is that the intent is better served by reversion to the status quo ante 1962. This conclusion follows fairly directly from the size of the "problem" with which the 1962 Amendments sought to cope. Consumer losses from purchases of ineffective drugs or hastily-marketed unsafe drugs appear to have been trivial compared to their gains from innovation. In this context, any perceptible deterrent to innovation was bound to impose net losses on consumers and the Amendments seem clearly to have provided such a deterrent. Indeed, the conclusion can be put more strongly. If our estimates of the gains and losses due to exceptionally beneficial and unsafe drugs respectively are at all reasonable, there was already a bias costly to consumers contained in the pre–1962 proof-of-safety requirement of the Act. If relaxation of that requirement would have compressed the new drug development process only slightly, the resulting gains would have left a considerable margin of lives saved and disability avoided to offset substantially increased losses. With the risk-return trade-off already biased against drug consumers in 1962, the Amendments have simply exaggerated the bias.

It is easier to state our conclusion than it is to be sanguine about the prospects for reduced regulation of drug innovation. Since the 1962 Amendments do not appear to have benefited any substantial group and have hurt some, one might question their political viability. The most important group that has been hurt, that is drug consumers, cannot be expected to offer substantial pressure for change. The damage to each member of this vast group can be no more than a few dollars per year, so that members of this group have little incentive to bear the costs of organizing politically. At the same time, reduced regulation of consumer goods quality sharply contradicts the thrust of most organized groups that today most assertively purport to promote the consumer interest. One organized group that might share in the gains of reduced regulation of drug innovation is the American Medical Association, but the AMA has not taken a strong position on the matter since it testified against requiring proof-of-efficacy for drug advertising in the Kefauver hearings. Finally, our results indicate that the producer group that has benefited from the Amendments may be at least as large as that which has been hurt, so coherent support for reduced regulation by producer groups cannot be confidently anticipated.

If, as now seems likely, there will be no substantial reduction of the formal restraints embodied in the Amendments, one must be pessimistic that any substantial reduction in the costs they have generated will be accomplished by purely administrative changes. The FDA is, after all, confronted by the same political forces that militate in favor of legislative inertia. Moreover, the FDA can expect little of the reward for extremely successful innovations, but substantial cost for wrongly certifying an unsafe or ineffective drug. Exhorting the FDA to speed up the NDA process or to substantially reduce its information requirements is, therefore, not likely to be very fruitful. It would also be misleading to seek the source of the inefficiency of drug regulation in the detail of FDA procedures. The important conclusion of this study is that perhaps even before, and certainly after, 1962, too many resources have been devoted to testing of drug safety and efficacy, and, unless at least that part of the law requiring proof-of-efficacy is rescinded, continued resource waste is inevitable. An unlikely change in FDA procedures can only reduce, but never eliminate, the waste that is commanded by the law.

# References

1. *American Druggist.* New York, various issues.

2. American Medical Association Council on Drugs. *AMA Drug Evaluations.* Chicago: American Medical Association, 1971.

3. ———. *Report of the Commission on the Cost of Medical Care,* Volume 3. Chicago: American Medical Association, 1964.

4. Arnold Bernhard and Co. *Value Line Investment Survey.* New York, various issues.

5. Bennett, D. M. J., "Liability of the Manufacturers of Thalidomide to the Affected Children." *Australian Law Journal,* 39 (1965): 256–68.

6. California Department of Health Care Services. *Medi-Cal Formulary.* Sacramento: California Department of Health, 1971.

7. Clymer, H. "The Changing Costs and Risks of Pharmaceutical Innovation," in *The Economics of Drug Innovation,* edited by J. D. Cooper, Washington, D.C.: American University, 1970.

8. Goodman, L., and Gilman, A. *The Pharmacological Basis of Therapeutics.* New York: Macmillan, 1965.

9. Harris, Richard. *The Real Voice.* New York: Macmillan, 1964.

10. Illinois Department of Public Aid. *Drug Manual for Physicians.* Springfield: Illinois Department of Public Works, 1971.

11. Jadlow, J. M. *The Economic Effects of the 1962 Drug Amendments.* Ph.D. dissertation, University of Virginia, 1970.

12. Jensen, M. C. "Risk, the Pricing of Capital Assets, and the Evaluation of Investment Portfolios," *Journal of Business* 42 (1969): 167–247.

13. Jones, D. D., and Follman, J. F., Jr. *Health Insurance and Prescription Drugs.* New York: Health Insurance Association of America, 1971.

14. Mintz, M. *By Prescription Only.* Boston: Houghton Mifflin, 1967.

15. Mishan, E. J. "Evaluation of Life and Limb: A Theoretical Approach." *Journal of Political Economy* 79 (1971): 687–705.

16. Paul de Haen, Inc. *de Haen Nonproprietary Name Index,* Volume 8. New York: Paul de Haen, Inc., 1971.

17. President's Commission on Heart Disease, Cancer and Stroke. *Report to the President*, Volume II. Washington, D.C.: Government Printing Office, 1965.

18. Pringle, M. L. K. and Fiddes, D. O. *The Challenge of Thalidomide.* London: Longman, 1970.

19. R. A. Gosselin, Inc. *National Hospital Audit.* Dedham, Mass.: R. A. Gosselin, Inc., 1971.

20. ———. *National Prescription Audit, Therapeutic Category Report.* Dedham, Mass.: R. A. Gosselin, Inc., various issues.

21. Schnee, J. E. *Research and Technological Change: The Ethical Pharmaceutical Industry.* Ph.D. dissertation, University of Pennsylvania, 1970.

22. Smick, K., Condit, P., Proctor, R., and Sutcher, V. "Fatal Aplastic Anemia, An Epidemiological Study of its Relationship to the Drug Chloramphenicol." *Journal of Chronic Diseases* 17 (1964): 899–914.

23. Standard and Poor's Corp. *Security Price Index Record.* New York, various issues.

24. U.S. Bureau of Labor Statistics. *Employment and Earnings.* Washington, D.C.: Government Printing Office, various issues.

25. ———. *National Survey of Professional, Administrative, Technical and Clerical Pay.* Washington, D.C.: Government Printing Office, various issues.

26. U.S. Bureau of the Census. *Census of Population.* Washington, D.C.: Government Printing Office, various issues.

27. ———. *Current Population Reports.* Series P–60, n. 80. Washington, D.C.: Government Printing Office, 1971.

28. ———. *Historical Statistics of the United States, Colonial Times to 1957.* Washington, D.C.: Government Printing Office, 1960.

29. ———. *Statistical Abstract of the United States.* Washington, D.C.: Government Printing Office, various issues.

30. U.S. Office of Business Economics. *National Income and Product Accounts of the United States, 1929–1965.* Washington, D.C.: Government Printing Office, 1966.

31. ———. *Survey of Current Business.* Various issues.

32. U.S. Public Health Service. *Estimating the Cost of Illness.* Health Economics Series, n. 6. Washington, D.C.: Government Printing Office, 1966.

33. ———. National Office of Vital Statistics. *Vital Statistics of the United States,* v. 1. Washington, D.C.: Government Printing Office, various issues.

34. ———. *Vital Statistics—Special Reports,* v. 37, n. 9. Washington, D.C.: Government Printing Office, 1951.

35. U.S. Senate. Judiciary Committee. *Administered Prices: Drugs.* 87th Congress. Washington, D.C.: Government Printing Office, 1961.

36. U.S. Senate. Select Committee on Small Business. *Competitive Problems in the Drug Industry,* pt. 4. 90th Congress, Washington, D.C.: Government Printing Office, 1968.

37. Weisbrod, Burton A. "Costs and Benefits of Medical Research: A Case Study of Poliomyelitis." *Journal of Political Economy* 79 (1971): 527–44.

38. ———. *Economics of Public Health.* Philadelphia: University of Pennsylvania Press, 1961.

# Comments on The Benefits and Costs of New Drug Regulation
Lester G. Telser

Professor Peltzman's study is a model of economic reasoning applied to a difficult subject. It is a comprehensive, imaginative, and laborious investigation of an important subject deserving of more attention by professional economists than it has so far received. Among the impressive achievements of Peltzman's work is the demonstration of the power of economic theory in predicting the outcome of the new drug regulations. As a result of this work we can reach certain definitive conclusions. First, there is now a two-year delay in the introduction of new drugs. Second, there is a reduction in the number of new drugs. Third, the risk involved in the use of new drugs prior to the new regulations is much exaggerated. Fourth, the losses imposed on the public, as the consequence of these new regulations, far outweigh the gains. It is implicit in Peltzman's results that the drug companies themselves have powerful incentives to exercise care in their introduction of new drugs, even in the absence of federal and state laws. At the outset, therefore, I wish to make it clear that Professor Peltzman's study is deserving of high praise.

It is convenient to divide Peltzman's paper into two parts: the first comprises Sections I to IV and presents estimates of the effects of the new regulations primarily in terms of the demand for drugs. Section V is a lengthy analysis attempting to estimate the loss incurred by the delay in the introduction of new drugs in terms of the lives that could have been saved, and the illness that might have been prevented or rendered less harmful. This Section also attempts to assess the frequency of important new discoveries and of mistakes. I wish to comment on these parts separately and state the points of agreement and the points of disagreement. My comments on the last section of the paper dealing with the effects of the new drug regulations on the market value of the drug companies will be brief. In the course of commenting on Section V, I shall suggest an analytical framework as an alternative to the one used by Peltzman.

In Sections II to IV, Peltzman's analysis proceeds through several stages beginning with the question of whether or not the new drug regulations have reduced the number of new chemical entities (NCEs) on the market since 1962. This problem is studied with a regression analysis designed to predict the number of new chemical entities as a function of three variables: the total num-

I am grateful to Gary Becker, Milton Friedman, Reuben Kessell, and George Stigler for their helpful comments. I assume sole responsibility for all errors.

ber of prescriptions, expenditures on physicians' services, and the total number of chemical entities. The need for this type of sophisticated treatment is made evident by the obvious fact that the number of NCEs has in fact gone down since 1962, and one must ascertain whether this might not have been the result of factors other than the introduction of the new drug regulations. Thus the regression analysis relates the number of NCEs to certain pertinent variables in order to predict what would have been observed in the period following 1962 had there been no new regulations. These results establish beyond reasonable doubt that the reduction in the number of new NCEs cannot be attributed to changes in the levels of the variables that normally operate. Neither the change in the size of the market nor changes in the expenditures on physicians' services can explain the reduction in the number of NCEs since 1962.

Peltzman goes on to provide a theoretical analysis of how to measure the gain or loss in consumer surplus resulting from the new regulations. This analysis employs the demand for drugs. The number of prescriptions is the measure of quantity, and the price per prescription is the measure of price. Most economists would accept this as a logically correct analysis. The chief problem is an empirical one. How can one estimate the demand for NCEs? As the empirical counterpart to the theoretical relation, Peltzman proposes the equation as follows:

$$(1) \qquad q_{nt}/Q_{Tt} = a + b\,(P_{nt}/P_{ot}) + c\,A_t + \text{random residual,}$$

where

$q_n$ = number of prescriptions for new drugs by therapeutic category,

$p_n$ = price per prescription of the NCEs in therapeutic category n,

$p_o$ = price of all other drugs in the therapeutic category,

$Q$ = total number of prescriptions in the therapeutic category,

$A$ = dummy variable which is zero before the amendment and one afterwards.

We should note that equation (1) is no ordinary demand relation. Its unit of observation is a therapeutic category, 58 in all, 31 in 1960–62, and 27 in 1964–69. You will forgive me if I reveal some ignorance about the practice of medicine, but let us suppose we have two therapeutic categories, one consisting of drugs for the treatment of diarrhea, and the other of drugs for treatment of emphysema. The equation postulates that if the NCEs in these two therapeutic categories decrease in price by the same amount, then the market share in these categories would both rise by the same amount. This is to say that NCEs used for treating diarrhea, which fall in price relative to the old chemical entities in this category, rise in share by just as much as NCEs used for treating emphysema. This is a strong assumption to make and it requires some empirical support. It is certainly not obvious to me as a layman that this is true. It may be that NCEs in one therapeutic category are better substitutes for the old drugs than are the NCEs in another. One could test this hypothesis by estimating the demand relation with time series data for a given therapeutic category and see whether the slopes are the same across therapeutic categories. That is, instead of pooling all of the therapeutic categories into one regression, one could estimate separate demand relations for each therapeutic category over time. In this way one could test whether the hypothesis implicit in Peltzman's specification of equation (1) is consistent with the evidence.

This is an important point because the estimate of the slope b is a crucial parameter in the measure of the consumer surplus that is lost as a result of the Amendment. Using the data in Table 2, I estimate the elasticities with respect to changes in the sample means from 1956–57 to 1960–62. With the latter period as the base, my estimate of the elasticity is — 7.37 and with the former period as the base my estimated elasticity is — 5.79. These are arc elasticities. The mean is — 6.58. Thus a 1 percent rise in the relative price of NCEs results in a 6.6 percent decrease in the market share of NCEs. This estimate corresponds to the one based on the regression equation, E4. These estimates have an interesting implication for the market shares of NCEs in the period 1964–69. Table 2 shows that, in fact, the price of NCEs relative to the prices of other drugs in the category is lower. Thus the ratio is 1.263 in 1960–62 and it is 1.165 in 1964–69. If I apply my estimate of the arc elasticity to the 1964–69 figures, I can estimate the market share of NCEs treating prices as given. The results are startling. Since there is a sizeable reduction in the relative price of NCEs, in 1964–69 the market share of the NCEs would have been between .168 and .159. In fact it was .064. On the basis of these estimates, therefore, one may conclude that there has been a 62 percent reduction in the market share of NCEs, presumably as a result of the Amendment! Peltzman's estimate of the slope is —.1871. My estimate of the slope is —.625. The use of my estimate would cut the estimated loss of consumer surplus by 30 percent. This gives a rock bottom estimate of the loss, and one that is consistent with Peltzman's E4. Clearly, the annual loss from the Amendment remains a large figure. Nor is this all. My estimate of the reduction in quantity, based on the time series work commented on above, is larger than Peltzman's, and it has the virtue of taking the price change into account, albeit crudely.

In my opinion the most ingenious empirical analysis is contained in the subsection "Expert Drug Evaluations." These data show that boards of experts are far more conservative than private practitioners, yet, the data indicate that the market share of NCEs chosen by the experts eventually attains the same level as the private practitioners' shares. It would be useful for Peltzman to supply us with some calculations, using his analytical apparatus, giving his estimates of the cost to society of the delays in the acceptance of NCEs by the committees of experts who devise the formularies for hospitals and for state and federal agencies.

In concluding my comments on the first four sections of this paper, I wish to record my objections to the material giving the estimates of the effects on prescription drug prices. First, the price of NCEs in a given therapeutic category exceeds the prices of the other drugs in the same category. Second, we know that the share of the NCEs by category is lower since the Amendment. Third, prices of NCEs tend to decrease over time. Hence the reduction in the market share of NCEs resulting from the Amendment in conjunction with these facts would tend to retard the decline in the average price of all chemical entities by therapeutic category. This evidence would seem, therefore, to be an arithmetic consequence of the preceding results.

The first four sections of the paper constitute a powerful set of results on the effects of the new drug regulation. The estimated losses given there are sufficient to show the magnitude of the effects. At this point Peltzman could rest his case and be confident of the jury's verdict. However, he proceeds in Section V to more conjectural terrain wherein he furnishes dollar estimates of the costs of illness and the deaths that may result. Even so, he could merely state the number of lives that would be lost if there is a delay in the introduction of a new drug and forego the attempt to place a dollar value on the loss. I would not object to this procedure, but I do wish to record my objections to the dollar estimates given in Section V. In any case, Peltzman's method assumes all lives are of equal economic value. Moreover, Peltzman's footnote 48 suggests to me that he may share some of my misgivings.

Peltzman does not give an explicit defense for the measures he uses to estimate the economic cost of death. One may divide the problem into two parts, the cost to society, excluding the victim, and the cost to the victim. One may attempt to estimate the cost to society of someone's death by calculating the present value of labor earnings. Obviously, this method does not apply to those with no prospect of future employment such as the aged. It is even difficult to apply this approach to male children, although the bold may attribute the average income of the pertinent part of the population to such males. In any case, the present value of future income does not represent the cost to society, excluding the victim, of the death of a given individual. Presumably, individuals consume as well as contribute to real output. To a first approximation there is no economic loss from death. Put differently, the only way in which society obtains an economic gain from the employment of an individual is if that individual makes a voluntary gift to society of some portion of his income. Hence this approach to measuring the economic value of saving a human life leads to absurd results.

The main loss is to the victim, his family, and his friends. This leads one to furnish a different defense for Peltzman's measure of the economic value of human life which draws an analogy between kidnapping and illness. Suppose a person is held for ransom by a bandit. The bandit offers the choice of life or death. The victim may live provided he pays the bandit a sufficiently large ransom. What is the maximum ransom the victim is willing to pay the bandit? In answering this question one is not constrained by the present value of the victim's labor earnings. Nor does one attach a zero value to an elderly person, an infant, a wife, or others not gainfully employed in the labor force. Indeed, the relation between the maximum ransom and the present value of the labor earnings of the interested parties is tenuous. Yet it is the maximum ransom that represents the value to the individual of his life and furnishes the theoretically correct concept that one may strive to estimate.

These lines of argument are distasteful to me and, I suppose, to others. Yet they seem to underlie the measures of the benefits of new drugs that Peltzman uses in Section V of his paper.

To deal with the questions posed in Section V there is another approach that is free of many of the riddles involved in measuring the value of human life or health. This approach concentrates on the cost of providing for health care. I favor that measure of the gains from new treatments which equals the savings in the cost of the resources that are allocated to the maintenance of a given level of health. This measure has several advantages. It avoids altogether the emphasis on earning capacity. All human beings are treated alike. It concerns itself only with the costs of the various treatments. The main complication arises in estimating the gains from the introduction of a wholly new treatment of a disease for which no treatment was previously available.

A simple model can illustrate the proposed measure of the gains from the introduction of a new drug. Consider the sub-population stricken with a certain illness. Let H denote recovery and — H nonrecovery. Let D denote treatment with the new drug and — D nontreatment. There are four possible states: first, (D, H) is the state of being treated with the new drug and recovering; second, (D, — H) represents treatment and a complication; third, (— D, H) represents nontreatment with the new drug and recovery nevertheless; and fourth, (—D, —H) represents nonuse of the drug and nonrecovery. Let p(X, Y) denote the proportion of the relevant sub-population in the state (X, Y). Table 1 gives the proportions for the various states.

|  | **H** | **— H** |
|---|---|---|
| **D** | p(D, H) | p(D, — H) |
| **— D** | p(— D, H) | p(— D, — H) |

**Table 1**

The sum of these over the four states is one. Each proportion may be interpreted as giving the probability of that state. In addition, it is convenient to define the proportion of the users, p(D), and the nonusers, p(— D) of the drug as follows:

$$p(D) = p(D, H) + p(D, — H)$$
$$p(— D) = p(— D, H) + p(— D, — H).$$

The probabilities measure only one aspect of the problem. In addition there are the costs to consider. Let c(X, Y) denote the cost of an individual being in state (X, Y). For instance, c(D, H) represents the cost of treating the illness with the drug for those who recover their health. The costs include hospital care, physicians' services, special therapeutic equipment and the other items representing the direct costs for the given state. Corresponding to Table 1 we have Table 2 to represent the various costs as follows:

| Table 2 | | |
|---|---|---|
| | **H** | **−H** |
| **D** | $c(D, H)$ | $c(D, -H)$ |
| **−D** | $c(-D, H)$ | $c(-D, -H)$ |

The expected cost of the illness to society is given by the expression as follows:

$$(2) \qquad C = c(D, H)\, p(D, H) + c(D, -H)p(D, -H)$$
$$+ c(-D, H)p(-D, H) + c(-D, -H)p(-D, -H)$$

This expression assumes that even after the new drug is available, there may be some with the illness who are not treated with the drug. To find the cost of the illness if it is not treated with D, we use the conditional probabilities $p(H/-D) = p(H, D)/p(-D)$ and $p(-H/-D) = p(H, -D)/p(-D)$. We obtain

$$(3) \qquad C(-D) = c(H, -D)\, p(H/-D) + c(-H, -D)$$
$$p(-H/-D).$$

Similarly, for the cost conditional on treatment we have

$$(4) \qquad C(D) = c(H, D)\, p\,(H/D) + c(-H, D)\, p(-H/D).$$

The gain from the use of the new treatment is, therefore,

$$(5) \qquad C(-D) - C(D).$$

We may also write the total cost C as follows:

$$(6) \qquad C = C(-D)\, p(-D) + C(D)\, p(D).$$

When there is a positive gain from the use of the new drug, a transition from nonuse, $p(-D) = 1$, to a state where everyone uses the new drug, $p(-D) = 0$, would lower the total cost to $C(D)$.

Peltzman gives persuasive evidence to show that $P(D)$ is lower and rises less rapidly as a result of the new drug regulations. Hence the gain to society of the new treatment is lower and accrues less rapidly.

The expected cost to society of an individual with the illness given by (6) or (2) has an empirical counterpart under certain favorable conditions. It is proportional to the actuarial cost of the illness to an insurance company which insures a random sample of the population. The factor of proportionality is the fraction of the population with the illness. Indeed, apart from loading costs, this measure suggests that the deflated cost of health insurance premiums may furnish a tolerable first approximation to the cost of illness.

There are at least two serious difficulties with the proposed measure of the gain from a new treatment as shown by (6). First, it begs the question of the relevant measure of quantity. Should we count the cost for a given number of recovered, a given number ill, or a given number treated? It is often reasonable to calculate the cost of treating a given number of cases of the illness. In fact, this is virtually the implicit quantity measure involved in (6), since the population under consideration is the number with the illness. The second question is more difficult. How should one measure the cost when there was previously no treatment for an illness? One may imagine illnesses where one can only comfort the victim as much as possible because there is no real treatment. Indeed, for some illnesses death is the inevitable result. Should death come quickly, then my measure of the cost before treatment may well be small. Let a new and costly treatment appear with some chance of recovery, and my measure will then show regress and not progress, if it looks to the number with the illness as the base. One may say that incurable diseases have an infinite cost of treatment for the purpose of bringing about recovery, hence the appearance of a treatment with some chance of recovery yields an infinite gain.

In recognition of this phenomenon one is tempted to suggest as the appropriate measure of quantity a given number of people in a certain state of health. One then seeks to measure the cost of maintaining this number in the prescribed state of health. The problem is that the cost may well be infinite. For example, take a population of 1,000 business executives with no current symptoms of heart disease. Is it sensible to ask what is the cost of maintaining them in the same state for one year? That is, is there any finite expenditure that can assure their remaining without heart disease over a period of one year?

We must admit that there are more serious obstacles in measuring the gains from innovation in the field of health than for most other commodities such as food or entertainment. Thus, one can calculate the cost of supplying certain well-defined quantities of food at different points in time so as to measure the changes in the cost of production. Similarly, we could measure the cost of supplying given quantities of various *medical services* at different points in time, but it is far more difficult to calculate the cost of providing given quantities of *health* at different points in time.

The source of the problem lies in our lack of control over all of the factors that govern a person's state of health. Let us reconsider the example of the business executives. Instead of asking how much it would cost to maintain all of them in a prescribed state of health, we might estimate the costs of maintaining this number in such a state that at most a certain percentage can be expected to develop symptoms of heart disease. As the percentage decreases, that is, as the proportion in the given state of health rises, the cost of supplying this amount of health services rises. The cost rises without bound only if the proportion to remain without heart disease exceeds a certain level.

Some of these issues become clearer with the aid of a few diagrams. In Figure 1 the quantity of "health" is measured along the horizontal axis and the price per unit of "health" is measured along the vertical axis. The demand for health services is represented by the negatively sloped schedule, DD, while the supply of health services is given by the positively sloped schedule SS. The equilibrium quantity of health is 0Q. Let a new treatment appear that lowers the cost of supplying a given quantity of health services. The new supply schedule is S'S'. I measure the gain by the reduction in the price per unit of health services times the initial quantity 0Q. The complication arises in the situation illustrated by Figure 2. Initially, there is no supply of the given type of health services. The equilibrium quantity is zero. Let a new treatment appear, so that the supply schedule is S'S'. In this situation it is unreasonable to describe the gain as the drop in price at the zero quantity since we have no way of reckoning this.

One may say that the situations illustrated by these figures show a close affinity between the measures I propose and those that Peltzman uses. Thus in Figure 1 the gain in consumer surplus holding quantity constant is the same as the reduction in the cost. Very well, this means that the correct measure for the gain in consumer surplus is the reduction in the cost. Note carefully that this has nothing to do with measuring the value of the lives saved. Indeed,

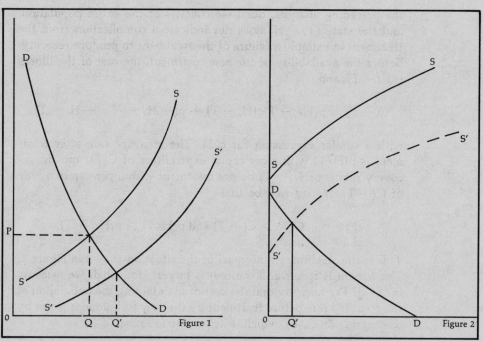

Figure 1

Figure 2

the area under the demand schedule for health has nothing in principle to do with attaching a money value to a human life.

It is helpful to demonstrate the nature of the difficulty with the aid of the algebraic framework described above. To avoid ambiguities I wish to furnish a somewhat different interpretation of the situation. Suppose we have a treatment T that can result in recovery under favorable conditions. The absence of treatment is denoted by $-$ T. The probabilities of the state (X, Y) are given in Table 3 as follows:

| Table 3 | | | |
|---|---|---|---|
| | **H** | **$-$ H** | |
| **T** | $p(T, H)$ | $p(T, - H)$ | $p(T)$ |
| **$-$ T** | $p(- T, H)$ | $p(- T, - H)$ | $p(- T)$ |

Before the availability of the new treatment, the proportion of the population succumbing to the illness is $p(- H/ - T)$ and the proportion that is well is $p(H/ - T)$. After the new treatment is available, the proportion that remains well is $p(H/T)$ and the proportion that succumbs despite the treatment is $p(- H/T)$. Thus, in contrast to the preceding analysis, our base consists of the entire population, and the state $(T, -H)$ does not indicate a complication from the treatment but simply a failure of the treatment to produce recovery. Before the availability of the new treatment, the cost of the illness is $C(-T)$, and

$$C(-T) = p(H/-T)c(H, -T) + p(-H/-T)c(-H, -T),$$

with a similar expression for $c(T)$. The recovery rate after treatment is $p(H/T)$ with a per capita expenditure of $C(T)$, and the recovery rate is $p(H/-T)$ before treatment with a per capita outlay of $C(-T)$. It may well be that

$$(7) \qquad C(T) > C(-T) \text{ and } p(H/T) > p(H/-T).$$

This is the algebraic counterpart of the situation shown in Figure 2. The benefit is larger and the cost is larger. How shall we measure the gain? We may say that the cost of maintaining the population at the recovery rate before treatment by the new technique is given by the expression $C_a(T)$, which is defined as follows:

$$(8) \qquad C_a(T) = p(H/-T)c(H, T) + p(-H/-T)c(-H, T).$$

Economists will recognize this expression as the numerator of a Laspeyre index. It calculates the cost of the base period bundle of goods, that is, the level of health available before the new treatment, at the post-treatment costs. Using this cost we would measure the gain (or loss) by the difference $C(-T) - C_a(T)$. Hence if $c(H, T) = c(H, -T) = 0$, so that only the ill incur the costs, then the estimated gain becomes

$$(8) \qquad C(-T) - C_a(T) = p(-H/-T)[c(-H, -T) - c(-H, T)].$$

This is positive only if the new treatment is cheaper than the old.

Economists are resourceful and they can measure the cost in another way. The alternative, the Paasche index, calculates the cost of providing the post-treatment level of health at the pre-treatment costs. Let

$$(9) \qquad C_b(T) = p(H/T)c(H, -T) + p(-H/T)c(-H, -T).$$

With this estimate of cost the gain is $C(-T) - C_b(T)$. If $c(H, T) = c(H, -T) = 0$, then the estimated gain is

$$(10) \qquad C(-T) - C_b(T) = c(-H, -T) \; [p(-H/-T) \\ - p(-H/T)].$$

If the new treatment is more effective then $p(-H/-T) > p(-H/T)$, so the estimated gain using (10) is always positive. Thus, the estimated gain with (8) focuses on the change in the costs, and the one using (10) emphasizes the difference in the recovery rate.

By this line of argument, the new treatment receiving the highest marks is the one with a higher chance of success that is also cheaper than the old treatment. The ambiguous case is the more expensive new treatment with a higher chance of success. One can have a cheaper new treatment with a lower recovery rate. Rational men would never choose a more expensive new treatment with a lower success rate than the old treatment. Therefore, both measures of gain can be positive or only one of them can be positive. We should never encounter a situation where the gain is negative with both measures.

These suggestions for measuring the gains for new treatments seem worth pursuing. They bring out different aspects of the problem. I am not competent to discuss the feasibility of gathering the data that would be required to construct these estimates, but the figures on morbidity and survival rates in Section V of Peltzman's paper imply that it may be possible to do so.

At the end of his article, Peltzman analyzes the effects of the new drug regulations on the market valuations of drug company equity shares. It is surprising to see the smallness of the effect of the variable labeled the rate of drug innovation. I have found in my studies of the relation between the market value of companies and their research and development outlays that the latter exert a significant positive influence on the former. This is because R&D outlays represent a component of a firm's capital reflected in the market value of its stock. Therefore, a variable better designed to represent the development costs of new drugs can be expected to furnish a clearer picture of how the new drug regulations affect the market value of the drug companies.

# Part III:
# Alternative Systems
# of New Drug Regulation

## The British System of Drug Regulation
Sir Derrick Dunlop


## Comments
Reuben Kessel


## Toward Better Systems
## of Drug Regulation
Hubert Bloch


## Comments
Louis Lasagna

# The British System of Drug Regulation
Sir Derrick Dunlop

Different countries exhibit great diversity in their control of the manufacture and use of medicines, and their many regulations prevent the free movement of medicines from one country to another. Such discrepancies are not surprising when the rapidly changing conditions and the varying circumstances in which legislation has had to be enacted in different parts of the world are considered. Nevertheless, these variations greatly complicate the production and marketing policies of international pharmaceutical companies attempting to comply with the diverse regulations that exist. It may be that in the course of time some common broad legislative measures will be evolved to control the marketing and sale of pharmaceutical products. In Europe this may be facilitated by the expansion of the European Economic Community.

Modern medicines are such formidable weapons that there is a general consensus that the sole responsibility for their production and use can no longer be left entirely to the manufacturer and prescriber. On the other hand, it is difficult to know how far government should assume responsibility for their production and prescription without unduly interfering with the advance of scientific therapeutics, the well-being of the pharmaceutical industry, and the cherished freedom of the physician, dentist, or veterinary surgeon to prescribe as he thinks best. Inadequate legislation can threaten public safety, but excessive regulation can also be prejudicial.

## Early Control of Medicines in the United Kingdom

Although the Food and Drug Administration in the United States is the premier drug control organization in the world and since the beginning of this century has done so much to protect the public—and not only the public of the United States—attempts to control drugs have gone on in the United Kingdom for hundreds of years. The earliest efforts were the herbals consisting of descriptions of poppies and mandragora, mercury and antimony, the eyes of newts and toes of frogs, which were intended to help physicians to recognize and use these agents. Though his head might be cut off if the results of their administration were dire, the physician of those times could not be summoned under the provisions of any act. Then came the London and Edinburgh Pharmacopoeias—essentially herbals themselves but given due authority by their respective Royal Colleges. The Gin Acts of the eighteenth century first recognized the need to protect the public and pioneered efforts to overcome the abuse of drugs. The first *British Pharmacopoeia*, published in 1864, and subsequent editions produced standards for quality control which have enjoyed international prestige although, until recently, the machinery for the enforcement of these standards has been inadequate. Since then, governments in the United Kingdom have been active in establishing standards for the purity and strength of medicines and in preventing their adulteration, abuse, and misdirection.

The Dangerous Drugs Acts recognized the danger of drug addiction and controlled the manufacture of certain drugs by license, together with a strict recording of their sale and supply. In consequence, the incidence of addiction to potent narcotics in Britain was so rare as to be a matter of almost incredulous envy in other parts of the world. It must be confessed, however, that during the last 12 years the United Kingdom has shared to some extent in the recent international epidemic of drug abuse.

The Cancer and Venereal Diseases Acts prevented the deception of the public by advertisements of quack nostrums for the treatment of serious disorders. Various Pharmacy and Poisons Acts elaborated control over the sale and supply of certain patent medicines, and the Therapeutic Substances Acts controlled agents such as vaccines, sera, and hormones, the purity and potency of which could not be established by chemical means.

This mass of legislation, involving control over the quality of medicines, their prescription, sale, and supply, their promotion and manufacture under license, was achieved within the context of a bewildering number of statutes in need of consolidation. Further, the multiplicity of organizations with varying degrees of authority —some reporting to the Home Office, others to the Ministry of Health or Agriculture, the Board of Trade, the Privy Council, and so forth—made British legislation on medicines complex, chaotic, and cumbersome.

# The Safety of Drugs Committee

Although the formidable nature of modern therapeutic agents had been recognized for years, there had been a curious complacency about them and no statute in the United Kingdom required the pre-marketing approval of medicines on the grounds of their safety: anyone could market any product no matter how dangerous or inadequately tested—apart from those products listed under the Therapeutic Substances Acts—without seeking official approval. It took the emotional reaction to the thalidomide tragedy to stimulate action. As a result, in 1963, the Minister of Health established the Safety of Drugs Committee as a temporary expedient until the more recent comprehensive legislation on medicines could be enacted. It was a purely voluntary arrangement, official only in the sense that its members were appointed by the Health Ministers who also provided its finance, accommodation, and secretariat. In spite of the complete absence of legal sanctions (there were, it is true, some unofficial ones) the Association of the British Pharmaceutical Industry and the Proprietary Association of Great Britain promised that none of their members would (a) put a new medicine to clinical trial or (b) market a new medicine without the Committee's approval—a promise loyally observed.

The Committee consisted of a small group of voluntary, unpaid experts—scientists, physicians, and pharmacists—whose assignment did not include the cost or comparative efficacy of medicines. Although the safety and efficacy of medicines are often inextricably entwined, efficacy *per se* was not the function of the Committee. Its object was to ensure as far as possible the safety of medicines for the purpose for which they were to be used rather than to act as an arbiter of therapy.

To undertake its function the Committee developed three subcommittees to advise them in their decisions: the first to scrutinize the adequacy of the pharmacodynamic studies undertaken before clinical trial was permitted; the second to scrutinize the adequacy of the clinical trials before marketing was approved; and the third to monitor adverse reactions to drugs after marketing, and to feed this information back to the profession.

A committee with freedom of action, relatively untrammelled by legal niceties, can often conduct business more easily and expeditiously than official organizations since there is a minimum of paperwork and it can make its own case law according to circumstances. Thus, much of the Committee's contact with the applicants —the requests for clarification and amplification—took place in robust but usually good-humored encounters over the telephone or in informal meetings rather than in official communications duplicated for the record.

It seldom took more than four months after an application had been filed for a completely new medicine to be passed for clinical trial or marketing, and new formulations of standard remedies were usually dealt with in a few weeks. The rejections of medicines for clinical trial or marketing were relatively few and constituted a comparatively minor part of the Committee's function: more important was the persuasion of manufacturers to alter their intentions, to modify their promotional claims, and to issue warnings to doctors when the register of adverse reactions suggested that a medicine was developing undue or unexpected toxic effects. In addition, the mere existence of the Committee may have tightened up standards.

As far as possible, the Committee attempted to solve its problems by voluntary compliance and mutual agreement which worked fairly well. Manufacturers seemed to appreciate this informal, elastic approach which paved the way for the present statutory controls. It might, therefore, be asked why government sought to effect through legislation what was being accomplished reasonably satisfactorily through the Committee's voluntary arrangements with the pharmaceutical industry. There were, however, many reasons for the new legislation which encompasses far more than the limited functions of the Committee. Probably the least important of these reasons was to give the Committee legal power, the lack of which had not proved a serious embarrassment. There was, however, a great need to consolidate and simplify the somewhat chaotic legislation on medicines which had developed in the United Kingdom over the last hundred years; to provide an inspecting and licensing system to ensure better conditions for the manufacture, storage, and distribution of medicines; to establish an effective machinery to enforce the quality control of preparations purporting to comply with British Pharmacopoeial specifications; to ensure better standards for advertisements and promotion; and to control veterinary products in the same way as human medicines.

## The Medicines Act

The Medicines Act was passed through Parliament in 1968, but it only became operative toward the end of 1971. The Licensing Authority (the Ministers of Health and Agriculture who are responsible to Parliament) is advised by the renamed Safety of Medicines Committee which has now become statutory with legal powers but has virtually the same functions as the previous Safety of Drugs Committee and a very similar membership. It is hoped, therefore, that it will continue to maintain the flexibility and exercise of professional responsibility which the experience of the unofficial Committee had shown to be desirable. A similar committee on Veterinary Products advises the Licensing Authority on veterinary medicines and medicated animal feeding stuffs.

The Act also established a Medicines Commission to advise Ministers on the broad aspects of policy regarding medicines, and to direct the preparation of the British Pharmacopoeia. It is also required to advise Ministers on the numbers, functions, and personnel of the expert committees giving advice to the Licensing Authority. Once established, however, such committees are not subject to the Commission's control, for the latter will act as an Appeal Tribunal should an applicant for a license wish to appeal against an adverse decision of the Authority given on the advice of one of the Safety Committees. The 14 members of the Commission are scientists, physicians, pharmacists, veterinarians, and representatives of the pharmaceutical industry, serving in a part-time, virtually honorary capacity, and appointed by the Ministers after consultation with interested organizations.

The Act involves the licensing of manufacturers, wholesalers, and persons responsible for the composition of medicines—or their importers. Licenses of Right refer to products which are already on the market prior to the commencement of the licensing system and do not as yet require appraisal for safety and quality. The second stage of the Act, to be implemented in the future, will involve a review of these Licenses of Right, a probable control of medical and veterinary devices, and the possible initiation by the Commission of compendia and publications, other than the British Pharmacopoeia, to give sound information on medicines to the professions.

The Act provides that all medicines must be sold from pharmacies except for simple, relatively innocuous home remedies which appear on a General Sales List drawn up by the Commission. Another list enumerates those medicines obtainable by "prescription only." When new medicines are licensed, the Safety Committees will specify to which classification they belong.

Finally, the Act requires that any promotional literature must be consistent with a data sheet which is approved by the Safety Committees and must accompany the product license. This sheet sets out concisely the essential facts about the medicine in a standardized way—its generic and brand names, its dosage, method of administration, indications and contraindications.

## Main Differences in the U.K. and U.S. Control Systems

It is perhaps inappropriate to contrast control systems in a vast country like the United States with those of a small one like the United Kingdom which has a more homogeneous population. Controls are easier in the United Kingdom because many of the leading physicians, pharmacists, veterinarians, and pharmaceutical industrialists are familiar with each other and often on friendly terms. Further, the political atmosphere and competitive commercial pressures are perhaps less fierce than in the United States.

**The licensing authorities.** The main difference between the two systems is that ultimate power to license medicines in the United Kingdom rests with the Licensing Authority (the Ministers responsible to Parliament) acting on the professional advice of the Safety Committees. The decisions of these committees are taken by professional men whose careers in no way depend on their membership of the committees on which they serve part-time in a virtually honorary capacity as an altruistic chore. They are assisted, of course, by a small staff of expert professional civil servants who do most of the preparatory work, but the decisions are taken by the committees. It is probable that the experience gained from the eight-years' informal Safety of Drugs Committee will tincture their subsequent official actions.

In the United States, on the other hand, ultimate power rests with the full-time professional civil servants of the FDA whose careers depend on the correctness of their decisions, and who are subject to formidable grillings by Congressional Committees. The FDA has to work under fairly rigid rules imposed by Congress which seem to rely more on animal experiments than is usual in the United Kingdom.

**Appeals.** There is no appeal against the decisions of the FDA save by recourse to a civil action in the courts. In the United Kingdom an applicant for a license can appeal against an adverse decision of the Licensing Authority, taken on the advice of one of the Safety Committees to the Medicines Commission on which the pharmaceutical industry is represented.

**Procrastination in licensing.** In the United States it usually takes much longer than in the United Kingdom for a new medicine to be licensed, and great expense is involved. This delay or procrastination saved the United States from the consequences of the thalidomide disaster, and it may be that the protracted checks result in the greater safety of medicines in the United States than in the United Kingdom, though there is no definite proof of this. It is often insufficiently appreciated, however, that excessive delay in clearing a valuable new remedy for the market may have results as unfortunate as those arising from the clearance of one that is undesirably toxic.

Certainly, the increasingly stringent regulations imposed by the FDA have resulted in a great decrease in the number of new medicines being introduced in the United States; and a few preparations considered valuable in the United Kingdom are also not available. Manufacturers are becoming increasingly reluctant to introduce medicines having only marginal advantages over those already available—medicines often disparagingly called "me too" drugs. This is often of great advantage since the number of almost identical medicines on the market has become embarrassing to the medical profession. On the other hand, this molecular roulette must not be disparaged unduly for it often results eventually in great improvements on the original preparations. Who, for example, would now use sulphanilamide or sulphapyridine rather than one of the modern sulphonamides?

**Advertisement and promotion.** During the last 12 years the control exercised by the FDA on the advertisement of medicines has resulted in far greater accuracy and truth in their promotion. In comparison, the promotion of medicines in the United Kingdom has often been subject to justifiable criticism. This will now be remedied to some extent by the data sheets that must accompany product licenses, and to which all subsequent promotion must adhere. Such sheets will be more concise than the package inserts insisted on by the FDA, which some consider to be excessively detailed.

**Efficacy.** Neither of the control systems allows comparative efficacy to be taken into account in the licensing of medicines, though their classification by the FDA into "effective," "probably effective," "possibly effective," and "ineffective" comes very close to doing so.

In the United Kingdom the primary concern of the Authority has been to ensure the safety and quality of the medicines it licenses for the profession's use, and it is felt that opinion on efficacy *per se* should be left to the free processes of scientific publication, debate, and undergraduate and postgraduate education. The Licensing Authority does not deny a minority the right to use any medicine it desires provided it is reasonably safe for its intended purpose. Herbal and homeopathic remedies are examples of the principle involved. There must be no chance of prejudiced individuals securing power to impose their ideas on the medical profession and community. It is considered that there is no safe depository of ultimate power in the use of medicines save the medical profession and, if doctors are thought to be insufficiently enlightened to exercise such power with a wholesome discretion, the remedy is not to take it away from them but to improve their discretion by education—particularly in clinical pharmacology.

In the United States, on the other hand, it is thought to be completely irrational to attempt to distinguish the safety from the efficacy of medicines: no medicine is safe if it fails to cure a disease for which a cure is available. Thus, it is the duty of the FDA to try to prevent the needless suffering, the protraction of illness, and the squandering of money on ineffective and unnecessary medicines. Whether a medicine is sufficiently safe and efficacious to be marketed must be decided by government helped by panels of experts from the National Academy of Sciences' Research Council, who are less often wrong than non-experts. Among the thousands of preparations available there are many that are of limited value, useless, or undesirable. Most doctors see insufficient numbers of patients with any one disease to evaluate critically the medicines employed for it and can only gather impressions about the ones they use. All doctors are not equally knowledgeable about all drugs and it would be absurd to expect them to be so. It is, thus, equally absurd not to expect appreciable misuse of medicines if doctors at all levels of seniority are not to be helped and guided. It is, therefore, the duty of the FDA to assist them in this respect by strict supervision of the efficacy as well as the safety of new and old remedies, for though there are many semi-official publications on therapy, textbooks of treatment, and medical journals, these publications are read to only a variable extent.

A former well-known Commissioner of the FDA poured scorn on the suggestion that a gradual process of medical education might in the long run produce sounder results than the more immediate effect of legal edicts. He said, in so many words, that when the house is on fire an academic lecture on how to prevent incendiarism is inopportune; what is needed is to put out the fire and only then is it appropriate to give lessons on how to prevent fires in the future. These are cogent arguments; it is, however, somewhat surprising that in the United States, the home of big business and free enterprise, the control of medicines should be more bureaucratically rigid than in the United Kingdom with its so-called socialized medicine.

# Comments on The British System of Drug Regulation
Reuben Kessel

It is clear that Professor Dunlop feels that the British have a better system for regulating the introduction of new drugs than we do in the United States. He makes no secret of the fact that we are more bureaucratically rigid than the British, and as a consequence, much slower. Moreover, we try to do more than the British; our regulators try to judge efficacy also—they don't want the public wasting money on useless drugs.

The evidence that I have encountered that is relevant for evaluating Professor Dunlop's judgment supports his view. Professor Wardell of the department of pharmacology of the University of Rochester's School of Medicine studied the pharmacological history of the United States and the United Kingdom in recent years and he concluded that (1) similar if not identical new drugs came on the market much sooner in the United Kingdom than in the United States, and (2) many more new drugs were introduced to the British market.[1] Most important, he concluded that the British have not suffered excessive new-drug toxicity as a result. Wardell's results are complementary with the findings reported by Professor Peltzman and constitute support for the view that, at least in the United States, our regulatory policy has had deleterious effects.

In view of the foregoing evidence, why do we find in Professor Dunlop's paper an endorsement of the U.S. Food and Drug Administration? Why is he so confident that this organization has done so much to protect the public? Clearly he believes the British system (possibly non-system is the appropriate word) is better than ours. Moreover, Wardell's detailed investigation supports Dunlop's thesis.

Much of Dunlop's paper is a description of changes in drug regulations in the United Kingdom to make them more like ours than they have been in the past. In general, Professor Dunlop favors these changes and justifies them by his judgment that the potency of drugs has been increasing. I should think that the comparison between Britain and the United States would suggest that he go slowly in endorsing recent changes in regulation in Britain. More to the point, I find no evidence in Dunlop's paper that the U.K. system of drug regulation in existence in the past was deficient, and that more regulation would work an improvement. Indeed, his principal explanation of the growth in support for more regulation is the emotion associated with the thalidomide tragedy. Yet he clearly recognizes that there is such a thing as too much control and he

1. William Wardell, "The Drug Lag: An International Comparison," unpublished paper.

intimates that this is the case in the United States. I find this ex-
plantation *ad hoc;* do airline regulations change from disaster to
disaster?

My guess is that in time the British system of drug regulation
will become more bureaucratic, with full-time regulators much like
ours. If that occurs, then I suspect these regulators will pursue policies designed to maximize their self-interest which will coincide
with the kind of arrangements that will forestall future thalidomide-
type disasters at the cost of forestalling the introduction of many
useful drugs. The lesson of thalidomide for regulators appears to
be: preclude the introduction of useful drugs in order to be confident of preventing the introduction of bad ones.

One proposition that Dunlop seems to accept without question is
that physicians should not be free to choose those drugs that will be
most suitable for their patients from among the drugs pharmaceutical concerns are prepared to provide. Despite the lengthy and expensive training physicians receive, this education is deemed to be
inadequate to prepare them for the free, to say nothing of the
optimal, choice of drugs in treating their patients.[2] Indeed this education is often regarded as inadequate for coping with the blandishments of drug house detail men.

This view is justified by the argument that it is unreasonable to
expect physicians to be able to evaluate the therapeutic value of
drugs, either new or old, by virtue of their own endeavors. Is it,
however, unreasonable to presume that physicians, as a result of
their interest in the welfare of their patients, will be interested in
selecting the drugs most suitable for treating their patients? If
such an interest exists, then it will be to the advantage of others,
more able than practicing physicians in evaluating the usefulness
of drugs, to provide this information to the profession.

On the surface, it appears that governmental regulations specifying what can and cannot be prescribed by physicians are redun-
dant. There is a potential role for the government in providing
resources to evaluate drugs because of the lack of private incentive
to produce this knowledge. It can be argued that without governmental subsidy there would be under-investment in the acquisition
of such knowledge. Granting the existence of a case for such subsidies does not support the case for direct controls over the choice
of drugs by practicing physicians.

One could rationalize governmentally imposed new drug testing

2. For evidence on the high costs of medical education, see Rashi Fein and
Gerald I. Weber, *Financing Medical Education.* New York: McGraw-Hill, 1971.

requirements upon pharmaceutical companies as a means for providing optimal quantities of information to the market that would otherwise not be provided unless their production were subsidized. However, this interpretation fails to justify the existence of a verboten list of drugs to the practicing physician.

Another line of explanation for direct state control over drug choice by the physicians stems from the view that medicine is a monopoly and that physicians earn monopoly returns. According to the eminent English economist, John Hicks, an easy, trouble-free life is one important class of monopoly return.[3] On this argument, physicians are not sufficiently interested or motivated to find out what drugs are harmful to their patients and (1) direct controls are necessary, (2) the monopoly should be eliminated, (3) licensing arrangements for the profession have failed, etc.

This explanation is not inconsistent with our experience in Illinois, where physicians have transfused blood that was obtained from members of the community that had the highest *a priori* probability of having hepatitis. Intervention by the state has now effectively eliminated this source of blood. Why physicians on their own initiative failed to insist on higher quality donors and hence higher quality blood for their patients is a mystery. The allegation that physicians fail to minimize the cost of drugs required to achieve a given therapeutic effect—prescribing by brand instead of specifying chemical entities—is another variant of the same problem.

Perhaps we are right to limit the choice of physicians in prescribing drugs for their patients, but I would like to see evidence that this prohibition has a beneficial effect. I believe that we have been all-too-willing to accept the proposition without any systematic examination of its truth content. If it is true that physicians cannot be trusted to prescribe adequately for their patients, then I am less sanguine than Professor Dunlop about the benefits of adding more courses in pharmacology to the medical curriculum. The fundamental problem here seems to be inadequate motivation for physicians to prescribe properly, and until physicians are so motivated, the problems will remain.

Finally, I wish someone would explain why the regulation of new drug entry into the market should be so much more severe in the United States than in the United Kingdom. Like Professor Dunlop, I would have expected the opposite to be the case and I wish I understood why our expectation proved to be false.

3. John R. Hicks, "Annual Survey of Economic Theory: The Theory of Monopoly," *Econometrica*, January, 1935, p. 8.

**Toward Better Systems
of Drug Regulation**
Hubert Bloch

## Drug Regulatory Systems: Aims and Purpose

The very fact that this conference has been called indicates that an ideal model of drug regulation has not yet been devised. Rather than describe the peculiarities of various systems as they presently exist in the United States, in Europe, or elsewhere, I would like to suggest possible improvements on existing systems, the merits of which may then be discussed. Surely, the time has come to learn from past experience and to draw certain conclusions, since we have now lived long enough with systems as rigid as the Japanese, as demanding and expensive as the FDA's, as personal as the French, as bureaucratic as the Indian, as reasonable and open-minded as the British, and as confusing or unrealistic as many others.

Any ideal system should meet the following requirements:

1. It should safeguard the patient from harm inflicted by the use of old drugs and the testing of new ones.

2. It should guarantee that only drugs with proven therapeutic usefulness be admitted to the marketplace.

3. It should make certain that there is an acceptable risk-benefit ratio between the incidence of possibly adverse reactions and the expected therapeutic benefits of a drug.

4. It should provide the physician with a choice of similarly acting drugs from which he may be able to satisfy the therapeutic needs of *all* of his patients, including those with metabolic or genetic peculiarities or with idiosyncrasies of one kind or another.

5. It should not stifle the creativity and the inventiveness of drug research by the way it is administered, and it should not burden the manufacturers (and the public) with unjustified developmental costs due to the request for data of little scientific value.

6. Finally, an ideal system should be universally applicable, allowing just sufficient leeway to take into account national preferences and traditions, and racial, geographic, or even economic particularities.

In discussing such a system, I start from a few axiomatic assumptions which should be accepted for as long as their validity is not disproved by evidence to the contrary.

1. Every drug therapy, just like every other effective therapetuic measure, constitutes a calculated risk which the doctor and the patient must be prepared to take. There are no effective remedies or other therapeutic measures entirely devoid of possible side effects. The risk of using a potent drug must be weighed against the risk of doing nothing.

2. Medicine is an experimental science. It proceeds by trial and error, and problems are eventually solved at the price of often and sometimes tragic mistakes. Although this is not different in principle from other technological applications of scientific findings, the fact that medicine deals with human beings gives it its peculiar sensitivity and vulnerability, especially since in our time the activity of the medical profession is no longer covered by a convenient cloak of secrecy.

3. Drug testing in laboratory animals and human beings is still characterized by a low order to quantifiable, unequivocal data.[1]

4. The pharmaceutical industry, like any other private commercial enterprise, is profit-minded and market-oriented. Nevertheless, the great majority of manufacturers are basically honest. They assume their responsibilities just as conscientiously and decently as, for example, the medical profession, if for no other reason than to stay in business. To deal with the rare exceptions, there exist adequate legal means and an ever growing public awareness that keeps them under control

5. By and large, the pharmaceutical industry has been singularly successful in improving the physicians' pharmacotherapeutic armatorium. Neither in capitalist nor in socialist economic systems have state-supported institutions up to now contributed significantly to the innovative process in the development of new and better drugs.

Within this framework of desiderata and axiomatic premises, I propose to discuss the subject further.

## The Nature of Modern Drugs

Modern drugs are potent agents with very specific activities. Their handling requires much specialized knowledge. They are sophisticated industrial products, placed at the hands of every licensed doctor, who often enough is not adequately trained in handling them.

Existing drug regulatory systems are often built on the tacit assumption that there is such a thing as a completely fool-proof, highly effective, and specific drug devoid of any side effects, and that sufficient animal testing for acute and chronic toxicity, car-

1. Cooper, J. D. (ed.). "Decision-Making on the Efficacy and Safety of Drugs." Washington, D.C.: Interdisciplinary Communication Associates, Inc., 1971.

cinogenicity, antigenicity, and development of dependence will eliminate all potentially hazardous compounds, eventually leaving us with 100 percent effective and 100 percent innocuous substances.

This assumption is wrong for the following reasons. Most pharmacologically active substances act differently when applied in different dosages. Below a certain amount, no effect may be seen. With increasing dosage, an effect may reverse itself, for example, from excitation to depression, and may end with producing irreversible damage ("*Facit dosis venenum*"). Thus, dosage is of prime importance, but the correct dosage cannot be fixed unequivocally and prescribed rigidly. There exist too many individual differences among patients, depending on age, sex, nutritional state, weight, genetic constitution, previous exposure to this or other drugs, concurrent ingestion of other drugs or certain foods, the particular disease against which the drug is meant to act, other diseases from which the patient may be suffering, and other factors. The half-life of the drug in the human body is important, but it may vary from man to man, and within the same individual from one application to the next.

Although some of these factors can be controlled and even predicted, others cannot, and individual variations leading to too much or too little drug action cannot altogether be eliminated. Drug trials can only yield average values, they can never provide data applicable at any time to every single patient and therefore can never assure optimal efficacy and total freedom from side effects.

Drug regulatory agencies should explicitly recognize these facts. In reaching their decisions they should take *all* available facts into consideration. For instance, because of different drug-licensing practices in various countries, it is not uncommon for a new drug to be marketed in some countries several years before it can be sold in others. The evidence accumulated in pre-marketing trials and post-marketing experience should be accepted and used by agencies of countries whose drug clearing process takes longer. By disregarding foreign data, a national agency not only frequently deprives itself of valuable information, it also burdens the manufacturers and the clinical pharmacologists with duplicate work which in many instances could be avoided, and is therefore not justified on ethical or on economic grounds. Moreover, to take cognizance of and to critically review foreign data would help to bring the format of clinical trials and of toxicological experiments to a common international denominator, which is an essential prerequisite for reaching the ultimate goal of a universal drug regulatory system.

## The Role of the Physician

Those who expect a drug regulatory system to eliminate all hazards and to provide perfectly fool-proof drugs are often forgetting the most essential link in the chain between the drug manufacturer and the patient, namely the doctor. In calculating and appraising the doctor's role, most drug control systems today are deficient.

The majority of physicians are scientifically naive. Even the best-trained doctors cannot fully keep up with medical progress. They lack the means and the basic knowledge required to understand all intricacies of modern drug therapy and are unable themselves to sift the true scientific value of all the information they receive. This not only applies to the practicing physicians; their academic colleagues are frequently subject to the same limitations.

Despite these objections, all existing drug administrations start from the assumption that all doctors are equal and that all are competent. An ideal system should recognize that some doctors are "more equal" than others, and that very specific skills are required for adequate administration of very specific drugs. Just as not every pilot licensed to fly a small plane may take the controls of a jumbo-jet, there should be limitations to the individuals who are permitted to administer certain drugs—unless, of course, the prevailing attitude about the inherent dangers of certain drugs were to be changed and a certain number of failures were accepted as inevitable. While this is really so, it is rarely, if ever, openly admitted. Instead, one tries to eliminate adverse reactions by further tightening the regulations of drug testing. Such efforts are inadequate as long as they do not include measures for better control of the part played by the physicians, as discussed later in this paper.

## Some Comments on Toxicology

Toxicity tests as they are usually performed today are demanding and time consuming, but the standard protocols are basically sound. Nevertheless, certain accepted practices might be seriously questioned and more room should be left for experimentation in the following areas:

1. The use of animals of uniform genetic stock facilitates experimentation, since the results tend to become more uniform than with randomly-bred animals. On the other hand, there exists a real danger that certain reactions may not occur in a certain breed, or, contrariwise, may occur in one specific breed only, which would

yield a distorted picture of the frequency or severity of certain drug reactions. Thus, with inbred animals, toxicity tests may have less predictive value for the human situation than would seem desirable.

2. There is a wide belief that toxicity tests of long duration will bring out effects not seen in experiments of shorter duration. This may be true for the testing of drugs for possible carcinogenicity but for all other effects, tests of long duration can largely be replaced by the application of higher single dosages over a shorter period of time.[2] More use should be made of this possibility and much time and money could be saved without the sacrifice of safety.

3. In the areas of testing for teratogenicity and damage to germinal cells, the testing procedures appear relatively crude and primitive. If existing practices would allow or indeed invite wider experimentation, much meaningful information might well emerge, and we could expect significant gains in knowledge which are presently almost excluded by the uniformity of the procedures employed.

4. The greatest weakness of existing practices lies in the way results are interpreted. In all doubtful cases, more consideration should be given to the experimental design and the meaningfulness of the models employed. Only by relating the model to the actual clinical situation it tries to simulate can the significance of animal findings be extrapolated to man. This is a difficult exercise demanding imagination as well as courage and sound scientific judgment. Care should be taken that the best available scientific judgment be applied in these decisions and that they will be made in an atmosphere of privacy, devoid of publicity and pressure of any kind. Unfortunately, too often these conditions are not met, and yet, given the right attitude of the drug agency, they could easily be obtained.

In summary then, as long as the predictive value of many experimental models, especially in the areas of chronic toxicity, carcinogenicity, and teratogenicity, is relatively low with regard to anticipated effects in man, a greater degree of freedom in the design and execution of experiments should be encouraged. This might not only produce more meaningful experimental models, it would also obviate a spurious sense of security which is now likely to result from the routine execution of tests, the inherent value and sig-

2. Bein, H. J. "Rational and Irrational Numbers in Toxicology." *Proceedings of the European Society for the Study of Drug Toxicity.* Excerpta Medica Foundation, 1963, pp. 15–24.

nificance of which are at least doubtful. The questionably predictive value of certain test results should be acknowledged and the results should be interpreted according to the best scientific judgment rather than used as a basis for the slavish application of administrative measures.

## The Value of Rules and Guidelines

Various countries issue guidelines advising drug manufacturers and clinicians on methods of testing new drugs, both in the laboratory and on patients. One might think that a near-perfect text could be elaborated and amended as experience grows, and that in this fashion the problem could be resolved. Surprisingly enough, this is not the case.

Guidelines have inherent weaknesses, and any set of rules applied mechanically tends to have a stultifying effect. He who follows the book to the letter does his duty and feels no longer obligated to look further; and he who reads the reports and interprets the results likewise tends to do so according to the rules of the statute-book. To both of them, codified rules give a false sense of security. They tend to stifle their curiosity and to blunt their individual judgment.

Rigid rules are necessary and useful when applied to experiments and data of a physical nature. There can be no doubt that statute-books such as those governing the "Good Manufacturing Practice" fulfill their purpose. The directives are clear and the results unequivocal. When applied to biological objects and to reactions in laboratory animals and man, however, rigid rules tend to become as much of an impediment as a help because, as the data become more ambiguous and vague, their interpretation becomes more important. Furthermore, interpretation cannot be regulated; it must be based solely on sound scientific judgment.

There is, moreover, always a danger that set rules followed to the letter will not only stifle any initiative to go beyond the limits set by the statute-book, but that such initiative may indeed render the investigators liable to punishment by the authorities for their scientific curiosity. Since many agencies require all experimental findings obtained with new drugs to be reported, there is a real danger for the industrial scientist who is too curious and looks into areas not prescribed by the book. Suppose a toxicologist is curious enough to study the effects of a new compound on the liver histology of laboratory animals or patients using an electron microscope instead of the light microscope which is the accepted standard practice. He may well find certain morphological changes not readily explainable from past experience. In reporting them to the drug agency, as he is required to do by law in many countries, he runs the risk that his findings may delay the clearance of the new drug by many months or years. So, for the manufacturer it is better not to be too curious, since he has no assurance that his findings will be interpreted according to the best scientific judgment. As a consequence, in such a situation the gaining of new knowledge will have been hampered.

In a more enlightened system, on the contrary, scientific curiosity would be encouraged. The widest possible range of experimentation would be invited, and it would be left to the discretion of the investigators themselves to decide when and how to report their findings. Never should they be penalized for pushing their experiments toward new frontiers. The highest aim of everyone involved in the testing of drugs must be to learn as much as possible at every level of investigation and to communicate and discuss the results freely among scientists, including government scientists. It remains for the scientists to tell the administrative officers what conclusions to draw from new findings and how these may affect the licensing policy of the authorities.

In summary, then, rigid rules for the control of drugs are called for and useful where they apply to precise investigations of a physical nature. Good manufacturing practice, quality control, analytical data, sterility requirements, etc., can be, and should be, clearly defined, and minimum standards should be postulated and enforced. With such data, little room is left for interpretation. The results are clear and unequivocal.

On the other hand, biological data, whether obtained in man or animal, do not lend themselves to strict codification. Quite often, they are equivocal. They must be interpreted, and the interpretation must be entirely free within a framework of scientific references.

Scientific judgment cannot be replaced by the mechanical application of rigid rules. In this area, therefore, good guidelines are useful, but only in the literal sense that they may guide experiments in a direction which in the past has proved to be useful. When applied rigidly, they tend to become senseless, because most biological systems are not sufficiently uniform and well defined as to allow the replacement of considered scientific judgment by rigid rules and computer-type yes or no answers.

## The Role of the Public, the Press, and the Politicians

Drug regulatory agencies are set up to protect the public. It might, therefore, seem logical that the public, through its elected representatives and the press, should have an eye on the functioning of such agencies. Yet, it appears to me that the drug regulatory agencies function best in countries where they are relatively sheltered from interference by politicians, the press, and the various pressures of populist and consumer groups. It is unfortunate that anything connected with health—and this includes drugs—commands an unrelenting public interest, because human nature is too weak and too corruptible for certain journalists and politicians to resist the temptation to abuse the public interest for their own personal goals.

To this it may be objected that the vigilance of an informed populace is the best means of ensuring that the powers of special interest groups, with their profit-mindedness and lack of morality, are not used to compel the regulatory agencies to set the interests of the industry before those of the public. Examples in support of this thesis could just as easily be found in many countries as instances to the contrary.

There is no foolproof way out of the dilemma, but some systems seem to provide more protection from irresponsibly motivated outside interference than others, while still protecting the public's interests in the best possible way. Personally, I feel that the British and the Swiss systems are superior to the American in this respect, because the ultimate responsibility for difficult decisions is borne by independent committees of part-time scientific experts, and the executive medical officers of the government are the servants of these committees. They provide the information, they collect and analyze the data, but the expert-committees are responsible for the decisions. It would be very hard for any politician or journalist to question the integrity and competence of duly constituted expert committees. Outside committees have performed outstandingly in the United States, for example, in the extramural programs of the National Institutes of Health (NIH), the National Science Foundation (NSF), and other agencies. It is rather odd that the institution of the independent committee, which is so typical of many U.S. institutions, should not be used more often to assist the FDA in its difficult task.

Obviously, in order to fulfill a useful purpose, advice must be sought from expert committees *before* the pertinent decisions are made, not afterward. The history of the banning of cyclamates is an outstanding example of how political and economic pressures are apt to becloud a problem that should be resolved on the basis of the best scientific judgment alone.[3]

In addition to disturbing the orderly process of reaching conclusions based on the best available scientific evidence, the interferences by politicians, by consumers, or others are bound to create among the public an atmosphere of unnecessary doubt and uncertainty, thus undermining confidence in the medical profession. This is unfair to patients as well as to their doctors, since no useful purpose is served by the premature release through the daily press of incomplete and often biased information.

## The Risk-Versus-Benefit Arithmetic in Therapy and the Misuse of Drugs

If we accept the statement that the use of every effective drug involves a certain risk and that in drug therapy—as indeed in any other type of therapy—the possible risk must be calculated against the expected benefit, we soon realize that the area where the administrative competence of the drug regulatory agency is competent is relatively small compared to the field that must be left to the physician's judgment. Obviously, one is prepared to take greater risks where the expected benefits or where the danger of doing nothing are great. In extreme cases, such as the chemotherapy of cancer, acceptable ratios of risk-versus-benefit can be agreed upon relatively easily.

Where it becomes difficult or impossible to define what is, or is not, reasonable, is with drugs that are not unique or life-saving but are nevertheless very useful therapeutic aids, although they may be causing rare but serious adverse reactions. In this area, to be guided by percentages is of little help. Even when side effects occur merely in one patient out of 100,000, the one who happens to represent the 0.00001 percent suffers 100 percent! It then becomes a matter of philosophy as to how much risk the doctor (and the patient) are willing to take—the same philosophy that we apply when boarding a car or an airplane, or when crossing the street or swimming in a river. In all of these instances, according to our nature, we either honestly try to calculate the risk and to act accordingly, or we act like an ostrich. The ultimate result may be about the same.

3. Cooper, J. D. (ed.). *The Quality of Advice.* Washington, D.C.: Interdisciplinary Communication Associates, Inc., 1971.

Obviously, no one would advocate licensing a new drug that is in no way superior to existing ones, except that it produces more side effects, but I find it questionable to bar from circulation drugs that are merely suspected, but not definitely proven, to be involved in causing side effects, or that have produced injury in laboratory animals under experimental conditions that are so far removed from the reality of therapeutic application that the animal experiment cannot seriously be regarded as a meaningful model of the clinical situation.

Drug therapy is but one aspect of medical treatment, and the risks involved in other therapeutic measures such as surgery or electroshock, or in diagnostic procedures such as X-ray or heart catheterization, are just as serious and frequent. Here, however, we discover a peculiar set of dual standards. While the sale and use of drugs is closely watched by the authorities, other diagnostic or therapeutic measures are freely administered by licensed physicians in the absense of any government supervision. I am not divulging any secrets in stating that not every surgical intervention is justified and that not everybody dying on an operating table or suffering from the sequelae of non-essential diagnostic or therapeutic measures should have necessarily suffered this fate.

Perhaps there are signs that the medical community is becoming aware of this state of affairs. Some hospitals are setting up peer committees to review the practice of their colleagues, just as there are peer committees to review the usage of drugs. These beginnings should be encouraged and institutionalized. They are an essential and necessary adjunct to any drug regulatory system. The relative incompetence of too many physicians in handling potent drugs has already been mentioned. The serious drug information provided by monographs and journal articles is useful if read, but I doubt whether busy practitioners find enough time to do so. To read package inserts and brief summaries or listen to salesmen is clearly insufficient.

To my mind, moreover, package inserts have a very serious shortcoming. At the request of the regulatory agencies, they contain long lists of contraindications, warnings, precautions, and adverse reactions. In many cases, these enumerations are considerably longer than the paragraphs on actions, indications, and dosage recommendations. What is the physician to do when he reads that the safe use of drug X, a widely prescribed sulfonamide, in pregnancy has not been established, that its teratogenic potential has not been thoroughly investigated in either animals or humans, and that a significant increase in cleft palates has been observed in the off-spring of pregnant rats that were injected with 10 to 25 times the human therapeutic doses?

An endless list of warnings, especially when devoid of quantitative information on the frequency of adverse reactions and their relationship to the duration of treatment, has about the same significance as have the paragraphs in small print on airline tickets or the signs occasionally encountered on American highways which say: "Road officially closed, proceed at your own risk." It serves as an alibi for the drug regulatory agency and scares the patient if he sees it. It also constitutes a useful tool for lawyers specializing in suing doctors for alleged malpractice.

When a state is reached where long lists of warnings are standard features on every package insert, they will almost necessarily be disregarded by the prescribing physician and thus simply lose their effect. Warnings should be limited to well-documented, significant side effects that can be expected to occur with a certain frequency. Only then will they be heeded and seriously considered. In the present practice, they serve no other purpose than to remind the physician that chemotherapy constitutes a calculated risk. Specifically, they fail to give the physician meaningful guidance in prescribing drugs of an effective nature.

As stated previously, the package insert illustrates that drug therapy is characterized by a low order of quantifiable data, that the prescribing physician lacks the means to take into consideration all parameters necessary for a scientific appraisal of the risks involved in chemotherapy, and that no amount of laboratory and clinical tests can completely eliminate the grey area between drug safety and drug efficacy.

It is still unclear who should ultimately be responsible for resolving these elements of uncertainty; it is certain that the responsibility can neither be fully assigned to the prescribing physician nor to the agency or the manufacturer. Until the state of the art has reached a much higher degree of perfection, these are the inherent risks and their existence must be acknowledged and accepted as such.

Continuing medical education in an age of rapid medical progress is such an obvious necessity that one can only wonder why it has not long been institutionalized and made compulsory in all countries. Clearly, medical refresher courses must include instruction on the correct usage of new drugs and a system of peer review must be found and implemented to allow the continuing control and improvement of the doctors' prescribing patterns.[4] Such institutions would form the most meaningful and most urgently needed addition to any drug regulatory system.

# Is Drug Innovation Necessary?

Drug innovation proceeds by leaps and bounds and then again by very small steps. It is a continuing process, and progress is made by design and intelligent planning as well as by clever observation and serendipity. It is not the purpose of this article to investigate the reasons for the decline in the number of newly-introduced drugs during the past decade or so. Suffice it to say that I strongly believe that this trend will reverse itself and new types of compounds with new indications will appear in the not too distant future.[5]

However, the very justification and necessity for drug innovation has sometimes been questioned and it has been said that existing regulations seriously hamper the progress of chemotherapy in some countries. A number of facts must be considered in this context:

1. Most physicians use only a small proportion of all the drugs available to them on the market. Physicians use those drugs with which they are best acquainted and which they feel they can handle best, but not all physicians make the same choice and the personal selection varies from doctor to doctor. Furthermore, the number of drugs available in each country varies within wide limits.

2. As the development of new drugs becomes increasingly expensive, drug companies are forced to consider the potential market value of their innovative goals with increasing care.

3. The great number of years it takes today to develop a new drug makes drug manufacturers less flexible in their plans than they were only a short time ago.

4. Theoretically, a constellation of economic, regulatory, and social pressures could lead to a state of affairs where it would become not only unprofitable, but even financially impossible for private manufacturers to stay in drug research, whereupon the public would have to decide whether nationalized industries should continue the tradition at the expense of the taxpayers or whether drug innovation should come to a standstill.

4. Stolley, P. D. and Lasagna, L. "Prescribing Patterns of Physicians." *Journal of Chronic Diseases* 22 (1969), pp. 395–404.
5. Bloch, H. "Zukunftsperspektiven der Pharmaindustrie." *Chem. Rundschau* 24 (1971), p. 689.

These points are not as theoretical as they may appear at first sight, and they are very germane to the present discussion of drug regulatory systems. Any such system must ultimately take them into account, because an ideal system should afford the maximum consumer protection while still preserving the greatest opportunities for progress and improvement.

I need not seriously discuss why innovation is necessary and why claims to declare a "moratorium on innovation" are totally unrealistic. Even when one generously acknowledges all the excesses and mistakes for which the pharmaceutical industry has at times been blamed, the most severe critic must concede that the industry has been singularly successful and that medicine has undoubtedly benefited from the continuing progress and improvement of chemotherapy. To stop its innovative activity would be tantamount to killing the research-based pharmaceutical industry, and ways must be found to permit its continued functioning in an atmosphere of mutual trust and openmindedness.

History has often demonstrated that significant innovative improvements were based on unplanned observations in the laboratory or the clinic and that these would not have been made had it not been for some research which perhaps was not necessarily rated as outstanding or particularly significant before the pertinent crucial observation was made. It should therefore be the aim of every drug regulatory system to allow the maximum freedom for qualified experimentation (including experimentation on patients) that is compatible with medical ethics and patient safety. Red-tape should be eliminated as much as possible, while meticulous record-keeping and sound experimental design should be vigorously enforced. The general improvement of controlled clinical trials is one of the most salutary side effects of modern drug regulations.

When clinical trials show that a new compound is merely equal to or insignificantly better than the standard drug with which it is compared, should the new drug be barred from introduction? I believe not. When 70 percent of a group of patients respond favorably to treatment with drug A and 70 percent of a comparable group respond similarly to drug B, this does not mean that *the same* 70 percent would have reacted similarly had the treatment groups been reversed. It is a safe prediction that in each cohort of 70 percent, certain individuals respond favorably to only one of the two compounds. Although this number may be small, it still represents a number of patients whose individual reaction makes the difference between getting well or remaining sick. All other pertinent factors being equal, the drug regulatory agency should see no reason not to license both drugs.

Some countries, such as Norway, have chosen a different way. They license only a small number of drugs for normal usage, but at the request of any physician every drug licensed in a foreign country may be immediately imported and made available for the treatment of particular patients. This system of "*à la carte* service" safeguards the doctor's freedom in prescribing and the patients' right to treatment with any drug that is available world-wide. It may work for a small country with a population of under 4 million, but it could never be adopted by countries with large populations and with active research-based pharmaceutical industries of their own.

## The Post-Marketing Surveillance of New Drugs

It is hardly necessary to reiterate the need for close surveillance and follow-up of newly-introduced drugs during their first post-marketing years, yet little seems to be done about this important issue in practice. Here, a meaningful collaboration between regulating agencies and drug companies could be established which, in my opinion, would be mutually beneficial.

It does not seem unreasonable that new drugs requiring special medical skills or patient monitoring devices for their successful administration should, for an initial post-marketing period, be restricted to use by hospital doctors and specialists. After this first post-introductory period, the experience obtained could be reviewed and the drug could then eventually be released for general use.

Similar restrictions could be imposed on the use of new antibiotics with selective spectra of activity where it would be in the public health interest to preserve their usefulness as long as possible by preventing the emergence of resistant bacterial strains resulting from indiscriminate use.

Both the industry and physicians would probably protest against such proposals, but if their implementation were restricted to selected, well-justified instances, both manufacturers and the medical profession would benefit in the long run. Drug misuse is bad from the public health point of view as well as from the manufacturer's point of view. The proposed restrictions would seem to be efficient means to counteract it.

Some time after an important new drug has been introduced,

drug companies are in the habit of organizing symposia to give
doctors who have had experience with the drug an opportunity to
exchange information and at the same time to obtain publishable
papers on the subject which may be used for promotional purposes. (Curiously enough, whatever has been published, in no
matter how obscure a journal, may be used for advertising purposes, whereas the most serious unpublished observations may
not!) I would suggest that symposia of this sort be made compulsory; that they be conducted and edited by committees of independent specialists in the field acting in trust for the regulatory
agency as well as the manufacturer; that the membership of the
symposia consist of participants nominated by the drug company
and of others invited by these committees; and that the regulatory
agency should bear an adequate share of the publication costs.

The proposed procedure would remove from these publications
the stigma associated with purely commercial advertising material
(which in most instances they are not) and would further ensure
that such symposia are not just "family affairs" but gatherings of
impartial specialists which would enhance the information value
of the ensuing publications. It is noteworthy that such symposia
are not unknown in socialist countries when the responsible government agencies plan to introduce foreign drugs after clinical
trials in their own country.

It is important to follow up and disseminate information on
newly-marketed drugs, not only with regard to possibly rare and
previously not observed side effects, but also to complete our
knowledge of their therapeutic profile, including new indications,
compatibility with other drugs or foods, etc. Such information
should be compiled in close collaboration with the parent drug
company which has by far the best knowledge, but it should be distributed in appropriate form by the regulatory agency.

Publications such as the British *Prescriber's Journal* or the
*Medical Letter* have had various degrees of success in imparting
knowledge on the experience obtained with newly-introduced
drugs. However, the articles are not always written by the most
neutral and knowledgeable experts in the field and most of the
time their sources are limited to what has been published in the
literature. It would seem possible to devise a system whereby
periodic evaluations could be published by an official agency *in
close and active collaboration with the drug manufacturer.* The
latter has direct access to his investigators and to physicians who
are using the drugs, and his files contain a wealth of information

on his product. Although a great deal of this information may be too fragmentary and raw for publication, much of it is valuable and could be used for objective reports co-authored by government and company scientists.

It follows from this proposal that the manufacturer would have to open his files. In reality, this should not present serious problems, since only data which are scientifically founded and sufficiently well controlled and documented would be published. On the other hand, since the manufacturer is in any case obligated to inform the regulatory agencies on any adverse reactions of which he is notified, a composite picture of all available information, screened and edited by a group of competent authors, would serve the interests of the public and the manufacturer considerably better than the procedures presently observed.

While these suggestions may seem strange and unrealistic at first, I am sure that with a little good will on both sides they would work out. Doubtless, the standing of such publications in the view of the medical community would surpass that of the glossy monographs distributed by a company's department of medical information.

## Should Drugs Be Licensed for Specific Indications Only?

Since the efficacy of a new drug is judged by the results of adequately conducted clinical trials, it seems logical that its use should be limited to those indications where the trial results have convinced the regulatory agency of the usefulness of the drug. In practice, however, things do not always work this way. There are famous examples of drugs cleared, as it turned out, for the wrong indication in one country and for the right one in another. There are many instances where new and useful indications were found by chance, often because drugs were prescribed for a disease for which they were not meant to be used, and there are cases where a drug reaches sales volumes far beyond the producing company's expectations and calculations, obviously because doctors prescribe it for indications other than those for which it was intended.

These facts are merely mentioned to illustrate that despite existing regulations drugs appear to be used not infrequently for indications other than those for which they were developed. Perhaps the medical community would be well served if such unorthodox usage became more widely known, so that it could be either supported or refuted after being checked by further clinical trials.

In addition, this state of affairs points to another problem which is unresolved in many existing drug regulatory schemes. Normally, drug trials are performed with hospitalized or otherwise confined patients, but a large proportion of all drugs is prescribed by practicing physicians to ambulatory patients for conditions that do not require hospitalization. Practitioner trials have been successfully performed in some countries, although they are always fraught with some difficulties. Some patients drop out, the taking of the medication is uncontrolled, the patients are poorly observed, etc., yet it seems that despite these shortcomings these trials should be encouraged and improved and their results should be accepted as evidence by the authorities as long as certain standards are met. Not only are there too few hospitalized patients and qualified clinical pharmacologists available to perform all the trial work that is needed, there are diseases for which medication is indicated which are rarely if ever seen in hospitals and where it would be well to test new drugs under field conditions and in proper double-blind fashion. It has been amply demonstrated that this can be done.[6, 7]

## The Case of the Placebo

There are two categories of placebos: the genuine, bona fide placebo and the drug for which there is a claimed efficacy that cannot be unequivocally proven by objective means. The latter group includes scores of old remedies and a number of new drugs introduced into the market in countries where NDAs are more easily granted, but which are still barred from introduction where licensing is dependent on objective proof of efficacy. It is this second group that is discussed here. Although these drugs are not placebos in the strict sense of the word, their action may be indistinguishable from that of placebos in controlled clinical trials. Nevertheless, in countries where they are available, experienced clinicians use them and are convinced of their efficacy. In this context, we may also mention drugs whose efficacy is uncontested

6. Imhof, P. "Prüfung neuer Arzneimittel durch Praktikergruppen in der Schweiz." *Therapiewoche* 20 (1970), p. 1690.

7. Wheatley, D. "The General Practitioner Research Group." *Clinical Pharmacology and Therapy.* 4 (1963), p. 542.

when used for the right indication, but questionable or nonexistent when not. The classical example is supplied by the vitamins, for which efficacy can be demonstrated in vitamin deficiencies, but where tons are prescribed or consumed with no clear indication. There are two schools of thought regarding the usage of drugs in this category. The strictly scientific opinion prevailing in this country and some others maintains that drugs without proven efficacy have no place in therapy.

There is an opposite view which pleads for the use of such drugs. Their development, so the argument goes, was often based on unequivocal findings in experimental animals where a clear-cut pharmacological action was demonstrable. This action, however, proved to be less pronounced and more questionable during clinical trials. The results never reached high statistical significance, often because of very high placebo rates, yet they always pointed in the right direction, and experienced clinicians were favorably impressed. Toxicity and side effects were low and the drug presented no particular problems. In the patients' view, the drug was helpful.

It can earnestly be argued that the failure to prove efficacy may be due to the inadequacy of the available methods of clinical pharmacology and not to the lack of effectiveness. Obviously, if the claimed action concerns an effect that is easily measurable, such as diuretic action or effects on blood pressure, there is little room for discussion and dissenting views. On the other hand, if the therapeutic target concerns more diffuse areas with clinical parameters less easily accessible to accurate measurements, a good case can be made that sufficiently sensitive analytical methods have yet to be developed; that not enough is known about the pathophysiology of the disease; and that in the meantime patients should not be deprived of the benefits of such drugs.

I suggest that in these areas where the state of the art still leaves plenty of room for improvement and where the clinical knowledge and methodology are not as far advanced as in others, regulatory agencies should be more tolerant; that the merits of such drugs should be decided in open discussion between clinicians and government doctors; and that in such instances the proven safety of a drug in question should bear more weight than its unequivocal efficacy. Once more, we should remember that many areas of clinical medicine are still characterized by a very high order of unquantifiable data.

At the same time, these circumstances should constitute an added stimulus to improving and refining the art of clinical pharmacology, and government agencies as well as medical schools and drug manufacturers should be encouraged to support institutions devoted to furthering this comparatively young branch of clinical medicine.

## The Socio-Economic Aspects of Drug Control

So far, only the medical aspects of drug control have been discussed. However, since certain socio-economic and political principles are involved, these must be briefly touched upon. It has been said previously that in drug therapy the danger of medication must always be weighed against the danger resulting from the omission of chemotherapy. If this is true for the individual patient, it is equally true for whole populations.

It has been pointed out that the development of a new anti-fertility drug under present FDA regulations in the United States would be an undertaking of such enormous dimensions and prohibitive costs that it would be impractical to tackle it.[8, 9] Nevertheless, one may ask whether the precautions and safety requirements concerning this type of drug are not out of proportion in comparison to, say, anticancer drugs where the regulations are so much easier to comply with? Is the cancer of an individual so much more threatening and so much more "relevant" a disease than overpopulation of the earth?

Birth control pills were illegal in India for many years after they had been introduced in the United States and in Europe, because the Indian Medical Research Council was not convinced that they were safe for Indian women. Thus, the pressing problems of over-population in India, with all its obvious consequences of malnutrition and famine, was less of a burden on that Council's conscience than the possible hazards of ovulation inhibitors for some of the women who took them. Clearly, a rethinking of these problems is indicated and control agencies should learn to appraise problems affecting the entire population in terms commensurate with their gravity, and to weigh individual safety standards against those of large population groups.

In some countries, particularly those with universal state health

8. Djerassi, C. "Prognosis for the Development of New Chemical Birth-Control Agents." *Science* 166 (1969), pp. 468–73.
9. Djerassi, C. "Birth Control After 1984." *Science* 169 (1970), pp. 941–51.

insurance schemes, the price of a new drug is also an important component of the drug licensing process. In these countries the state is practically the industry's only customer. It is ultimately paying all the drug bills and licensing a drug is tantamount to accepting that its price will be charged to the social security system. A completely new dimension thus enters the drug scene: the consideration of drug prices in the socio-economic context. Although the degree to which medicine is "socialized" varies from one country to the next, it may be safely predicted that, with the ever-rising costs of medical care, the state's and therefore the taxpayer's share will be steadily increasing everywhere. Although drug prices have risen but little in comparison to the costs of hospitalization and medical services, they constitute a hot political issue.

Just as on medical grounds drugs are weighed in terms of risk versus benefit, they should be similarly appraised in the economic context. The price of drugs must be weighed against the savings in hospital days and absenteeism from work resulting from their therapeutic action. Health has its price, and society must ultimately decide how much it is willing to pay for it.

## Conclusion

You need only a relatively small amount of good clinical work to establish that a drug is effective and reasonably safe. It takes a lot of work, however, to pinpoint safety and efficiency with precision. It takes years to find out all the potential toxic mischief that drugs have. One might argue that you could introduce new drugs, therefore, rather early on the market if you could feel assured that there would be some sort of gradual use of the drug as opposed to massive prescribing by every doctor in the country to every patient. What you would like to have is gradual introduction and efficient monitoring of the safety and efficacy aspects of that new drug so as to revise, as frequently as necessary, the indications and contraindications for the drug. Also, you would like to have an effective means of communicating this to doctors. All of these aspects are tied together. If you believe, as I do, that it is possible to get a pretty good feeling for a drug relatively early in the game, it seems wasteful to spend years getting more data just so that people can have a spurious sense of confidence in what they know and do not know about a drug.

This statement by Professor Lasagna admirably summarizes what I would consider the essential elements of a reasonable approach to the problem of drug control.[10] I have tried in the present essay to point out the elements that have more or less interfered in many countries with the practical implementation of these principles.

1. The false assumption that there exist highly efficacious drugs with specific pharmacological action completely devoid of any toxicity, and that with an ever-increasing amount of toxicity tests and clinical trials such drugs will eventually be found.

2. Overemphasis on safety which tends to neglect the therapeutic effects of drugs by not considering the risk versus benefit ratio in realistic terms.

3. In drug therapy, the role of the physician is all-important; he cannot be relieved of his responsibility in decision-making by the work of the regulatory agency.

4. The physician is often inadequately trained to handle potent drugs, and continuing medical education is a necessary task with which regulatory agencies ought to concern themselves in close collaboration with medical schools, medical associations, and the drug industry.

5. Insufficient use is made of systems of peer review of doctors' prescription patterns which should improve the correct usage and reduce the misuse of drugs.

6. In many countries the existing drug regulations are counterproductive in that, as they are administered, they inhibit rather than encourage experimentation designed to further our knowledge about drugs.

7. The nature and quality of drug information available to the physician might be greatly improved if industry and government agencies could find a way to funnel their information into the same channels through which it would reach the doctors in a completely objective manner.

8. The aforementioned overconcern with drug safety tends not only to withhold the benefit of new drugs from patients in certain countries for unjustifiably long periods of time, but by putting the concern for individual safety before that for the well-being of

10. Bloch, H. and Paget, G. E. "Responsibilities of the Pharmaceutical Industry and the Assessment of Drug Safety and Efficacy." *CIOMS Round Table Conference on "Evaluation of Drugs."* Geneva: World Health Organization, 1968.

entire populations, it tends to jeopardize the interests of public health.

9. Many regulatory agencies take too little outside expert advice, and agencies in general perform better in countries where critical decisions are left to consultant groups of sterling merit rather than to government scientists and administrators.

10. An all-too-active interest in drug regulatory affairs by politicians, populist or consumer groups, and the press is bad inasmuch as it results in forcing decisions under pressure which then tend to be shaped by political rather than by scientific considerations.

Finally, a plea is made that national agencies should also take into account as far as possible the results of foreign drug trials and laboratory data which would greatly reduce unnecessary duplicative work, save money and manpower, and pave the way to an international system of drug regulation which would incorporate the best features of all existing national schemes.

# Comments on Toward Better Systems of Drug Regulation
Louis Lasagna

It may be profitable to delineate, as sharply as possible, what a drug regulatory system can and cannot do. No system currently in force can, for example, safeguard all patients from harm caused by the use of old drugs. In recent years we have been berated with horrendous figures about the incidence of adverse drug reactions. Without question, any active chemical can cause untoward effects. This is the price we pay for therapeutic benefits. It does not help the quality of debate about drug development and usage to take an isolated study on a few patients on one service at one hospital, however, and confabulate some national figure on the "cost" of adverse drug reactions. Not only are the various assumptions involved in such extrapolations of dubious validity, but the answer supplied is in any case not really to the question of major interest.

It is unpleasant to develop a skin rash from penicillin while under treatment for pneumococcal pneumonia, but such an event in a patient without an allergic history is hardly comparable to the same rash in a patient known to be sensitive to penicillin, or in a patient who received the drug for infectious mononucleosis or uncomplicated influenza. In any case, the public welfare is best protected not by regulatory fiat but by the education of physicians (and patients) and the monitoring of professional performance.

These latter functions are best reserved, I submit, for academic and professional bodies and mechanisms, not governmental regulatory agencies—unless the non-governmental means are so ineffective that the potential dangers of federal or state intervention seem worth risking in desperation. (This is not the moment to discuss the deficiencies of academic efforts in this regard, or the absence of good data on the quality of prescribing, but I am not unaware of these matters.)

Nor can regulatory agencies alone guarantee freedom from drug toxicity in the evaluation of new drugs. All such research involves calculated risks, and the best that can be accomplished by a distant bureaucracy is to request (and review) the preclinical data on a new chemical, the suggested plans for its study in humans, and the qualifications of the investigators who propose to evaluate it. These steps are by no means useless, but they are certainly imperfect, and we need not pretend that they are (or can be) better than they are.

The same type of unreasonableness characterizes the demand that a regulatory system allow on the marketplace only drugs of guaranteed merit and acceptable cost-benefit ratios. Certainly, no new drug will be marketed in the future in this country without reasonable evidence of efficacy and safety; but clinical studies will always be imperfect, the safety record of a drug is never known with any assurance prior to extensive and prolonged use, and (most importantly) *the regulatory system can only determine that in general the cost-benefit picture is acceptable when the drug is properly used for the right patients.* (This concept not only emphasizes individualistic decision-making by patient and doctor, weighing the specific and idiosyncratic benefits, risks, and alternatives, but lays open the possibility of limited approval of drugs for use only by certain specialists or in certain hospitals.)

It has been suggested that drug regulation would be better if it worried less about Type I errors than about Type II errors. A drug that is erroneously judged to be active may at least be correctly identified as ineffective ultimately by the test of performance in the marketplace. A drug that is kept off the market by the fallacious judgment that it is ineffective, however, will never have the chance to set its record straight.

I am bothered by the statement that "no one would advocate licensing a new drug which is in no way superior to existing ones," because I worry about what is meant by "superior" and who is making that judgment. Is a new hypnotic that is statistically indistinguishable from an old hypnotic in clinical trials admissable? Its only superiority may lie in its ability to work well for some patients not treated adequately by the old drug—a point very hard to prove in clinical trials of the usual sort. What of a highly toxic antibiotic which is not a first line drug but may save the life of a patient with endocarditis who has not responded to "better," "safer" antibiotics? What would the epileptologist do without his "backstop drugs" for refractory cases? Is a "minipill" that is less effective than the conventional oral contraceptives but almost devoid of thromboembolic risk "superior" or "inferior"?

On the other hand, I fully agree with Professor Bloch that we must concern ourselves with the impact of a drug regulatory system on the creativity and inventiveness of the drug industry. Implacable enemies of pharmaceutical firms seem to have given very little thought to this problem. (Nor has the discussion been helped by the unwillingness of industry to admit candidly that the increased cost of drug development is forcing them into overseas research, "diversification," and neglect of new products whose potential sales would be so small as not to justify the costs of bringing the agents to market.) It is indeed a pity that we can so poorly quantify the harm that society suffers from the absence of new, better drugs, as opposed to the well-publicized mischief caused by available drugs.

On another tack, it seems to me that drug regulatory systems—
like national industrial policy—may need to be quite different from
country to country, depending on the state of local drug development, the availability of local experts and clinical investigators,
and the caliber and availability of medical practice.

A comparison of drugs marketed abroad and in the United States
certainly shows differences. How much we are gaining and how
much losing by such differences is hard to say. United Kingdom
experts would say that American patients are suffering significantly
from not having available such drugs as carbenoxolone, sulfa-
trimethoprim combinations, and a number of drugs in the cardio-
vascular-pulmonary area. Some U.S. experts would disagree with
these judgments (although some of these experts seem egregiously
ignorant about, or inexperienced with, many of these overseas
drugs).

Perhaps one specific example may convince you that there are
problems in the way our system now functions. Propranolol is a
betablocker that is approved for use in the United States only as an
anti-arrhythmic agent. It is widely used both abroad and here for
an indication not approved by our FDA—the relief of angina pectoris. A high-placed FDA official has asserted that the FDA's "experts" have looked at "the evidence" and ruled that the benefits of
the drug are trivial compared to the risks, and that one could not
find a significant number of competent cardiologists who would
disagree with this judgment. I asked the manufacturer for a list of
cardiologists who had worked with the drug and wrote to each of
them for an opinion. These men—including chiefs of cardiology at
some of the most prestigious medical centers in the country—
unanimously expressed amazed disbelief at the FDA stance. They
all use the drug regularly and consider it a major advance in the
management of angina pectoris. Several of them volunteered the
information that propranolol has saved any number of patients
from the hazards of cardiac surgery.

Why this disagreement? Does the FDA use "inexpert experts"?
Are the FDA files inadequate to document the drug's true performance? Has the sponsor not supplied the FDA with the right
kind of data? Are the distinguished cardiologists I polled all fools
or drug-house lackeys? Do the FDA officials involved simply have
bad judgment about this drug (and possibly other ones)?

I don't know where the fault lies, but I submit to you that something's badly wrong when FDA policy disagrees so thoroughly both
with outside experts and with the prescribing physician. (As far as

I can tell, most propranolol in the United States is actually used for angina, not for arrhythmias, showing how far behind clinical practice is the FDA position.)

The very concept of "the experts" also bothers me. Anyone who wishes to see how experts disagree with one another has only to survey them on an issue. We must usually expect such disagreement, and I believe, therefore, that our national drug regulatory posture should be both pluralistic and fallibilistic. We should approve a drug for use if even a significant minority of qualified and experienced physicians find the drug useful. This does not mean that the lack of unanimity or the presence of controversy should be ignored. Quite the contrary; doctors should be fully apprised of it —I advocate neither unbridled license nor ostrich-like head-in-the-sandedness. But let us not be trapped into pharmacologic Lysenkoism.

I am also troubled by the undue emphasis on "controlled trials" by experts and the denigration of more "naturalistic" trials by "ordinary" practitioners. A drug is now evaluated primarily by its performance in what is in some ways a very artificial setting—inpatients (usually), expert investigators, reasonably homogeneous populations, a minimum of other medications given concomitantly, and supervised drug intake. Once marketed, the drug is used under circumstances almost totally different. There is every reason in the world for the performance to be different, yet we pay little attention to studying the drug as it will be used. Why not at least do such studies after introduction on the market?

The ultimate surrealism will be the demand that the safety and efficacy of over-the-counter (OTC) drugs be tested by formal controlled trials. Surely the performance of drugs used in the process of self-diagnosis and self-treatment is best gauged as such. The primary criteria should be patient satisfaction and a reasonable safety record when used as an OTC drug, not when given under supervision by doctors in a double-blind trial. We seem headed for a Heisenberg-type trap wherein we will destroy the utility and relevance of the data by the very process we choose to measure performance.

I am not an expert on animal toxicology, but I suspect that enlightened empiricism is often neglected in this area. I am really not worried about the inbred nature of beagle dogs if pathological changes due to drugs are easier to detect by the lack of variability in the biological material, provided the data can be extrapolated to man. The latter caveat cannot be determined *a priori*, but only experientially. The same consideration applies to the duration of animal testing.

The rigidity imposed by the Delaney Amendment philosophy is hard to defend. All of life is a cost-benefit analysis, in a sense—or should be!—and I would like to be able to weigh benefits against risks in *all* areas, including food additives. The possibility of spreading the Delaney approach to cover drugs chills my marrow.

The idea of developing guidelines for drug evaluation sounds attractive, but it will prove disastrous if the rules are rigid or stupid, and I have seen a tendency to both in some of the proposed guidelines. The temptation to force investigation into Procrustean molds so that some robot can easily plug the data into a computer will be great for the overworked bureaucrat, and must be resisted if it deleteriously affects the quality of the clinical work to be done (as it often will).

What sort of "package inserts" do we need for patients? What sort for doctors? Is our current compulsive demand for "completeness" and "fair balance" destroying communication by imposing an information overload on the audience? How can we ensure that the doctor not fall prey either to the improper blandishments of manufacturers or the nihilistic biases of academic critics? These are important matters, and for the moment I only wish to plug again for a pluralistic, fallibilistic approach. Just as a city is better off with a number of newspapers rather than just one, I believe that the doctor and the patient are best served by exposure to a variety of opinions, as unpleasant as that will be to those (unfortunately in the majority) who prefer the illusion of certainty to the ambiguousness of reality.

# Appendixes
## Appendix I: Synopsis of Discussions

## Appendix II: Conference Participants

## Appendix III: Center for Policy Study Faculty Fellows

# Appendix I: Synopsis of Discussions
## Edited by Richard L. Landau
## and Margot Doyle

## Part I: Preclinical and Clinical Problems of New Drug Development

The 1962 Amendments to the Food and Drug Act were designed to insure the flow of safe and effective new drugs to the market with all possible speed, and to protect the public from dangerous preparations. The regulations stemming from the Amendments, however, have found favor with neither the medical profession nor the pharmaceutical industry, since they appear to have reduced the number of new drugs licensed since 1962, and to have greatly prolonged the periods of pre-clinical and clinical testing. The doctors are dissatisfied because they see their patients deprived of some useful drugs that are readily available to their colleagues in foreign countries; and the pharmaceutical houses are unhappy with the increased costs of prolonged testing which make the development of new chemical entities a more doubtful financial venture.

Under present regulations, the drug companies are responsible for pre-clinical and clinical evaluation and submitting data on a proposed new drug to the Food and Drug Administration. The decision to grant a license, or to send the drug back for further tests, is made by the agency's professional civil servants who may be advised by experts drawn from the academic and professional community. These advisors, unfortunately, have no decision-making responsibility.

A further cause for dissatisfaction is the fact that the professional experts who are responsible for the clinical tests have no part in the licensing decisions. They are not permitted to serve as advisory experts, they have no way of knowing how their data are presented to the FDA, and their identity is unknown to the government agency. In this situation, many physicians feel that a regulatory agency more on the lines of that operative in the United Kingdom (see chapter by Dunlop) would serve them better. There, the *decisions* on licensing are made by advisory committees of voluntary experts, drawn largely from the academic community. The onus for the decision thus rests upon the scientific community and not upon civil servants.

It is regrettable that the information submitted to the FDA is normally shrouded in such a cloak of secrecy. This is apparently done to satisfy the pharmaceutical firms that their trade secrets are being protected. It is probable that the interests of the profession and the public would be best served if this scientific information were available for open discussion by the medical community before licensing, rather than after it. It should not be difficult to accomplish this without jeopardizing the exclusive rights of the sponsoring corporation.

It cannot be doubted that the tragic events that followed the use of thalidomide by pregnant women in 1958 have greatly influenced subsequent FDA regulations and implementation of the requirements for pre-clinical and clinical testing. Perhaps the fear that such a tragedy might occur again has had a greater impact on the regulation of clinical testing than the 1962 Amendments themselves. Presumably, one of the principal aspects of the new 1962 law was the addition of the requirement that drugs be efficacious as well as safe. However, Phase III testing has become very much longer (about 10 times as many patients are studied in the United States as are considered necessary in the United Kingdom). The extended Phase III testing is not intended to determine efficacy (the new criterion demanded by the Amendment), but rather to pick up idiosyncratic reactions and rare contraindications. It is widely acknowledged that the prolonged Phase III testing has greatly increased the costs of developing and marketing a new product. Whether this extended testing actually serves the purposes intended, that is, whether the program demanded for the purpose of discovering unusual reactions makes sound statistical sense, is indeed questionable. Over a comparable period of time, there seems to be no evidence that the United Kingdom system is less safe. This purpose of the Phase II tests is apparently achieved more effectively in the United Kingdom by the post-licensing reports from practicing physicians, who communicate observations of adverse reactions to a special sub-section of the Safety of Drugs Committee, an activity which must be expanded and improved in the United States. For example, it was by such post-licensing reports from practicing doctors that the thromboembolic effects of oral contraceptives and the lethal effects of the overuse of isoproterenol nebulizers by young people were pinpointed.

There is no doubt that the most significant proof of a drug's qualities is manifested after it reaches the market place. The new chemical entity must gain acceptance by the practicing physicians who, despite the impact of extensive advertising promotion, retain their professional judgment. This has been demonstrated by the fact that many drugs developed prior to 1962 remain in demand and (on re-examination) have satisfied the scientific medical community that they are useful.

More important, we tend to forget, when considering regulations, that neither the pharmaceutical industry nor the Food and Drug Administration can reliably predict the areas of therapeutic effectiveness of any new product. It is certainly unlikely that drug administration governed by carefully controlled protocols (Phases II and III) would do more than determine efficacy for the originally intended purpose. Once the drug reaches the market, however, its potential is multiplied several-fold. Through serendipity and the deliberate efforts of thoughtful physicians, many unforeseen uses of approved drugs are discovered—and most of these without securing investigational new drug (IND) exemption. Probably the most glowing example of such a discovery was Hench's observation that cortisone acetate had antirheumatic activity. Although he foresaw this possibility, one can be sure that even he did not anticipate the ramifications of his great discovery. If a committee of endocrinologists had been shown his idea in advance, there is a good chance it would have earned only derision. The line between clinical practice and clinical research is fuzzy indeed; and the Food and Drug Administration would certainly be unwise if it were to attempt to sharpen this dividing line, for in doing so it would risk impeding the discovery of many new drug uses.

As far as efficacy is concerned, valid judgments can be made with considerable certainty on much smaller samplings of cases than are required by the FDA in Phase III. The methods of appraisal have been standardized to a certain extent and answers can be obtained early, in part because one knows what one is looking for. From this viewpoint the question of efficacy is then easier to answer than the question of safety. The FDA license implies that a drug is safe and efficacious in the dosages recommended and for the purposes stated, and no pharmaceutical house of repute would be interested in developing a product that did not meet these requirements. The package insert, which has been so widely criticized, has the ostensible purpose of informing the physician of uses, indications, dosages, limitations, and contraindications. Even more important is the opinion of the FDA that statements in the package inserts prevent false claims by the manufacturers.

It is then the task of the physician to choose a drug with due care for a patient's illness and special needs; it should be the patient's responsibility to follow his doctor's instructions. The value of having patients well informed about the medicinals which they receive is easily underestimated; after all, they take the risks, and they stand to profit from the treatment. Patients who take part in Phase III testing are supposed to be carefully instructed on the defined risks and the potential benefit, and presumably are convinced of the wisdom of their participation. When well informed, they are then a part of the decision-making process. Similar considerations must hold for patients after a drug has been licensed. Well-informed patients would probably provide some protection against malpractice suits for physicians and for pharmaceutical houses.

The thalidomide incident has also laid great stress on the subject of liability in the damage suits that inevitably follow a tragedy of such magnitude. At the present time it does not appear that the differences in licensing procedure as exemplified in the United Kingdom and the United States have much influence on financial liability. It has been the pharmaceutical houses that have made the financial settlements in Europe; it would probably be the pharmaceutical houses who would make the payments in the United States under similar circumstances.

It would seem, nevertheless, that when a new drug has been developed, tested, manufactured, and licensed under conditions that meet all the highest requirements of the "state of the art" at a given time, the drug house in question should not necessarily be the sole culprit in the event of a catastrophe. For example, in the thalidomide case there were no tests current at that time that could have forecast the teratogenic effects of the drug.

In such circumstances it would not seem unreasonable to absolve the pharmaceutical manufacturer of financial liability for drug reactions. A limited liability ruling would hold the drug house responsible for adverse reaction in patients only if it could be proven that appropriate, available pre-marketing testing was not carried out, the tests were badly done, or the results falsified. If there were no federal regulatory agency and liability were restricted to those cases in which fault could be proven, the pharmaceutical firms would not be so susceptible to catastrophic judgments.

There have been cases of doctors who made errors in prescribing; and of patients who have misused prescriptions. Moreover, as scientific horizons widen and we become aware also of carcinogenic or genetic effects, who would care to speculate on all of the eventual effects of a drug? How long might it be before a genetic effect became manifest; who could establish or refute causes? The question of future liability then raises its head. Under almost any system of licensing, the long-term effects of a drug and related court cases, whether based on scientific or emotional evidence, are going to raise difficulties. It is impossible to foresee and provide for all possibilities.

Two additional points should be mentioned here in considering the desirability of the tort liability system: first, during the several years before the 1962 Amendments were passed, the benefits from the introduction of successful new drugs were overwhelming compared to the disasters suffered from the occasional failures; second, we have not yet had to deal with the far-reaching political and social consequences that might accrue if the FDA should license a drug that had deleterious effects on large numbers of the public. In the latter context, large financial losses by a drug company might well be considered a much more tolerable evil than an indictment (real or implied) of the government's concern for the health and safety of its people.

A total liability system would, however, assume, to some extent at least, that all pharmaceutical houses were equally scrupulous in their activities, that all doctors were equally competent and responsible, and that all patients could be relied on to follow their physicians' instructions. The system might break down at any of these three points. Certainly the public would not be completely protected against the marketing of inefficacious or even dangerous drugs, and the burden of proof would still be on the patient. Again, as was noted by Dr. Hubbard, it would be extremely difficult to leave the doctor's responsibility out of the picture. Furthermore, it would be undesirable to give a doctor a *carte blanche* as far as malpractice suits are concerned. Whether a total liability system would flood the market with new drugs, restrict their production still further, or result in the pharmaceutical houses resorting to heavy insurance against all possible contingencies, is impossible to forecast.

# Part II: The Legal and Economic Effects of Drug Regulatory Policies

## A. The Patent System and the New Drug Application

It is evident from Professor Kitch's paper that under the present FDA regulations the patent laws do not operate to encourage the development and production of new drugs. It is not clear whether revision of the laws in order to allow a drug patent to run for a longer time—from the time of a new drug application or from the time of licensing, for example—would serve this end. But even if there were agreement on the desirability of such changes, the delays that have attended revision of the copyright laws make it seem unlikely that the patent laws could be revised with any measurable speed. It is possible, however, that under a non-regulated system of absolute liability there might not be any need for a patent system at all, since a drug company would not act to release a drug until it was sure that all its liabilities were covered in a way that would justify its taking risks. Both the patent laws and the new drug applications eventually act to weed out the non-effective from the probably effective, since both patents and NDAs indicate the areas from which the compounds have been selected and hence the direction in which the research is tending. Thus, in a way, both systems carry the costs of the failures (that is, the compounds that have been discarded along the way) and the successes.

When allocating their funds for research, the drug companies calculate that it will take about 11 years' marketing of a new drug entity before the company can recoup the funds expended in its research and development. Any incentive system considering the time for which a new drug entity must be protected in order to be a profitable investment, must therefore allow for this 11-year period.

The greatest incentive for research is the successful marketing of an exclusive entity: a company that has succeeded in the very successful marketing of such an entity is more likely to assign a large portion of its available income to research. Many of the larger drug companies spend more money on research than is paid out in dividends to stockholders.

It should be emphasized that the investment in the identification of interesting new biological activity is minute in comparison with the very high cost of clinical testing. Thus, the discovery phase of a new chemical entity is controlled by the cost of the clinical phase —and this is determined by the regulatory agency, which decides the amount and kind of data that must be available to justify the marketing of a drug. As far as patents are concerned, these usually come so early in the story that they have nothing to do with the possible human efficacy. Dr. Hubbard said that the Upjohn Company had never pursued human efficacy studies, nor even serious animal studies, on an unpatented entity.

L-dopa is one of the unpatentable drugs that has been marketed. Its limited application to victims of Parkinson's disease makes it unlikely that the two separate companies concerned in its development were able to profit from it, and probably, in retrospect, they would not repeat the experiment of developing another compound with similar limitations. In general, there must be a potential market of significant size before a company would be interested in whether or not a patent is involved. Given the role of the NDA, if there is a large market involving continuous maintenance of a new drug, perhaps a four or five year head start on the market might be sufficient to compensate for the increased research expenditure.

However, a certain number of financially unprofitable drugs with very limited application are discovered, tested, and eventually marketed by the drug houses in the interest, at least partially, of good public relations. Undoubtedly, a number of potentially useful drugs with limited applications still remain, unmarketed and unlicensed, on the shelves of the drug manufacturers because they could not possibly pay for their development under present conditions. It should be possible to set up a different system for dealing with such substances. There can be little doubt that it is worthwhile (in the best sense) to develop something like L-dopa, even though it may command a small unprofitable market. As long as clinical testing remains so expensive, government subsidies seem to be the only solution if we are to be assured that funds will be available to develop substances that have shown definite promise for purposes which do not appear to be financially rewarding. Perhaps the National Institutes of Health might help with grants at this stage. The FDA at the present time is faced with three alternatives in considering such compounds: (1) to find the funds for the necessary research; (2) to approve licensing on a very special and individual basis; (3) to remove such compounds from the market. Obviously neither alternative 2 nor alternative 3 is a very satisfactory solution.

Most of the arguments advanced here apply mainly to the patent and regulating systems in the United States. There are, of course, international companies that operate and also do some research and development in countries that have very weak patent laws, or none at all. The foreign branches of these companies have, however, shown little disposition to flood other nations' markets with competitively cheaper new drug entities, their policies being determined by the general demands of the international trade balance. Moreover, in regard to the "state of the art" of drug development, in situations where the patent laws are weaker, it is becoming more evident that it is the knowledge and know-how that are most important in gaining a marketing success. Although a substance may not be patentable per se, the company developing it has acquired

sufficient expertise to keep it's products ahead of other, later competitors in the market.

## B. The Benefits and Costs of New Drug Regulation

Professor Peltzman's analysis of the effects of the 1962 Amendments to the Food and Drug Act on the development of new drugs
is particularly valuable because it examines in scientific detail a
subject that has previously been estimated in guesses or in "feel-
ings." Peltzman utilizes the valuations of human lives implied in
the decisions society makes to estimate the costs of delays in the
introduction of new drugs. Professor Telser points out that the costs
and gains of delay can be expressed equally well without introducing money by computing the years of life lost as a result of delay
and the years of life gained by preventing the introduction of drugs
that subsequently turned out to be deleterious.

The development of time lag in the introduction of new drugs
had become evident before the 1962 Amendments were passed.
The peak year for the development of new drug entities was 1958,
when about 60 new molecular entities were approved (see Table 1
of Professor Peltzman's paper). The number of new drugs decreased each year from 1959 on, and by the time the new drug
laws were passed in 1962, it was down to about 20.

Other factors principally attributable to refined techniques and
elaboration of procedures, and to increased information about the
structure, physiology, and pharmacological responses of living
organisms, have contributed to the slow-down. There is also a new
appreciation that drug effects are not simple and direct. Many more
avenues need to be explored than was previously realized, as, for
example, in the problems related to carcinogenesis, teratogenesis,
and mutagenesis. Recognition of the complexity of pharmacological
problems has led to a general scientific uneasiness which has probably contributed to increased experimentation in animals, even
when it is conceded that such experimentation may not supply
meaningful data in terms of the human clinical situation.

The rate of entry of all new drugs into the United States has
decreased, and there are significant new drugs widely used abroad
that are not available in this country. The reasons for this steady
maintenance of the low number in the United States may in some
measure be due to: (1) the fact that many areas of promise have
already been pre-empted by previous research with the effect of
reducing the size of the fields still open; and/or (2) the fact that

clinical pharmacology has lagged behind other disciplines in developing new experimental models that would reveal new therapeutic potentials.

In support of Peltzman's view on the effect of the 1962 Amendments, three counter-arguments are offered: (1) The fact that, since 1962, the leadership in new drug development seems to be passing from the United States to the Western European nations. This statement is supported by the fact that an increasing number of the "significant" new drugs entering the American market were developed elsewhere, and marketed elsewhere, months and occasionally several years before being approved here; (2) the improvement in the sciences related to "the art" of new drug development should, while increasing the amount of scientific data acquired for each entity, also increase the flow of potential pharmaceuticals; (3) the idea that areas of promise have been preempted is retrogressive. All practicing physicians are aware of a number of disorders for which the ideal drug is not on the scene, but these drugs may be around the corner. It is also far too easy to depreciate the importance of the less "significant" new drugs, that is, those that are distinguished from pre-existing compounds by only minor chemical differences. Often progress is characterized by small steps forward; witness the 35 years of progress through a series of relatively trivial chemical manipulations from sulfanilimide to the modern derivatives presently on the market.

Professor Peltzman's paper emphasizes the costs of reducing the rate of introduction of new drugs. It should, however, be considered whether speeding up the flow of drugs to the market per se, is entirely desirable. A too rapid rate of introduction of new drugs may not give a practicing physician sufficient time to evaluate their practical use, or, since they are sensitive tools, to master the techniques of their use.

It is clear that a freer flow of information and international cooperation is both desired and desirable. It would be of great help to know why another country has discarded one drug, or was especially enthusiastic about another. Such exchanges would cut down on wasteful duplicative research, and would save valuable time and money, as well as, perhaps, lives. Certainly, in the case of the isoproterenol nebulizers, it might have been important for the British authorities to know that the American drug companies had never felt the need to introduce preparations with the higher concentrations that were prevalent in the United Kingdom.

Despite Peltzman's results, it is probable that most physicians and drug houses would consider that a return to the pre-1962 position is neither practical nor desirable, even if it were possible. They would prefer to work with the FDA in an improved framework that would insure that the number of the new chemical entities reaching the market were not reduced in number, nor the rate of their release slowed down unreasonably.

# Part III: Alternative Systems of New Drug Regulation

## A. The British System of Drug Regulation

An ideal system of drug control would seem to lie somewhere between the limits of extreme permissiveness and undue repression. Professor Peltzman's paper suggests that a formidable number of new drugs have been withheld from the U.S. market by the restrictive practices of the FDA; his conclusions have been confirmed by Dr. William Wardell of the University of Rochester Medical Center.[1] It is, of course, impossible to say at this time how many of those drugs that are not available in this country would be novel or substantial improvements over existing marketed products, or whether any of them might have to be withdrawn later, as Aminorex was in Germany. A second paper by Dr. Wardell[2] lists some drugs in current use in the United Kingdom, but not licensed in the United States, which are considered by British specialists to be very valuable in the treatment of gastric ulcer, hypertension, angina pectoris, urinary tract infections, and infectious diseases in general. Since these products are virtually unknown in America, most U.S. physicians are unaware of what they are missing. This study clearly supports the view that present regulations in the United States are too restrictive.

It is not altogether easy to pinpoint the reasons why the British committees approve their drugs so much more rapidly than does the FDA; but there must be some rationale for requiring less evidence of safety—the British Phase III of the clinical testing covers hundreds of cases, the U.S. testing covers thousands. However, the results of studies done in other countries are taken into consideration in the United Kingdom, while they are used to a very limited degree, if at all, in this country. With the exceptions noted

1. William Wardell, "The Drug Lag: An International Comparison," unpublished paper.
2. William Wardell, unpublished paper.

by Wardell, the drug formularies in the United States and the United Kingdom contain substantially the same array of drugs.

Perhaps the difference lies with whether the licensing is regulated by a professional bureaucracy or through the judgment of the experts in the field; that is, whether the government, advised by experts, makes the decisions, or whether the experts make them and the government sees that they are adequately implemented.

Since safety and efficacy are value judgments, one can never expect to achieve either absolute safety or absolute efficacy: the best that can be expected is that satisfactory trials are carried out to produce the necessary data. What needs to be asked here, then, is how many cases are required to produce data that will validate judgments on safety and efficacy. This is the task of the bio-statistician who can design the experiments and the formulae that say how many cases make a valid sample. Rare and unforeseen reactions may not be predicted, at least in some cases, even by the several thousand Phase III studies that may be required.

It should be noted, moreover, that the results that are used to certify a compound will never be precisely the same as those achieved in clinical practice. No regulating agency can predict what will happen in the uncontrolled (in the strictly scientific sense) clinical settings. The prolonged Phase III clinical testing is partly designed to catch as many contraindications as possible, and to place these, via the package insert, at the physician's disposal— not the patient's. The FDA apparently believes that requiring more extensive pre-marketing testing permits the agency to exert a tighter control on the honesty of advertising by the pharmaceutical industry. Package inserts in the United Kingdom seem to be designed more for the patients' information than for the physicians', and are certainly not as lengthy as they are in the United States. Exaggerated advertising claims are treated more permissively in the United Kingdom.

It is interesting to compare mechanisms of control as they relate to surgery and to medicine. In the United States, a qualified physician can practice surgery in any hospital that will permit him to do so. There are no legal requirements and no legal controls. The controls are supplied by the profession itself, which has gone to extraordinary lengths to try to establish standards. There are very strong local peer review mechanisms in most communities, and a national organization which is a coalition of the various specialty boards in the American College of Surgeons. Nevertheless, surgery is still practiced by some qualified physicians who are not certified specialists in direct opposition to repeated recommendations that the existing criteria for certified physicians be recognized legally and become a requirement for quality control.

It may also be interesting to note here the development of controls for medical devices. The American National Standards Institute, which has a very elaborate mechanism for setting up standards for all kinds of engineering electronic devices, has agreed to a request from the Artificial Internal Organs Committee on Medical Device Standards to establish an advisory panel that will use its independent review mechanism to pass on the standardization of new medical instruments. This process would occur outside the FDA, which has approved the program but does not have any legislation to propose. It is hoped that review will then come from representatives of consumers, industry, and the professions, thus avoiding some of the problems that have beset regulation of the drug industry. If the system is successful, it may well prove a model for re-orienting the FDA's thinking on new drug licensing.

## B. Toward Better Systems of Drug Regulation

It is known that there are many instances of valuable drugs being used by highly competent physicians for purposes not described on the package insert; for example, lidocaine was used for years on cardiac patients, lithium salts were used to treat manic depressive psychosis, and propanalol for the treatment of angina pectoris and hypertension. These uses have been discussed widely at scientific conventions, and papers on them have appeared in a number of reputable scientific journals. Other drugs have similarly passed into general and beneficial use without FDA endorsement. Moreover, there is evidence that the FDA is aware of this situation and does not act to deter it, unless a deleterious effect is detected. The limitations of the "description of use" on the package insert, however, jeopardizes the physician who uses a drug for purposes not noted—if challenged, he could be liable for malpractice. The risks to the doctor in such a situation are compounded because the package insert often does not, or cannot, take into account all the circumstances governing individual cases. The adverse reactions that may show up during treatment could be due to other causes, such as concurrent administration of and interaction with other drugs, the stage of the disease, and so on. As far as indications of uses beyond the package insert are concerned, the drug manufacturers are stringently warned by the FDA against oral or published recommendations for any uses not specifically approved.

With regard to new and potentially dangerous drugs, it is possible that the best solution might be to release them early, restricting their use to experts in the field, at least for a well-defined trial period. The difficulty encountered here is defining and selecting such experts. However, with medical school appointments and specialty board examination as criteria, this should not be an insurmountable problem. The release of drugs to experts has already been recognized in two situations—the use of isotopes and methadone. L-dopa was also released under special circumstances, with the requirement that the company keep careful track of the way in which it was used. Another way to help solve the problem of early use of new drugs might be for the physician to explain the potential risks and benefits to the patient, with a view to having the latter sign a release authorizing the treatment. However, such a system might place an intolerable burden on the physician and is also subject to misuse either in ignorance or by intent. From a legal point of view, it is not very highly recommended.

There are indications that the FDA appreciates the difficulties that have arisen from the 1962 Amendments and is ready to modify its approach to licensing. This is shown by its approval of the way in which standardization of medical devices is being handled, and in recent attempts to improve and revise the package inserts. The legal provisions of the Food and Drug Act amendments are in fact very general, and the agency has a great deal of latitude in the administration of the statute: it could reduce the amount of premarketing proofs and increase the amount of post-marketing information required; it could put resources into post-marketing monitoring and it could even label drugs "To be released only for use by certain kinds of special experts." All that the statute actually says is that the FDA must have substantial evidence of safety and effectiveness. It also says that the court must defer to the FDA on the determination of scientific facts. If the FDA should decide that proof of a less complex, less time-consuming, and less costly nature is required for safe marketing, it can require this. It can also require continuous reporting from a marketer that he is selling the drugs as described.

Thus, in the final analysis, the FDA could use its existing authority to face some of the issues and to change the practice of some of its administering officials. We might then go forward into the 1970s to a more satisfactory system of regulation without any need for new legislation.

# Appendix II: Conference Participants

**Dr. Daniel Azarnoff,** Professor of Pharmacology and Medicine ar
Director of the Clinical Pharmacology Unit, Kansas Univers'
Medical Center.

**William F. Baxter,** Professor of Law, Stanford University.

**Dr. Hubert Bloch,** Director, Friedrich Miescher-Institut, Basle,
Switzerland.

**Stephen G. Breyer,** Professor, Harvard Law School.

**Yale Brozen,** Professor in the Graduate School of Business, The
University of Chicago.

**D. J. R. Bruckner,** Vice-President for Public Affairs and Director of
the Center for Policy Study, The University of Chicago.

**Dr. Thomas E. Bryant,** President, The Drug Abuse Council.

**Guido Calabresi,** the John Thomas Smith Professor of Law, Yale
University.

**Ronald H. Coase,** the Clifton R. Musser Professor of Economics in
the Law School, The University of Chicago.

**William S. Comanor,** Professor of Economics, Stanford University
Business School.

**Joseph D. Cooper,** Professor of Political Science, Howard University.

**Dr. J. Richard Crout,** Acting Director, Office of Scientific Evaluation, Bureau of Drugs, Food and Drug Administration.

**Kenneth Dam,** Assistant Director, Office of Management and Budget, Executive Office of the President.

**Kenneth Culp Davis,** John P. Wilson Professor in the Law School,
The University of Chicago.

**Harold Demsetz,** Department of Economics, University of California at Los Angeles.

**Sir Derrick Dunlop,** Professor Emeritus of Therapeutics and Clinical Medicine, The University of Edinburgh.

**Dr. Jarl E. Dyrud,** Professor and Director of Clinical Services, Department of Psychiatry, The University of Chicago.

**Dr. Daniel X. Freedman,** Chairman and Louis Bloch Professor in the Department of Psychiatry, The University of Chicago.

**John P. Gould, Jr.,** Associate Professor in the Graduate School of Business, The University of Chicago.

**Dr. Clifford W. Gurney,** Professor in the Division of the Biological Sciences and in the Department of Medicine, The University of Chicago.

**C. Eric Hager,** The Drug Abuse Council.

**Clark C. Havinghurst,** The Institute of Medicine, National Academy of Sciences.

**Dr. Leo Hollister,** Medical Investigator, Veterans Administration Hospital, Palo Alto, California.

**Dr. William Neil Hubbard, Jr.,** Executive Vice-President, The Upjohn Company.

**Dr. Lee S. Hyde,** Professional Staff Member, House of Representatives Committee on Interstate and Foreign Commerce.

**Reuben Kessel,** Professor of Business Economics and Director of Research, Graduate School of Business, The University of Chicago.

**Edmund Kitch,** Professor in the Law School, The University of Chicago.

**Dr. Richard L. Landau,** Professor in the Department of Medicine and in the College, The University of Chicago.

**Dr. Louis Lasagna,** Professor of Pharmacology and Toxicology and of Medicine, School of Medicine and Dentistry, University of Rochester.

**Dr. Robert Levine,** Department of Medicine, Yale University M
ical School.

**Dr. George E. Maha,** Executive Director, Clinical Research, Mer
Sharp & Dohme Research Laboratories.

**Philip J. Nelson,** Department of Economics, State University of New
York at Binghampton.

**Sam Peltzman,** Associate Professor of Economics, University of
California at Los Angeles.

**Richard A. Posner,** Professor in the Law School, The University of
Chicago.

**Dr. Thaddeus E. Prout,** Chief of Medicine, Greater Baltimore Medical Center.

**Robert Rabin,** Professor of Law, Stanford University Law School.

**Lord Ritchie-Calder,** Senior Fellow, Center for the Study of Dem-
ocratic Institutions, Santa Barbara, California.

**Dr. Lloyd J. Roth,** Professor and Chairman in the Department of
Pharmacology and Professor in the College, The University of
Chicago.

**Dr. John H. Rust,** Director of the A. J. Carlson Animal Research
Facility and Professor in the Departments of Radiology and Pharmacology, The University of Chicago.

**Dr. David B. Skinner,** Dallas B. Phemister Professor of Surgery and
Chairman of the Department, The University of Chicago.

**George J. Stigler,** The Charles R. Walgreen Distinguished Service
Professor of American Institutions in the Department of Economics
and in the Graduate School of Business, The University of Chicago.

**Lester G. Telser,** Professor in the Department of Economics, The
University of Chicago.

# Appendix III: Center for Policy Study
# Faculty Fellows

**Robert McC. Adams,** Dean of the Division of Social Sci
Professor in the Departments of Anthropology and N
Languages and Civilizations, and Professor in the Orient

**George W. Beadle,** President Emeritus and the William
Distinguished Service Professor in the Department of B.
in the College, and Honorary Trustee of The University of

**Saul Bellow,** Professor and Chairman in the Committee on
Thought and Professor in the Department of English.

**Brian J. L. Berry,** Professor in the Department of Geography and
Chairman of the Training Program, Center for Urban Studies.

**R. Stephen Berry,** Professor in the Department of Chemistry, in the
James Franck Institute, and in the College.

**Leonard Binder,** Professor in the Department of Political Science.

**Walter J. Blum,** Professor in the Law School.

**Jerald C. Brauer,** The Naomi Shenstone Donnelley Professor in the
Divinity School.

**D. J. R. Bruckner,** Vice-President for Public Affairs at The University of Chicago, and Director of the Center for Policy Study.

**James W. Cronin,** University Professor in the Department of Physics and in the Enrico Fermi Institute.

**Dr. Jarl E. Dyrud,** Professor and Director of Clinical Services in the Department of Psychiatry.

**Edgar Epps,** The Marshall Field Professor of Urban Education in the Department of Education.

**John Hope Franklin,** The John Matthews Manly Distinguished Service Professor in the Department of History.

**Dr. Daniel X Freedman,** Chairman and the Louis Block Professor in the Department of Psychiatry.

**Milton Friedman,** The Paul Snowden Russell Distinguished Service Professor in the Department of Economics.

**Jacob W. Getzels,** The R. Wendell Harrison Distinguished Service Professor in the Departments of Education and Psychology.

**Julian R. Goldsmith,** The Charles E. Merriam Distinguished Service Professor in the Department of Geophysical Sciences.

**Chauncy D. Harris,** The Samuel N. Harper Professor in the Department of Geography, and Director of the Center for International Studies.

**Philip M. Hauser,** Professor in the Department of Sociology, and Director of the Population Research Center of the Chicago Community Inventory.

**Roger H. Hildebrand,** Dean of the College, and Professor in the Department of Physics and in the Enrico Fermi Institute

**Ping-ti Ho,** The James Westfall Thompson Professor in the Departments of History and Far Eastern Languages and Civilizations.

**Philip W. Jackson,** Director of Pre-Collegiate Education, Laboratory School, and Professor in the Department and Graduate School of Education and the Committee on Human Development.

**Morris Janowitz,** Professor in the Department of Sociology and Director of the Center for Social Organization Studies.

**D. Gale Johnson,** Professor and Chairman of the Department of Economics.

**Harry G. Johnson,** Professor in the Department of Economics and Editor of the *Journal of Political Economy.*

**Morton A. Kaplan,** Professor in the Department of Political Science, Chairman of the Committee on International Relations, and Director of the Arms Control and Foreign Policy Seminar in the Center for Policy Study.

**Philip B. Kurland,** Professor in the Law School.

**Edward H. Levi,** President and Trustee of The Universit[cut]
cago, and Professor in the Law School.

**Julian H. Levi,** Professor of Urban Studies in the Divisio[cut]
Sciences, and Executive Director of the South East Chi[cut]
mission.

**Donald N. Levine,** Associate Professor in the Departme[cut]
ciology and in the College.

**Richard C. Lewontin,** The Louis Block Professor of Biologi[cut]
ences, Professor in the Department of Theoretical Biology, in[cut]
Committee on Conceptual Foundations of Science, and in the C[cut]
lege, and Chairman of the Committee on Evolutionary Biology.

**James S. Lorie,** Professor and Director of the Center for Research
in Security Prices in the Graduate School of Business.

**Martin E. Marty,** Professor and Associate Dean of the Divinity
School.

**William H. McNeill,** The Robert A. Milliken Distinguished Service
Professor in the Department of History.

**Soia Mentschikoff,** Professor in the Law School.

**William R. Polk,** President of the Adlai Stevenson Institute of International Affairs and Professor in the Department of History.

**Stuart A. Rice,** The Louis Block Professor and Chairman of the
Department of Chemistry, The Louis Block Professor in the James
Franck Institute, in the Department of Theoretical Biology, and in
the College.

**Margaret K. Rosenheim,** Professor in the School of Social Service
Administration.

**Robert G. Sachs,** Director of Argonne National Laboratory, and
Professor in the Department of Physics, and in the Enrico Fermi
Institute.

**Edward Shils,** Distinguished Service Professor in the Committee on
Social Thought and in the Department of Sociology.

John A. Simpson, The Edward L. Ryerson Distinguished Service Professor in the Department of Physics, in the Enrico Fermi Institute, and in the College.

Dr. David B. Skinner, Chairman and the Dallas B. Phemister Professor in the Department of Surgery.

George J. Stigler, The Charles R. Walgreen Distinguished Service Professor of American Institutions in the Department of Economics and the Graduate School of Business, and Editor of the *Journal of Political Economy*.

Bernard S. Strauss, Professor and Chairman of the Department of Microbiology and Committee on Genetics, and Professor in the College.

Robert E. Streeter, Professor in the Department of English and in the College, and Dean of the Division of the Humanities.

Sol Tax, Professor in the Department of Anthropology and in the College, and Director of the Smithsonian Institution Center for the Study of Man.

Tang Tsou, Professor in the Departments of Political Science and Far Eastern Languages and Civilizations.

Anthony Turkevich, The James Franck Distinguished Service Professor in the Department of Chemistry, in the Enrico Fermi Institute, and in the College.

Paul Wheatley, Professor in the Department of Geography and in the Committee on Social Thought.

John T. Wilson, Provost of The University of Chicago, and Professor in the Departments of Education and Psychology.

Robert R. Wilson, Professor in the Department of Physics, in the Enrico Fermi Institute, and in the College, and Director of the National Accelerator Laboratory.

Albert Wohlstetter, University Professor in the Department of Political Science.

Aristide R. Zolberg, Professor in the Department of Political Science.